INTRODUCTION

WELCOME TO THE MILLENNIUM EDITION of the Taste of Scotland Guide in what are proving to be momentous times for Scotland, its people – and its food.

Having achieved political self-determination for the first time in almost 300 years, we have the exhilarating prospect of rising to the challenge of the new millennium – and the new Scottish Parliament – and showing exactly what we can do.

And the food? The last few years have brought tremendous advances for Taste of Scotland and, indeed, taste *in* Scotland. Recent improvements in our industry can now be seen as building blocks for even greater things. There are many reasons why cooking has become one of the most popular leisure time activities. You may be enjoying rediscovering your own kitchen or sampling the delights of someone else's.

Some of the world's finest cooks and chefs are working in our establishments across the country. It has never easier been for them to access our wonderful local produce.

If it is your intention to eat and stay in Scotland – you can rely on this Taste of Scotland book to guide you. The time and expertise of our fully qualified, experienced and professional Inspectors is devoted to ensuring that they recommend only the best eating places for Taste of Scotland.

The very best need not be elitist, however.

As ever, we aim to represent all types of establishment from tea-rooms and coffee shops to every conceivable type of restaurant, formal and informal. We are simply looking for the best Scottish hospitality, skilful cooking and presentation and, of course, a commitment to quality.

By using this Guide, you can be sure that you have a reliable recommendation. Apart from enjoying this hospitality to the full, all we ask of you is your feedback. What you think of our recommendations is important to us as an organisation and we hope to be able to meet your expectations and, if we do not, we need to know why.

Enjoy a Taste of Scotland 2000.

Amanda J Clark

Amanda J Clark
Chief Executive

PRODUCT OF SCOTLAND

Walkers

• ESTABLISHED 1898 •

The gift from the Highland

Like the Scottish Highl
themselves, once you l
experienced Walker
shortbread, nothing else
comes close to the orig
This pure creamery bt
shortbread is baked in
Highland village of Abe
in Speyside to an orig
family recipe, first perfe
by Joseph Walker in 1
Guaranteed to be n
from only the fine
ingredients – with
an artificial flavour
colouring or preserv
in sight – just as it
always been. Can yc
imagine a better gift t
that of the world's cla
pure butter shortbrea
Beautifully presented
distinctive tartan packa
Walkers irresistible ra
of varieties means it
always a welcome gi

The world's
classic
pure butter
shortbread

Walkers Shortbread Ltd Aberlour-on-Spey Scotland AB38 9PD
Telephone +44 (0)1340 871555 Fax +44 (0)1340 871355 E-mail enquiries@walkers-shortbread.co.uk

CONTENTS

How to use this Guide 4
The Macallan Taste of Scotland Awards 6
Scottish Tourist Board Quality Assurance 8
Local Tourist Information 9
Say cheese – and you're smiling! 10
Out with the old, in with the new – or not quite?......13
Matthew Algie – 'The Coffee People' 14
The Macallan – A Masterpiece Among Malt Whiskies....17
Classic shortbread 20

**LIST OF TASTE OF SCOTLAND
MEMBER ESTABLISHMENTS 2000** 33
How to order the Taste of Scotland Guide 2001 235
Nomination forms 237
Comment forms 238
The Taste of Scotland Scotch Lamb Challenge 1999...242
Recipes 244
Index 266
Map 270

THE TASTE OF SCOTLAND
2000

This is to certify that

The Lochnagar

has been selected for membership of
The Taste of Scotland Scheme

in recognition of its commitment to the pursuit
of excellence in food preparation and service

*Taste of Scotland current
members are identified by
the 2000 Certificate of
Membership which should be
prominently displayed.*

**TASTE OF SCOTLAND IS GRATEFUL
FOR THE CONTINUED SUPPORT OF**
**Scottish Tourist Board • Scotland the Brand
Scotch Quality Beef and Lamb Association
The Macallan • Walkers Shortbread
Matthew Algie • Alexander Wines**

TRADE BOARD MEMBERS
Laurie Black (Chairman, Taste of Scotland Board),
Fouters Bistro Restaurant.
Annie Paul, **Taychreggan Hotel,
and The Waterfront Restaurant.**
David Wilson, **The Peat Inn.**
Nick Nairn, **Nairns.**

PRODUCT OF
Scotland

HOW TO USE THIS GUIDE

ENTRIES

All members are listed in the Guide in alphabetical order under the nearest town or village. Island entries are shown alphabetically under I for Isle. A full list of all members is given in alphabetical order in the index at the end of the Guide. Alternatively, consult the map at the rear of the Guide to see where current Taste of Scotland Members are located.

DOGS/PETS

Some establishments welcome guests' pets – we advise that you check with the individual establishment in advance to avoid any difficulties.

ACCOMMODATION RATES

Taste of Scotland establishments with accommodation have the number of rooms stated in their entry and whether they offer special rates at given times of the year. Dinner Bed & Breakfast and Bed & Breakfast rates are per person unless otherwise stated. Rates quoted are intended as an indication of the prices charged – as these may change from time to time, you should obtain specific rates for the dates you request.

MEAL PRICES

£ symbols indicate the price category that the establishment has indicated to us they fall into. They are as follows:

$£$ = up to £10 per person
$££$ = £11 – £20 per person
$£££$ = £21 – £30 per person
$££££$ = over £30 per person

LUNCHES

Because lunchtime eating may be less formal in some establishments than others, the Taste of Scotland criteria extend to establishments who are open for a lighter lunch or bar snack. To avoid disappointment please establish when booking whether lunchtime opening is for dining room lunch or bar meals.

TIPS TO AVOID DISAPPOINTMENT

Make an advance reservation whenever possible – establishments may occasionally vary their opening times, in response to business demand, from those printed in the Guide. Please mention that you are using the Taste of Scotland Guide. Check that the prices quoted in the Guide have not changed. If you are planning to pay by credit card, please ensure your credit card will be acceptable.

COMMENTS

We welcome comments – both good and bad – about your experiences using this Guide.

However, if you have an unsatisfactory meal we always advise you to speak to the person in charge at the establishment concerned and let them know of your disappointment. It gives an immediate opportunity for the situation to be rectified.

If this fails to resolve the problem, please write to us about your experience. We will pass a copy of your letter or comment form onto the establishment for reply and investigation. We will also conceal your identity if you specifically request this. We do believe that for our establishments to continue to be the best they should be given the information and feedback we receive from their customers.

Please let us hear of your good experiences as we also pass these on to our members. There are comment forms towards the end of the Guide.

GUIDE TO SYMBOLS

The symbols listed here indicate more information about the facilities available at each member establishment.

🏠 Number of rooms

🛏 Accommodation rates

[SP] Special rates available

✕ Information on meals

[V] Vegetarians welcome

✗ Smoking restrictions

[UL] Unlicensed

🍷 Licensing status

★ Scottish Tourist Board Star rating

💳 Credit Cards

🏛 Proprietor or Manager

🧒 Children

♿ Facilities for disabled

🚢 Shipboard restaurant

🧺 Packed meals provided

🅿 No parking

🎪 Opening hours during local festival

🐕 Information on pets

🐄 Member of the Scotch Beef Club

🌱🌱🌱 Green Tourism Award

Town and Map Reference	**OBAN** — **B5**
Address & Telephone Number, etc	**ARDS HOUSE** Connel, by Oban Argyll PA37 1PT Tel: 01631 710255 E-mail: jb@ardshouse.demon.co.uk
How to get there	On main A85 Oban–Tyndrum, 4½ miles north of Oban.
Brief description	**Small family-run hotel overlooking Loch Etive.**
Type of building **Style of cooking** **Inspector's 1999 comment**	• Victorian villa. • Traditional Scottish cooking. • "Scottish hospitality at its best – good food, warm and friendly hosts."
Description	This is a comfortable small hotel standing on the shores of a loch, with views over the Firth of Lorn and the Morvern Hills. Six of the seven bedrooms are en suite, and there is a happy air of the family home here. This is encouraged by the owners John and Jean Bowman. John, who is an innovative cook, along with Jean, an exceptionally warm and friendly hostess, who treat their guests like friends. The daily changing set menu is displayed in the afternoon and any special requirements are easily catered for. The dishes rely on local produce where possible, combining a taste for detail and fresh home cooking.
Seasonal limitations	Open Feb to mid Nov 🏠 Rooms: 7 (6 en suite, 1 with private facilities) 🛏 DB&B £40–£54 B&B £30–£45 [SP] Special rates available ✕ Non-residents – by arrangement 🍷 Restricted licence ✕ Dinner 4 course menu £££ [V] Vegetarians – by arrangement 🧒 Children over 14 years welcome ✗ No smoking throughout
Menu specialities	Tomato, pear and tarragon soup with home-baked bread. Fettucine of local grey sole and smoked salmon roulade with a curry and coriander velouté. Almond and prune tart with an angelica and camomile syrup.
STB Rating **Credit Cards**	STB ★★★ Hotel 💳 Credit cards: Mastercard/Eurocard, Visa, Switch, Delta
Contacts	🏛 Proprietors: John & Jean Bowman

The MACALLAN.

THE 1999 WINNERS OF THE MACALLAN TASTE OF SCOTLAND AWARDS ARE:

OVERALL EXCELLENCE AWARD.............................Three Chimneys Restaurant and the
House Over-By, Isle of Skye *(listed on page 163)*

HOTEL DINING AWARD ....No 1 Princes Street, The Balmoral Hotel,
Edinburgh *(listed on page 84)*

CITY RESTAURANT AWARD ....Stravaigin, Glasgow *(listed on page 118)*

COUNTRY LUNCH AWARD..............................Greywalls, Gullane *(listed on page 127)*

RURAL RESTAURANT AWARD ....Gordon's Restaurant, Inverkeilor
(listed on page 132)

RESTAURANT WITH ROOMS AWARD ....Three Chimneys Restaurant and the
House Over-By, Isle of Skye *(listed on page 163)*

SMALL RESIDENCE AWARD ......The Old Smiddy Guest House, Laide *(listed on page 178)*

COMMENDED ESTABLISHMENTS SHORTLISTED:

▥ **HOTEL DINING**...The Georgian Room, Cameron House Hotel, Loch Lomond
..............................The Turnberry Restaurant, Turnberry Hotel, Turnberry

▥ **CITY RESTAURANT** ....Atrium, Edinburgh
....Exceed, Perth

▥ **COUNTRY LUNCH**..............................Cringletie House Hotel, Peebles
....Kinloch House Hotel, Blairgowrie

▥ **RURAL RESTAURANT**........................Ostler's Close Restaurant, Cupar
....The Seafood Restaurant, St Monan's

▥ **RESTAURANT WITH ROOMS** ....Gordon's Restaurant, Inverkeilor
....Scoretulloch House Hotel, Darvel

▥ **SMALL RESIDENCE**............................Ardvourlie Castle, Isle of Harris
....Argentine House Hotel, Isle of Arran

NOW IN THEIR TWELFTH YEAR, these Awards were set up to encourage the pursuit of excellence and, by so doing, encourage others to emulate the winners. This ethos remains unchanged – with public nominations being the starting point, inspectors' nominations follow and then each short-

listed establishment is further judged by an expert panel. All the establishments listed here have consistently demonstrated their commitment to excellence.

The Macallan Single Malt is renowned for its unique character and unrivalled quality and as such makes a perfect partner for these Awards. This partnership certainly captures the imagination of the public as every year a record number of nominations are received.

The Awards are restricted to establishments which are listed in the previous Taste of Scotland Guide and thus are already highlighted as leaders in their specific category.

This year, once again, the judging for the Awards was an exceptionally difficult task with nominations coming in from all areas and for all types of establishments. It is particularly heartening that the standards encountered across Scotland are continually rising, resulting in a growing number of eligible contenders.

We again invite Taste of Scotland customers to nominate establishments in which you have received outstanding experiences this year. In addition, Taste of Scotland Inspectors are being asked to nominate their favourite places throughout the inspection season. Please use the coupons towards the back of this Guide to forward your nominations for The Macallan Taste of Scotland Awards 2000. Nomination cards are also available at some Taste of Scotland establishments. Letters and postcards are also welcome and taken into consideration.

Simply nominate an establishment which has impressed you greatly, tell us why and leave the rest to us.

Closing date for entries – 30 June 2000.

The 1999 Winners have been highlighted in the listings with this symbol:

STB Quality Assurance

FOLLOW THE STARS and you won't be disappointed when you get to the inn. The new Scottish Tourist Board Star System is a world-first. Quality is what determines our star awards, not a check-list of facilities. We've made your priorities our priorities.

Quality makes or breaks a visit. It is only the quality of the welcome and service, the food, the hospitality, ambience and the comfort and condition of the property which earns Scottish Tourist Board Stars, not the size of the accommodation or the range of available facilities.

This easy-to-understand system tells you at a glance the quality standard of all types and sizes of accommodation from the smallest B&B and self-catering cottage to the largest countryside and city centre hotels.

★★★★★ Exceptional, world class
★★★★ Excellent
★★★ Very Good
★★ Good
★ Fair and acceptable

A trained Scottish Tourist Board inspector grades each property each year to give you the reassurance that you can choose accommodation of the quality standard you want.

To help you further in your choice the Scottish Tourist Board System also tells you the type of accommodation and the range of facilities and services available.

All the latest Star ratings are listed at the end of each Taste of Scotland entry where applicable.

ACCOMMODATION TYPES

Guest House: A guest house is usually a commercial business and will normally have a minimum of 4 letting bedrooms, of which some will have en suite or private facilities. Breakfast will be available and evening meals may be provided.

B&B: Accommodation offering bed and breakfast, usually in a private house. B&B's will normally accommodate no more than 6 guests and may or may not serve an evening meal.

Hotel: A Hotel will normally have a minimum of 6 letting bedrooms of which at least half must have en suite or private bathroom facilities. A hotel will normally have a drinks licence (may be a restricted licence) and will serve breakfast and dinner.

International Resort Hotel: A Hotel achieving a 5 Star quality award which owns and offers a range of leisure and sporting facilities including an 18-hole golf course, swimming and leisure centre and country pursuits.

Inn: Bed and breakfast accommodation provided within a traditional inn or pub environment. A restaurant and bar will be open to non-residents and will provide restaurant or bar food at lunchtime and in the evening.

Restaurant with Rooms: In a Restaurant with Rooms, the restaurant is the most significant part of the business. It is usually open to non-residents. Accommodation is available, and breakfast is usually provided.

LOCAL TOURIST INFORMATION

FOR SPECIFIC INFORMATION ON A PARTICULAR PART OF SCOTLAND, CONTACT THE FOLLOWING:

Aberdeen and Grampian Tourist Board
Tel: 01224 632727 Fax: 01224 620415
Web: www.holiday.scotland.net

Angus and City of Dundee Tourist Board
Tel: 01382 527527 Fax: 01382 527550
Web: www.angusanddundee.co.uk

Argyll, the Isles, Loch Lomond, Stirling & Trossachs Tourist Board
Tel: 01786 475019 Fax: 01786 471301
Web: www.holiday.scotland.net

Ayrshire and Arran Tourist Board
Tel: 01292 288688
Fax: 01292 288686
Web: www.ayrshire-arran.com

Dumfries and Galloway Tourist Board
Tel: 01387 253862 Fax: 01387 245555
Web: www.galloway.co.uk

Edinburgh and Lothians Tourist Board
Tel: 0131 473 3800 Fax: 0131 473 3881
Web: www.edinburgh.org

Greater Glasgow and Clyde Valley Tourist Board
Tel: 0141 204 4400 Fax: 0141 204 4772
Web: www.holiday.scotland.net

The Highlands of Scotland Tourist Board
Tel: 01997 421160 Fax: 01997 421168
Web: www.host.co.uk

Kingdom of Fife Tourist Board
Tel: 01334 472021 Fax: 01334 478422
Web: www.standrews.co.uk

Orkney Tourist Board
Tel: 01856 872856 Fax: 01856 875056
Web: www.orkneyislands.com

Perthshire Tourist Board
Tel: 01738 627958 Fax: 01738 630416
Web: www.perthshire.co.uk

Scottish Borders Tourist Board
Tel: 01750 20054 Fax: 01750 21886
Web: www.holiday.scotland.net

Shetland Tourism
Tel: 01595 693434 Fax: 01595 695807
Web: www.shetland-tourism.co.uk

Western Isles Tourist Board
Tel: 01851 703088 Fax: 01851 705244
Web: www.witb.co.uk

For general enquiries, please contact the
Scottish Tourist Board
23 Ravelston Terrace
Edinburgh
Tel: 0131 332 2433
Fax: 0131 343 1513

SAY CHEESE – AND YOU'RE SMILING!

AMONG SCOTLAND'S MOST DISTINCTIVE FLAVOURS – and there are many – its cheeses can claim a special place in defining the essence of the taste of Scotland. The diversity of tastes and textures reflects something of the country itself.

In the past, the seasons dictated the nation's diet and the people relied on food which could be stored to keep them going through the long winter months, and those winter months still seem longer than the summer ones! The farmers and crofters, or in most cases their wives, who made their own cheeses were well aware that lengthy periods of storage allow it to mature and improve.

Perhaps that's why cheese and wine go so well together. At any rate, it's a tradition which explains the predominance of hard or pressed cheese in Scotland – Scottish Cheddar accounts for the bulk of the total output. As you will see from the rest of this feature, however, today's Scottish cheesemakers are painting on a much broader canvas than their ancestors. The range of cheeses produced around the country are varied enough to suit the most discerning and adventurous of palates,

The advent of modern temperature-controlled facilities and refrigerated transport ensures that the country's cheesemaking fraternity again encompasses the enthusiastic artisans and farmhouse producers as well as the large industrial Cheddar creameries. The main creameries are located at Lockerbie and Stranraer in the south, at Campbeltown on the Mull of Kintyre, and on the islands of Bute, Arran, Islay, Mull, Gigha and Orkney. They are often open to the public.

Improved distribution methods mean that most of Scotland's cheeses should be easy to find, even those from the smaller producers. If you come across interesting local cheeses while eating out, ask where you can buy them. It's worth wandering round some of our specialist cheese shops in various parts of the country. And wherever you find them – enjoy!

THE FINE CHEESES OF SCOTLAND

AYRSHIRE & SW SCOTLAND
Scotland's most productive dairying region containing the largest creameries. Galloway and

Lockerbie are the established large scale cheddars. Bonnet: (goatsmilk), Burns (unpasteurised Dunlop), Swinzie (unpasteurised ewe's milk) and Loch Arthur (unpasteurised, organic cheddar) are a few of the distinctive small scale cheeses to look for.

BORDERS & LANARKSHIRE
Traditional hill farming region with a few small, but excellent farmhouse cheesemakers. Teviotdale, Kelsae, Stichill, Lanark Blue (unpasteurised ewe's milk), Dunsyre Blue (unpasteurised blue veined). All emanate from this area.

CLYDE & WESTERN ISLES
Includes many of Scotland's surviving smaller island and mainland creameries by virtue of the historical difficulty (and cost) of moving fresh milk to market. Arran (cheddar), Arran Blue (blue veined), Crotin (goatsmilk-Arran), Drumleish (Bute), Isle of Bute (cheddar), Inverloch (Gigha – goats), Mull of Kintyre (mature cheddar), Highland (Campbeltown) and Isle of Mull (or Tobermory Cheddar).

EAST SCOTLAND & PERTHSHIRE
Fine, relatively dry agricultural district with many large farms. A remarkable range of award-winning speciality cheese including: Bishop Kennedy (a unique 'Trappiste' cheese washed in malt whisky), Howgate Farmhouse Brie and Howgate Farmhouse Camembert, Pentland, St Andrews and Strathkinnes emanate from this region.

NORTH & NORTH EAST SCOTLAND
Mainly highland area with difficult climate for large scale commercial dairying. Cheeses include Highland Crowdie, Galic, Hramsa, Gruth Dhu and Caboc (Tain, Ross-shire), Caithness and Strathdon Blue (Aberdeenshire).

ORKNEY
Climate well suited to dairying and with a long tradition and heritage of distinctive cheesemaking, ranging from the two commercial creameries to several small, seasonal farmhouse makers depending upon milk availability. The main creamery produces Orkney Cheddar (Claymore) whilst there is a smaller family-run farmhouse creamery at Swannay Farm (Evie). There are several seasonal, but quite distinctive farmhouse cheeses available locally and often known only by their makers' names.

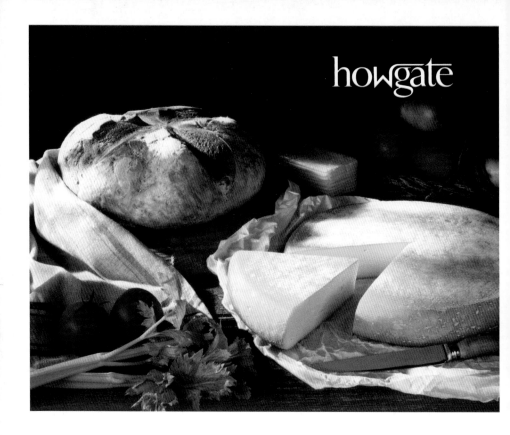

howgate

St Andrews • Bishop Kennedy • Pentland

Howgate Farmhouse Brie • Camembert

❖ ❖ ❖ ❖ ❖ ❖ ❖ ❖ ❖ ❖ ❖ ❖ ❖

 howgate

farmhouse cheesemakers

Kinfauns Home Farm
Kinfauns • Perthshire • Scotland • PH2 7JZ
Tel: (01738) 443440 Fax: (01738) 443439

OUT WITH THE OLD, IN WITH THE NEW – OR NOT QUITE?

ALTHOUGH THE GENERAL WINE-DRINKING PUBLIC may not realise it, there is a perennial debate among the imbibing professions as to whether or not wines from the countries of the New World (Australia, New Zealand, California et al) can really hold a candle to the classics of the Old World (for which read Europe, principally France), especially when it comes to making a match with food.

Detractors of the New World point to the rich, up-front flavours typical of many Antipodean and American offerings which, they claim, tend to dominate whatever food is being served. Old World wines, they argue, are much more versatile at table, their natural restraint and elegance allowing them to complement – rather than dominate – a wide range of foods, To followers of the New World camp, of course, this is nothing more than sour grapes. European wine-makers, they say, are merely jealous of the ripe, juicy fruit which their colleagues in warmer climates manage to pack into the bottle every year without fail.

The truth is, of course, that there is no right answer. Culinary trends in Scotland, as across Britain generally, have changed so much in recent years that, in some restaurants at least, you are just as likely to sit down to a plate of sushi or Cajun chicken as you are to roast beef or sole meunière. The bold, often exotic flavours of New World and Asian cuisine can make excellent partners for wines which might be wasted on more subtle styles of cooking.

But let's not be exclusive. After all, there are a good many elegant, restrained wines coming out of New World vineyards these days, just as there are plenty of bold, exotically flavoured dishes coming out of European kitchens. The key, as always, is to choose a wine which matches your chosen food in terms of body, texture and depth of flavour. In a restaurant or brasserie, this may mean relying on the wine list – and your waiter! – to suggest something suitable, bearing in mind that the wine list should have been designed in the first place to complement the cuisine on offer. True, some foods are not particularly friendly to wine – asparagus, chocolate and oily fish, to name a few – but, by and large, you should be able to find at least one wine to provide an acceptable, if not necessarily perfect, accompaniment.

There is, it seems, only one surefire way to minimise your chances of disappointment: taste, taste and keep tasting. It's tough, but someone's got to do it.

MATTHEW ALGIE – 'THE COFFEE PEOPLE'

SCOTLAND HAS MORE THAN ITS FAIR SHARE of long established family-owned businesses. One such company is Glasgow-based coffee roaster Matthew Algie. In the offices and production facilities of the 136-year-old firm, however, talking about 'the old days' is strictly forbidden: there simply isn't the time!

There is a feeling of vibrancy in the air when one visits the Matthew Algie 'roastery' in Glasgow. Here the coffee experts are never at rest, overseeing a computerised facility where age-old skills and modern technology combine to produce 25 million cups worth of roasted beans every week.

The roastery is a mass of equipment but seems anything but industrial. As if the incredible aroma of tons of coffee beans wasn't enough (imagine being placed inside a giant bag of your favourite roast and you begin to get the idea!) there is a multitude of machines all painted in bright carnival colours. Overhead, transparent tubes whoosh and hiss as freshly roasted beans are transported by jets of air to protect the delicate cargo. A glass-walled control room, apparently suspended in space, is illuminated by banks of monitors. This is food manufacturing with a theme park twist.

All the noise and theatre of the roastery is matched by the focus groups who gather in the company's purpose-built Espresso Lab. In this caffeine-fuelled think tank, the 'coffee people' spend their day arguing about the future. This is the place where Matthew Algie comes up with ideas to shape the market. As the country's largest independent producer, the company has introduced groundbreaking products such as the Espresso Cart, Single Origin coffees, double-roasted espresso beans, and now gourmet coffees over the Internet with the Espresso Warehouse Online service.

It's hard to say what Mr Algie would make of all that's going on in his family firm. Chances are, his notoriously 'upstanding' Victorian character might be a little affronted by the amount of fun being had in the company's offices.

But one thing's for sure: he'd love the coffee.

THE HOUSE OF
BRUAR

The people, the food,

the landscape,

and the warmest of Highland welcomes.

The home of all the classic beauty and flavour of the Scottish Highlands. Taste the wholesome good value fayre of Scotland in our restaurant. Breathe deep the Highland air by the "Falls of Bruar" or as you wander our garden. Enjoy the many natural fibres and colours found in our clothing halls which so perfectly reflect the

THE HOME OF
COUNTRY
CLOTHING

classic landscape and textures that surround The House of Bruar. With china, glass and gifts that epitomise the quality and tradition of Scottish life, you can afford to take home more than just good memories.

ON THE A9, BLAIR ATHOLL, PERTHSHIRE. OPEN 7 DAYS. TELEPHONE 01796 483236.

See entry page 58

A MASTERPIECE AMONG MALT WHISKIES

DAVID ROBERTSON is a young Scot with a huge responsibility on his shoulders. As the latest in a distinguished line of Whisky Makers at The Macallan, he is responsible for maintaining the quality of The Macallan single malt whisky that has been produced exclusively at the distillery, on the Easter Elchies estate, since it first officially opened for business back in 1824.

Perched high above the banks of the River Spey, close to the village of Craigellachie, the distillery at Easter Elchies was one of the first to be licensed – as whisky makers across early nineteenth century Scotland were given legal consent to create a drink that would captivate the world. Nine British Monarchs later, it is one of the few distilleries which is still operational that can trace its origins back to those first days of legal whisky making.

Upholding 175 years of tradition, David and his team labour long and hard to ensure that their malt whisky remains the malt against which all others must be judged. It is a dedication born of a passion to produce the very best.

THE PILLARS OF SPIRITUAL WISDOM

Within the walls of Easter Elchies House, David and his team talk frequently about "The Six Pillars of Spiritual Wisdom" – those unique elements which combine to make The Macallan peerless. An absolute loyalty to these Pillars ensures that whatever else may occur in the world, The Macallan remains The Macallan.

1. THE BARLEY

The Macallan continues to use traditional Golden Promise Barley, a costly practice long abandoned by most other distilleries. It lends the spirit a rich, full fruity character which balances with the wood and sherry flavours.

2. THE YEASTS

No less than four yeasts combine to ensure a perfect fermentation, which creates a more complex spirit and in turn a more complex whisky.

3. THE COPPER STILLS

The Macallan has retained the original size and shape of its particularly small hand-beaten copper stills, heated in the traditional way by direct furnace from below, in order to preserve its unique spirit character. By running them traditionally and slowly, the spirit remains complex and pure.

4. THE CUT

The cut of spirit taken from the distillation is exceptionally selective – the proportion of spirit deemed worthy to bear The Macallan name is smaller than even the most fastidious of its competitors.

5. THE NATURAL COLOUR

Unlike other malts, The Macallan does not have its colour enhanced by adding caramel. The deep, rich golden glow of The Macallan is derived wholly naturally from marrying different casks – which means its rich natural colour is matched by its rich, natural taste.

6. SHERRY CASKS

The Macallan continues to insist on maturing its whisky exclusively in Spanish oak sherry casks. This oak creates the rich, resinous spicy character in the whisky. Due to the

increasing expense and scarcity of these containers, it is many years since other distillers have insisted exclusively on their use. Only The Macallan still does – and has no intention of stopping.

"About the most delicious malt ever."
Sir Kingsley Amis

AN INTRODUCTION TO THE MACALLAN SINGLE HIGHLAND MALT SCOTCH WHISKIES

A good many Taste of Scotland establishments offer a bewildering array of whisky from which to choose. To help ease selection, David Robertson, The Macallan's Whisky Maker, offers a guided tour around The Macallan's superlative range – along with a few observations from other distinguished Macallan lovers.

The Macallan 10 Years Old Single Malt Whisky: is slightly sweet with a hint of almonds, pears, heather and sherry.

". . . a Rolls-Royce among malts"
The Harrods' Book of Whisky

The Macallan 18 Years Old Single Malt Whisky: is more honeyed, with an assertive sherry character with a hint of almonds, pears and long oak-flavoured dry finish.

"Due to the unfailing regularity with which it wins, we no longer include The Macallan 18 Years Old in our tastings. We have instead enshrined it in our Hall of Fame."
US Quarterly Review

The Macallan 25 Years Old Single Malt Whisky:

is elegant, rich, full bodied with heather and honey notes and a distinct silky complexity and sweetness.

"Every whisky lover knows how good The Macallan is."
The Sunday Times

The Macallan 30 Years Old Single Malt:

has a taste of rich dried fruit and sherry, overlaid with hints of orange.

"...a sensational nose"
Whisky Magazine

SPECIAL BOTTLINGS

The Macallan Gran Reserva is suffused with rich and complex spicy characters, delicious dried fruit flavours and a background of resinous wood – lending the whisky a profound depth of character, owing much to its Spanish oak sherry wood heritage.

"The Dom Perignon of Scotch"
Maxim Magazine

The Macallan 1948 is a rare 51 Years Old malt which owes much of its character to the post-war era of fuel scarcity when barley would have been kilned over a combination of local peat and coal. It has a distinctively rich phenolic and citrus character with apples and coriander. Only 366 bottles have been produced and individually dated, one for each day of 1948, a leap year.

"I love The Macallan"
Omar Sharif

The Macallan Millennium Decanter:

is a limited edition bottling of very rare 50 Years Old malt, selected to celebrate the end of this Millennium and the start of the next.

"The Macallan taste is as distinctive as the Hapsburg nose and the Cecil chin."
Sir Clement Freud

VISIT EASTER ELCHIES – HOME OF THE MACALLAN

If you are in Speyside and would like to visit Easter Elchies, home of the finest single malt whisky in the world, then The Macallan would be delighted to welcome you. Simply call 01340 871471 to make an appointment and we will give you a warm Speyside welcome.

Or why not join **The Advocates of The Macallan** – a select band of whisky lovers who share notes, tales and news on their favourite malt – The Macallan. Call 01340 871471 for details.

WALKERS SHORTBREAD – FROM 1898 TO THE MILLENNIUM AND BEYOND

WALKERS SHORTBREAD LTD. is one of Scotland's success stories. Founded in 1898 by Joseph Walker as a village bakery in Aberlour, the company has expanded into a highly respected international concern, specialising in traditional, quality products baked to original recipes which are widely considered to be the finest in the UK.

Proud of their heritage, Joseph's three grandchildren – Joseph, James and Marjorie developed the business from the original bakery to purpose built factories in Aberlour, in the heart of the Scottish Highlands.

During the sixties, demand for their shortbread increased dramatically and accounts were opened with top stores, such as Harrods, and Fortnum and Mason. Further expansion led to successful exporting of their products which are now available in the world's finest food stores.

Walkers combines modern technology with age-old craftsmanship and traditional family recipes to produce luxury gifts and treats in distinctive tartan packaging and decorative tins featuring renowned Scottish paintings.

Each Walkers product is made from the finest ingredients with no artificial additives, flavourings or colourings, certified Kosher (OUD), without animal fats and suitable for vegetarians.

The choice is endless, from traditional shortbread to mouth watering variations including almond, hazelnut, stem ginger and macadamia nut shortbread. Walkers Ginger Royals must be the ultimate in shortbread. Each contains tangy, moist pieces of ginger and is generously coated with smooth melt in the mouth dark chocolate.

Walkers has recently added organic shortbread to its ranges. Made to the same well-loved shortbread recipe but using the finest organic flour, sugar and butter, this unique product is the true taste of natural goodness.

As well as shortbread, Walkers produces other traditional Scottish specialities which include oatcakes, cakes and biscuits.

To commemorate the Millennium, Walkers has introduced two innovative new shortbreads – whisky and champagne. These new products are available in striking silver packaging. A specially selected assortment of shortbread in a unique silver, dome-shaped tin, which provides the perfect keepsake long after the product has been enjoyed, ensures that the year 2000 is celebrated in style.

$\mathcal{A}uchen\ \mathcal{C}astle$

HOTEL & RESTAURANT

BEATTOCK · MOFFAT · DUMFRIESSHIRE · DG10 9SH
TEL (01683) 300407 · FAX (01683) 300667

The towers, spires, turrets, gilded staircases and shining silver of a magnificent Victorian Mansion. Once the home of Sir William Younger, Auchen Castle stands proudly amidst 30 acres of exotic woodland with its own trout loch and boats.

The Italian terrace with playing fountain and secluded wedding garden are ideal for memorable photographs.

Our public rooms are grand, elegant and comfortable, while the bedrooms offer true luxury.

Fresh local produce is the key to our cuisine – Solway Salmon, Galloway Beef, Annandale Lamb and Haggis are featured on our menu. Menu changed daily.

Auchen Castle is a unique and magical hotel.

Nr. Moffat just off the A74/M74 Junction 15 Children, pets and helicopters welcome.

See entry page 55

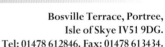

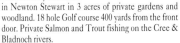

Culloden House

Inverness IV2 7BX Scotland
Telephone 01463 790461 or 0800 980 4561
Facsimile 01463 792181
Email info@cullodenhouse.co.uk
Website www.cullodenhouse.co.uk

STB★★★★   AA ★★★★ ❀ ❀

This Adam styled Georgian Country House incorporates hundreds of years of history, culture and luxury together with superb cuisine using the best of Scottish produce, individually appointed bedrooms and personal service. Associated with both Jacobite uprisings and Bonnie Prince Charlie's last battle 16 April 1746 on Culloden Moor. Central to the whisky trail, 35 golf courses, castles, fishing and shooting.

GOLF • STALKING • FISHING • HORSE RIDING
CLAY PIGEON SHOOTING • 4X4 OFF ROAD DRIVING
BY ARRANGEMENT

See entry page 133

See entry page 213

Fernhill Hotel

PORTPATRICK

★★★★
STB

AA ROSETTE
FOR FOOD

The Fernhill overlooks the picturesque village and harbour of Portpatrick and commands breathtaking views over the Irish Sea. Comfortable lounges and restaurant share the same everchanging view, as do most of the bedrooms. The hotel's rosetted conservatory restaurant is a fine setting for lunch and dinner where chef John Henry and his team serve a wonderful variety of local seasonal produce. Fresh lobster, caught in the waters off the Mull of Galloway, is the house speciality either as a delicious starter or as a main course, with a variety of sauces.

 Fernhill Hotel, Portpatrick DG9 8TD
Tel 01776 810 220 Fax 01776 810 596
e-mail fernhill@portpatrick.demon.co.uk

FLODIGARRY
COUNTRY HOUSE HOTEL
Isle of Skye

Country House Hotel of the Year
Taste of Scotland   Macallan Award

OPEN ALL YEAR

A REAL TASTE OF ISLAND LIVING

THE SUNDAY TIMES

The Sunday Times Scotland says *'it is worth beating a path to Flodigarry which enjoys one of the finest situations of any country house hotel in Scotland, … in the restaurant the scallops came with a Pernod sauce, superb, fresh and milky, as well cooked as any scallops I have had this year'.*

Flora Macdonalds Cottage at Flodigarry Hotel

STB ★★★★

**STAFFIN   ISLE OF SKYE
SCOTLAND   IV51 9HZ
TEL 01470 552 203 FAX 01470 552 301**

www.milford.co.uk/go/flodigarry.html

See entry page 159

See entry page 72

See entry page 46   See entry page 158

welcome to

The

Guide

ALL THE TASTES OF SCOTLAND

FOR MORE THAN 20 YEARS, the Taste of Scotland Scheme has acted as a standard bearer for the best of Scottish catering and cuisine. As an organisation it has remained true to its original quest – to identify eating establishments who use fresh local produce to create the kind of quality menus, textures and flavours that diners are unlikely to find anywhere else in the world.

In that time, there has been a growing sense of pride in the part the catering industry has played in defining the country's confident new identity. What makes today's Scottish cooking unique is the ability of our cooks and chefs to combine a great tradition with all that is good and exciting in world cooking.

Much improved transport links make it easier to source all kinds of fresh produce from virtually any part of the country. But that is only part of the story. Fresh ideas are easier to source, too, and influences from all over the world have made dining out in Scotland an exciting and exhilarating experience.

The Scottish tradition is thriving and its practitioners are not afraid to be bold and adventurous when they come to prepare new dishes. For a comparatively small country, the variety of styles on offer in such a wide range of establishments is quite remarkable.

While The Taste of Scotland Scheme is doubtless the most reliable guide to Scottish cuisine, we cannot claim it to be totally comprehensive. The diner in Scotland can, for instance, choose from an almost limitless array of international and ethnic restaurants. Although they are not listed in this Guide, they form a very important part of the culinary scene and continue to add to the diversity of eating out in Scotland.

There is also a small handful of establishments serving Scottish dishes, using Scottish produce, who are not listed in this Guide because they choose not to join the scheme. What Taste of Scotland can say about each of the 400 plus eating places listed in this Guide is that they have agreed to submit themselves to a thorough incognito inspection and assessment. Only by achieving the high standards our inspectors are seeking, do they merit a place in the Guide.

Eating out in Scotland can and indeed should be a wonderful, unique experience. You can regard this Guide as our invitation to you to share in that experience.

ARDOE HOUSE HOTEL
South Deeside Road
Aberdeen AB12 5YP
Tel: 01224 867355
Fax: 01224 861283
E-mail: info@ardoe.macdonald-hotels.co.uk

B9077, 3 miles west of Aberdeen. Turn left at hotel sign and up driveway.

Just outside Aberdeen this baronial-style hotel provides very good accommodation and hospitality.

- Scottish baronial mansion converted to a comfortable country house hotel.
- Modern and traditional Scottish cuisine.
- "Relax, be pampered and sample the fine food."

Ardoe House is a classic Scots baronial granite mansion. As day turns to night Ardoe turns into a fairytale castle and it is a delight to relax in the original palatial rooms. The bedrooms have private facilities and there are also function rooms available for conferences and weddings. An extension of a ballroom and full leisure club to the house is planned for the end of 1999. The addition of 43 bedrooms will be operational by May 2000. Dining is à la carte (or house menu if on an exclusive rate) from an extensive menu of unusually treated dishes and imaginative combinations. Chef Ivor Clark draws inspiration from classic French cooking, whilst using fresh Scottish produce. The hotel has 2 AA Rosettes. *See advert page 22.*

Open all year
🏠 Rooms: 71 en suite
🛏 DB&B from £65   B&B from £45
SP Special rates available
✗ Food available all day £££
✗ Lunch ££
✗ Dinner £££
Ⓥ Vegetarians welcome
🕏 Children welcome
♿ Facilities for disabled visitors
🚭 No smoking in dining room

Fillet of hot-smoked Scottish salmon, with lemon and barley risotto. Loin of Highland venison, with warm apple and blueberry marmalade and malt whisky jus. Hot clootie dumpling with baby pear flamed in Drambuie and honey cream.

STB ★★★★ Hotel
💳 Credit cards: Mastercard/Eurocard, Visa, Diners Club, Switch
👤 General Manager: Ewan Kirkpatrick

THE ATHOLL HOTEL
54 King's Gate
Aberdeen, Grampian
AB15 4YN
Tel: 01224 323505
Fax: 01224 321555
E-mail: info@atholl-aberdeen.co.uk.

Follow signs for A96 north. Turn right at King's Gate roundabout, the hotel is situated ½ mile along King's Gate in the heart of the city's West End.

Comfortable and friendly city centre hotel.

- Granite building.
- Traditional Scottish cooking.
- "A well-placed hotel with good food being offered to suit the shopper, visitor or business clientele."

The Atholl Hotel is under the personal supervision of Gordon Sinclair who has an eye for detail and high standards. The rooms are well-appointed and attractively decorated and the hotel has a comfortable and warm atmosphere – the staff are friendly and enthusiastic. The cooking is simple and straightforward with high quality ingredients and there is much evidence of local quality produce. Menus change monthly with specials changing nightly depending upon availablility.

Open all year except New Year's Day
🏠 Rooms: 35 en suite
🛏 B&B £71–£81
SP Special rates available
✗ Lunch ££
✗ Dinner ££
Ⓥ Vegetarians welcome
🕏 Children welcome

West Coast scallop, prawn and smoked salmon in a light wine cream sauce served in a savoury tartlet. Oven-roasted venison fillet with a herb crust accompanied by a rich game and port jus. Sticky toffee pudding with fudge sauce.

STB ★★★★ Hotel
💳 Credit cards: Mastercard/Eurocard, American Express, Visa, Diners Club, Switch
👤 Managing Partner: Gordon Sinclair

THE COURTYARD RESTAURANTS ON THE LANE

Alford Lane
Aberdeen AB1 1YD
Tel: 01224 213795
Fax: 01224 212961

In Aberdeen's West End, between Holburn Street and Albyn Place, just round the corner from Union Street.

A gourmet's paradise in central Aberdeen.

- City centre restaurant and bistro.
- Scottish cooking with a Mediterranean influence.
- "Good service, atmosphere and food all add to a fine dining experience."

The Courtyard on the Lane is a small stone building in a cobbled lane in Aberdeen's commercial district. It is a sanctuary of good food and a great discovery. Martha's Bistro (downstairs) has an informal atmosphere for lunch and dinner. Upstairs, the Courtyard Restaurant is more formal, the atmosphere intimate, and encourages you to linger over dinner. Head chef Martin Bühler and his team have created a fresh and innovative menu with daily selections of fish, game and poultry. Fine dining menu served in Courtyard Restaurant (upstairs) everyday, lunch and dinner. Bistro-style menu served downstairs. It is advisable to book.

Open all year except first week Jan
Closed Sun
✗ Lunch except Sun £-££
✗ Dinner except Sun Mon ££-£££
Ⓥ Vegetarians welcome
✸ Children welcome
♿ Facilities for disabled visitors – bistro restaurant only
✗ No pipes or cigars in bistro + no smoking in restaurant

Local Brie cheese wrapped in smoked salmon and filo pastry, baked and served with a spiced apricot chutney. Loin of Highland venison wrapped in a wild mushroom and rosemary coat sliced on a roasted parsnip and red onion compote edged by a light port wine and thyme jus. Blackcurrant crème brûlée with shortbread biscuits.

💳 Credit cards: Mastercard/Eurocard, American Express, Visa, Diners Club, Switch, Delta
👤 Manager: Martin Kennedy

CRAIGLYNN HOTEL

36 Fonthill Road
Aberdeen AB11 6UJ
Tel: 01224 584050
Fax: 01224 212225
E-mail: craiglynn@compuserve.com
Web: craiglynn.co.uk

On corner of Fonthill Road and Bon Accord Street, midway between Union Street and King George VI Bridge. Car park access from Bon Accord Street.

An intimate and charming hotel, close to the centre of Aberdeen.

- An impressive late Victorian house built with local granite.
- Lovingly prepared Scottish cooking.
- "A traditional granite town house hotel offering a high standard of accommodation and food."

Craiglynn Hotel was once the home of a wealthy Aberdeen fish merchant and has attractive rooms with high moulded ceilings and carved fire surrounds. These features have been carefully preserved by the hotel's owners, Chris and Hazel Mann, as have the parquet flooring and rose-wood panelling in the dining room (which was originally the billiard room). Service is friendly and attentive, and guests are made to feel part of the family. In the handsome dining room menus are short, since everything is prepared from fresh produce (even home-grown), and the cooking homely. The bedrooms are very comfortable and have unique en suite facilities.

Open all year except Christmas Day + Boxing Day
🛏 Rooms: 8 en suite
🍴 B&B £27.50–£39
✗ Non-residents – by reservation
🍷 Restricted licence
✗ Dinner ££
Ⓥ Vegetarians welcome
✗ No smoking in dining room + bedrooms

Parsnip and apple soup. Lamb noisettes garnished with fresh rosemary. Freshly prepared desserts.

STB ★★★★ Hotel
💳 Credit cards: Mastercard/Eurocard, American Express, Visa, Diners Club, Switch
👤 Partners: Hazel & Chris Mann

LAIRHILLOCK INN & RESTAURANT
Netherley
by Stonehaven
Aberdeenshire AB39 3QS
Tel: 01569 730001
Fax: 01569 731175
E-mail: lairhillock@lairhillock.force9.net
Web: www.welcome.to.lairhillock/

Take A90 south from Aberdeen, pass Portlethen then take right-hand turn for Durris for 3 miles. From the South, once on straight after Cammachmore, turn left at the Durris junction.

A charming old coaching inn between Stonehaven and Aberdeen. Inn on left-hand side.

- Atmospheric country pub with restaurant.
- Modern cooking, with continental influences.
- "A popular inn engulfed with charm, hospitality and fine food."

Lairhillock is a traditional small coaching inn (originally a farmhouse). It stands on the old Stonehaven-Aberdeen road, and was certainly there when Bonnie Prince Charlie took this road north to ultimate defeat at Culloden in 1746. The place has been extensively refurbished by owners, Frank and Anne Budd, in a way which enhances the original rustic features (low ceilings, dark beams, carved oak bar front, large open hearth with real log fires). Friendly, helpful staff complete the picture to make a very welcoming inn. Beef comes from a local farm; daily fish from Gourdon; fruits from local suppliers. Sauces are interesting and appropriate, and the overall treatment of the food sensitive and unusually good. An interesting wine list features some unusual wines, and some first growths. The Lairhillock is a great favourite with business people, locals and tourists.

Open all year except 25, 26 Dec, 1 + 2 Jan
✗ Lunch £
✗ Dinner ££
Ⓥ Vegetarians welcome
🧒 Children welcome
♿ Facilities for disabled visitors

Fresh crab and smoked salmon terrine with chive and sour cream dressing. Grilled fillet of venison in a black pepper crust with Madeira and redcurrant sauce.

💳 Credit cards: Mastercard/Eurocard, American Express, Visa, Diners Club, Switch, Delta
👤 Proprietors: Frank & Anne Budd

THE MARCLIFFE AT PITFODELS
North Deeside Road
Aberdeen AB15 9YA
Tel: 01224 861000
Fax: 01224 868860
E-mail: reservations@marcliffe.com
Web: www.nettrak.co.uk/marcliffe/

On A93 to Braemar. 1 mile from A92. 3 miles from city centre.

An outstanding country house hotel on the outskirts of Aberdeen.

- A large modern building tastefully in keeping with the older house it encompasses.
- Modern classic cooking with French influence and the best of Scottish ingredients.
- "At the Marcliffe you have outstanding quality of food, service and accommodation."

The Marcliffe at Pitfodels is a clever combination of old and new. Its atmosphere is luxurious, and enhances modern design with antiques and baronial detailing – the spacious new foyer has a stone flagged floor, comfortable sofas and an open fire. The hotel is set in eight acres of wooded grounds in the Deeside area of the west end of the city. There are two restaurants: the Conservatory, and the Invery Room. Menus in both are well-balanced and extensive; and the cooking is accomplished. Fresh lobster is available from May to October. 100 malt whiskies and 400 wines available. *See advert page 261.*

Open all year
🛏 Rooms: 42 en suite
🛎 DB&B £82.50–£150   B&B £52.50–£125
SP Special rates available
✗ Lunch £££
✗ Dinner £££
Ⓥ Vegetarians welcome
🧒 Children welcome
♿ Facilities for disabled visitors
🚭 No smoking in Invery Room Restaurant
🐂 Member of the Scotch Beef Club

Finnan haddock and leek filled with rösti potato. Peppered chump of Buchan lamb, dauphinoise potatoes, minted peas. Warm coconut pie with orange marmalade ice cream.

STB ★★★★★ Hotel
💳 Credit cards: Mastercard/Eurocard, American Express, Visa, Diners Club, Switch
👤 Proprietor: Stewart Spence

NORWOOD HALL HOTEL
Garthdee Road
Aberdeen AB15 9FX
Tel: 01224 868951
Fax: 01224 869868

1 mile from the Bridge of Dee roundabout off the
A90 and the A96.

The country house hotel in the city.

- Victorian mansion house.
- Modern Scottish with international influences.
- "A country house hotel offering hearty and
  flavoursome food."

Built in 1887 on the site of Pitfodels Castle this
Victorian mansion house hotel retains much of its
original features and has been sympathetically
restored to its former glory. This country house
hotel in the city offers true Scottish hospitality
together with the best of local produce. The hotel is
run by a professional and dedicated team. Food is
presented pleasingly in the Victorian dining room
and flavours do not disappoint.

	Open all year
🛏	Rooms: 21 en suite
🍴	DB&B £70–£102 B&B £50–£82
SP	Special rates available
✗	Lunch from £
✗	Dinner £££
V	Vegetarians welcome
⚹	Children welcome
♿	Limited facilities for disabled visitors
⊬	No smoking in dining room

**Assiette of smoked venison and chicken served
with an olive and grape salad. Rack of lamb with a
mustard and herb crust, set on a bed of ratatouille.
Walnut bread and butter pudding with caramelised
banana and warm butterscotch sauce.**

STB ★★★ Hotel
- Credit cards: Mastercard/Eurocard, American
  Express, Visa, Diners Club, Switch, Delta
- General Manager: Morag MacIndoe

SIMPSONS HOTEL BAR/BRASSERIE
59 Queens Road
Aberdeen AB15 4YP
Tel: 01224 327777
Fax: 01224 327700
E-mail: address@simpsonshotel.com

Follow signs for A96 North. Turn right at Queens
Road Roundabout, hotel is 500 yards down the road
on right-hand side.

**Contemporary-style restaurant attached to smart
modern hotel.**

- Three traditional granite town houses.
- Modern Scottish cuisine with international
  influences.
- "The high quality of the surroundings,
  atmosphere and the food are all on equal terms
  here."

Simpsons is a modern-style hotel brasserie with
much of its designer furniture and tiles coming from
Spain. Rich colour schemes with clever use of tiles,
ceramics and plants adorn the interior. The vaulted
ceiling restaurant has this theme extending to the
sophisticated hotel, even the courtyard has a
Mediterranean feel with the terracotta washed
walls and bright busy floral window boxes. Head
chef Graham Mutch mixes the traditional and
original in innovative recipes using the best of
Aberdeenshire local products. Simpsons has 1 AA
Rosette.

	Open all year
🛏	Rooms: 37 en suite
🍴	B&B £105–£145
SP	Special rates available
✗	Lunch ££
✗	Dinner £££
V	Vegetarians welcome
⚹	Children welcome
♿	Facilities for disabled visitors
⊬	Rooms non smoking. Smoking area in
Restaurant

**Cajun spiced West Coast crabcakes with a lime
and mango chutney. Saddle of venison filled with a
veal and Strathdon Blue cheese mousse, glazed
with a juniper berry and blueberry jus. Black
cherry chocolate ganache with cardamom ice
cream.**

STB ★★★★ Hotel
- Credit cards: Mastercard/Eurocard, American
  Express, Visa, Switch, Delta
- General Manager: Shona Stewart

THE VICTORIA RESTAURANT
140 Union Street
Aberdeen AB10 1JD
Tel: 01224 621381

In the middle of the main street, on the first floor above Jamieson and Carry the Jewellers.

A city restaurant on Aberdeen's main street.

- Victorian.
- Modern and traditional cooking.
- "A centrally situated restaurant for that badly needed rest from shopping."

Although the entrance to the Victoria Restaurant is through the gift department of Jamieson and Carry, the Jewellers, on Union Street it is run independently and the proprietors have a 'free hand' to do their own thing. The Victoria has been a restaurant for at least 50 years and is now owned by Gillian and Gordon Harold. Gillian is head chef and Gordon is in charge of the front of house. There is an evident commitment here to quality with highly visible sourcing of Scottish produce and skilful cooking.

Open all year except 2 weeks Jan
Closed local holidays, Christmas + New Year
Closed Sun
✗   Food available all day except Sun £
✗   Lunch except Sun £
Ⓥ   Vegetarians welcome
⚘   Children welcome
✉   No smoking in restaurant

Home-made bread topped with Scottish Brie, baked in the oven and served with Gillian's apple chutney. Local haddock, pan-fried in herb breadcrumbs with sauteed new potatoes and salads. Fresh Perthshire strawberries with peach sauce and locally-made ice cream.

💳   Credit cards: Mastercard/Eurocard, Visa, Switch, Delta
𝕏   Proprietors: Gillian & Gordon Harold

FARLEYER HOUSE HOTEL
Aberfeldy
Perthshire
PH15 2JE
Tel: 01887 820332 Fax: 01887 829430
E-mail: reservations@farleyer.com
Web: www.farleyer.com

Follow signs to the Castle Menzies and Weem on the B846. The hotel is situated 1 mile past the castle on right, approx 2 miles from Aberfeldy.

An award-winning country house hotel in beautiful surroundings.

- A small, formal and intimate hotel, rightly renowned.
- Sensational Scottish cuisine.
- "Outstanding in every respect."

In the heart of the old Castle Menzies estate, Farleyer was built as a croft in the 16th century. Enlarged twice since then Farleyer retains its air of calm opulence. Thirty-four acres of grounds enhance the house's tranquillity. Its Bistro offers imaginative Scottish cooking in a relaxed and informal atmosphere. The semi-formal Glenlyon Room offers an à la carte menu which reflects the outstanding quality of local game, meat and fish.

Open all year
🛏   Rooms: 19 en suite
🛏   DB&B £85–£130   B&B £60–£105
SP   Special rates available
✗   Food available all day ££
✗   Lunch ££
✗   Dinner ££
Ⓥ   Vegetarians welcome
⚘   Children welcome
♿   Facilities for disabled visitors
✉   No smoking in Glenlyon Room
🐂   Member of the Scotch Beef Club

House smoked venison with redcurrant and shallot dressing. Roasted woodcock on a garlic croute with rhubarb compote, port wine and game jus. Hot raspberry gratin with home-made vanilla ice.

STB ★★★★ Hotel
💳   Credit cards: Mastercard/Eurocard, American Express, Visa, Diners Club, Switch, Delta
𝕏   General Manager: Andy Cole

GUINACH HOUSE
by The Birks, Aberfeldy
Perthshire PH15 2ET
Tel: 01887 820251
Fax: 01887 829607

On A826, south-west outskirts of Aberfeldy, on road to 'The Birks', Guinach is signposted from Urlar Road.

This small hotel is run by international Master Chef Bert MacKay and his wife, Marian.

- This Victorian house is set in three acres of secluded gardens and birch woods with stunning views across Perthshire.
- Best Scottish sophisticated cuisine combining a range of national and international influences.
- "Relax in the friendly and hospitable atmosphere with true Scottish hospitality and outstanding cooking!"

Guinach House is a seven-roomed hotel immersed in the rolling countryside around Aberfeldy. It is an ideal location for those who simply wish to relax in tranquil surroundings and indulge in gastronomic inspiration. For those who prefer to build up an appetite more actively, there are nearby facilities for swimming, golf, fly fishing and riding. The MacKays are attentive and friendly hosts who run Guinach more like a home than a hotel. Bert's culinary expertise allows him to create rich and varied menus, while maximising on the availability of fresh local produce. Guinach has 2 AA Rosettes.

Open all year except Christmas Eve to 27 Dec
🏠 Rooms: 7 en suite
🛏 DB&B £68   B&B £45.50
✕ Dinner 4 course menu £££
Ⓥ Vegetarians welcome
🕏 Children welcome
🚭 No smoking in dining room

Soft poached egg on warmed nan bread topped with mushrooms and ham in cheddar cream sauce. Rosettes of beef fillet set on celeriac and bacon rösti edged with Guiness and muscovado jus. Florentine of milles feuilles with soft berries.

STB ★★★★ Hotel
💳 Credit cards: Mastercard/Eurocard, Visa
👤 Proprietors: Mr & Mrs MacKay

BIRKWOOD LODGE
Gordon Crescent
Aboyne
Aberdeenshire AB34 5HJ
Tel/Fax: 013398 86347

In Aboyne take the A93 towards Ballater. Gordon Crescent is the first lane on left after village green at Roman Catholic chapel.

High quality family run B&B.

- Victorian pink granite house.
- Scottish home cooking.
- "Taste the best of Scottish cooking as Jim and Elizabeth completely spoil you."

Birkwood Lodge is a typical Victorian Deeside house in pink granite and the interior has many features typifying the exuberance of the period. Two of the bedrooms are en suite and attractively decorated and furnished. The public rooms are equally very comfortable and include such little extras as a game board and excellent reading materials. The Thorburn family are your hosts and have superb local knowledge to ensure that you do not miss any of the attractions in the area. Jim also lets fishing on the Dee which often influences items on the menu and Elizabeth is in charge of the cooking which is highly accomplished, using only the freshest produce. Menus are well-balanced and the food is flavoursome and presented in an appetising style.

Open all year
🏠 Rooms: 3 (2 en suite, 1 with private facilities)
🛏 DB&B £45   B&B £25
✕ Residents only
Ⓤ Unlicensed – guests welcome to take own wine
🧺 Packed Lunch on request £
✕ Dinner ££
Ⓥ Vegetarians welcome
🕏 Children welcome
🚭 No smoking in dining room + bedrooms

Goujons of sole. Local roast pork with crackling. Blairgowrie raspberry mousse.

STB ★★★★ B&B
💳 No credit cards
👤 Owners: Jim & Elizabeth Thorburn

THE WHITE COTTAGE RESTAURANT
Dess
Aboyne
Aberdeenshire AB34 5BP
Tel/Fax: 013398 86265

On main A93 Aberdeen-Braemar, 2½ miles east
of Aboyne.

**Award-winning restaurant in the heart of Royal
Deeside.**

• Pink granite 150 year old converted cottage.
• Creative Scottish cooking.
• "A delightful restaurant with charm and
  character in the heart of Deeside."

Laurie and Josephine Mill have built a strong
reputation with local clientele for their special style.
Chef/proprietor Laurie is enthusiastic about the best
raw materials he can source and believes in
allowing the intrinsic flavours to emerge simply on
the plate. Fish and vegetables are minimally cooked,
soup and stocks are long in the making and sauces
complement rather than dominate. There is also a
vegetarian menu. The cottage is delightful, in the
winter log fires add to the intimacy and in the
summer the conservatory and pond garden lends
itself well to the relaxed atmosphere that pervades.
This commitment to the food is also reflected in a
carefully compiled wine list with wines from the Old
and New World and all reasonably priced. White
Cottage has 2 AA Rosettes.

Open most of the year except 24 Dec to 4 Jan
Closed Mon
🏠 Room: 1 en suite
🛏 DB&B £46–£52   B&B £21–£26
🍷 Restaurant licence
✕ Lunch and supper except Mon £-££
✕ Dinner except Mon 4 course menu £££
Ⓥ Vegetarians welcome
♿ Facilities for disabled visitors
🚭 No smoking in restaurant

**Little pan-fried rösti sea cakes with a lemon butter
sauce. Baked tarragon chicken with spiced apple
and crème fraîche. Dark chocolate and espresso
roulade with sugared cashew ice cream.**

💳 Credit cards: Mastercard/Eurocard, Visa,
    Switch
🅝 Proprietors: Laurie & Josephine Mill

SUMMER ISLES HOTEL
Achiltibuie
Ross-shire IV26 2YG
Tel: 01854 622282
Fax: 01854 622251
E-mail: smilehotel@aol.com

A835 to Ullapool and beyond – 10 miles north of
Ullapool turn left onto single track road to
Achiltibuie. Village is 15 miles on (i.e. 25 miles
from Ullapool).

**Award-winning country hotel in the West
Highlands.**

• A country hotel in a converted croft house.
• Innovative modern Scottish cooking.
• "A breath of fresh air for the finest of diners!"

Achiltibuie is another world. The village itself is a
straggle of white cottages at the end of which you
find the hotel, facing out over the bay to the Summer
Isles and the Hebrides beyond. Proprietors Mark
and Gerry Irvine are natural hosts, and offer a
unique experience for even the most discerning
diner. As well as a light lunch, a more formal lunch
(tablecloths, crystal, etc) is also available. Dinner is
served promptly at 8 pm using some of the finest
unadulterated produce Scotland has to offer. Chef
Chris Firth-Bernard creates sumptuous dishes to
tempt the palate and there is a well-sourced wine
list, with up to 400 bins, to choose from. Everyone
who goes there leaves reluctantly, determined to
return.

Open Easter to mid Oct
🏠 Rooms: 13,12 with en suite facilities (plus log
    cabins adjacent to hotel)
🛏 DB&B £79–£110   B&B £44–£75
✕ Food available all day £
✕ Lunch £££
✕ Dinner ££££
Ⓥ Vegetarians welcome
☆ Children welcome
🚭 No smoking in restaurant + bedrooms

**Carpaccio of Aberdeen Angus beef fillet, served
with a piquant relish. Fresh fillet of halibut with
langoustine tails and steamed mussels in white
wine. Hot steamed syrup sponge pudding.**

STB ★★★★ Hotel
💳 Credit cards: Mastercard/Eurocard, Visa,
    Switch
🅝 Proprietors: Mark & Gerry Irvine

BOUZY ROUGE

1 Rochsolloch Road
Airdrie
Lanarkshire
ML6 9BB
Tel: 01236 763853
Fax: 01236 770340
Web: www.scotscape.com/bouzy-rouge

At junction of Rochsolloch Road and Deedes Street on A89 Glasgow-Airdrie Road.

Stylish, contemporary all-day restaurant and bar.

- Large, ground floor of tenement building.
- Light modern cuisine.
- "A warm and relaxed atmosphere where good food can be found using finest Scottish ingredients with European influence."

The name Bouzy Rouge originates from the village of Bouzy in France, famous for producing fine Champagnes – the rouge being the village's most unusual red wine made from the Pinot Noir grape. Deceptively large, this city bistro has style. Furniture is individually hand crafted by Scottish wood-craftsmen and sculptors and the food matches the interior being colourful, eclectic and having flavoursome appeal. Run by a young yet experienced husband and wife team with similar popular eateries in Glasgow and Edinburgh.

Open all year except New Year's Day
✕ Food available all day ££
✕ Lunch £-££
✕ Dinner ££
Ⓥ Vegetarians welcome
☩ Children welcome
♿ Facilities for disabled visitors

Smoked haddock and Scottish cheddar tartlet with a rich crayfish and brandy bisque. Fillet of Perthshire ostrich roasted pink and set on pommes dauphinoise with a juniper berry reduction. Butterscotch mousse with a praline crust and a coffee bean anglaise.

💳 Credit cards: Mastercard/Eurocard, American Express, Visa, Diners Club, Switch, Delta
Ⓜ Proprietors: Alan & Audrey Brown

FARRIERS COUNTRY HOTEL

Alva Stables
Woodland Park
Alva
Clackmannanshire FK12 5HU
Tel: 01259 762702 Fax: 01259 769782
Web: www.scoot.co.uk/farriers-country-hotel/

From Stirling take A91 through to Alva. As you leave Alva turn left at hotel sign, then drive ½ mile to end of road.

Historic building.

- Converted stables.
- Good home cooking.
- "Country hotel in pleasurable rural setting, with good standards."

Farriers is situated at the foot of the Ochil Hills. The restaurant occupies a tastefully reformed stable block looking onto the cobbled courtyard. The atmosphere is complete with the use of attractive wooden furniture, and an impressive feature fireplace divides the restaurant into two intimate dining rooms. The original building dates back to 1820 when it provided space for 17 horses and two coach houses. Today the building offers tastefully decorated bedrooms, coffee shop and craft shop and, of course, the restaurant where the finest local produce is served in modern-style.

Open all year except Boxing Day
🛏 Rooms: 6
🛏 DB&B £65–£90 B&B £50–£55
SP Special rates available
✕ Food available all day
✕ Lunch ££
✕ Dinner £££
Ⓥ Vegetarians welcome
☩ Children welcome
♿ Facilities for disabled visitors
🐕 Dogs welcome

Home-smoked Barbary duck with hot gooseberry chutney and rocket. Pan-seared Tay salmon on garlic mash with sweet pepper coulis and crispy leek. Raspberry and Drambuie creme brûlée.

💳 Credit cards: Mastercard/Eurocard, American Express, Visa, Switch, Delta
Ⓜ Chef Proprietor: Gary Turner

'THE OVEN BISTRO' AT DRUMNACREE HOUSE

St Ninians Road, Alyth
Perthshire PH11 8AP
Tel/Fax: 01828 632194
E-mail: allan.cull@virgin.net

Turn off A926 Blairgowrie-Kirriemuir to Alyth. Take first turning on left after Clydesdale Bank. Hotel 300 yards on right.

An excellent small hotel with high standards of cuisine and comfort.

- Restored Victorian mansion.
- Eclectic Scottish cuisine with continental influences.
- "Highly accomplished cooking, comfort and informal hospitality."

Drumnacree is situated within lovely gorunds with mature shrubs. The former lounge/bar area is now 'The Oven Bistro' and is decorated in warm Mediterranean colours. Owner/proprietor, Allan Cull, cooks at Tayside's only wood-burning oven, which is located in the bistro, enabling guests to view their choice from the imaginative and innovative menus. Results are really delicious and very succulent. Eleanor Cull is professional and attentive as front of house. There is an evident commitment to good food and freshness here – the hotel has its own vegetable and herb garden – very impressive. Drumnacree has 2 AA Rosettes.

Open all year except New Year
Closed Mon
🏠 Rooms: 6
🛏 DB&B £55–£75 B&B £35–£60.50
🆂🅿 Special rates available
✕ Lunch except Mon £
✕ Dinner except Mon ££
Ⓥ Vegetarians welcome
🕇 Children welcome
🚹 Facilities for disabled visitors
🐕 Dogs welcome
🐄 Member of the Scotch Beef Club

Warm Arbroath smokie mousse with a tomato, fresh basil and virgin olive oil sauce. Lamb shanks with red wine, balsamic vinegar, rosemary and garlic, slowly braised in the wood-burning oven and served on a bed of mixed beans and potatoes. Little pots of chocolate topped with Glenturret liqueur.

STB ★★★★ Hotel
💳 Credit cards: Mastercard/Eurocard, American Express, Visa, Switch, Delta
🙎 Owner/Proprietor: Allan Cull

BEAUMONT LODGE GUEST HOUSE

43 Pittenweem Road
Anstruther
Fife KY10 3DT
Tel/Fax: 01333 310315
E-mail: reservations@beau-lodge.demon.co.uk

Coming from west on A917, 300 yards past 30 mile limit sign on right-hand side.

Small friendly guest house in the centre of Anstruther.

- Small guest house.
- Good home cooking.
- "Guests are made to feel very much at home in this friendly guest house."

Beaumont Lodge is a family-run guest house in the picturesque village of Anstruther. The lodge is situated in a large walled garden and has been run by the Anderson family for the past four years. Everything is prepared in-house with a strong commitment to represent fresh local produce. Dinner orders are placed on arrival and everything is prepared to order. Menus offer good choice – all the food is cooked with a light hand by Mrs Anderson who is a keen and accomplished cook. Beaumont Lodge offers the best of good guest house hospitality and dining in an area with an abundance of interests and pursuits.

Open all year
🏠 Rooms: 5, 4 en suite
🛏 DB&B £34–£43 B&B £22–£28
✕ Residents only
Ⓤ Unlicensed
✕ Dinner ££
Ⓥ Vegetarians welcome
🕇 Children welcome
🚹 Ground floor room suitable for guests with limited mobility
🚭 No smoking throughout

Home-made soup accompanied by fresh dinner rolls. Leg of lamb steak with minted hollandaise sauce. Scotch mist.

STB ★★★★ Guest House
💳 Credit cards: Mastercard/Eurocard, Visa, Delta
🙎 Proprietor/Owner: Julia Anderson

FEORAG HOUSE
Glenborrodale
Acharacle
Argyll PH36 4JP
Tel: 01972 500 248 Fax: 01972 500 285
E-mail: admin@feorag.demon.co.uk
Web: www.feorag.demon.co.uk

36 miles or 1 hour's drive from Corran Ferry. Take
A861 then B8007 to Glenborrodale. 200 yards beyond
school on left.

**A handsome country house on the shores of Loch
Sunart in Glenborrodale.**

- Luxury country house.
- Skilful home cooking.
- "A wonderful guest house with delicious food."

Feorag House (Feorag means squirrel in Gaelic) was
designed and built by its present owners, Peter and
Helen Stockdale, in 1994 on the wooded northern
shore of Loch Sunart. It has a lovely situation, within
yards of a rocky inlet and facing south. The view
can best be appreciated from the large balcony
attached to the sitting room, with open log fire, or in
less clement weather, from the broad bay windows
in the luxurious dining room. Altogether, the house
has been sensitively designed, furnished and
decorated to a high standard. The food is delicious:
both Peter and Helen cook and bake on their Aga;
everything is fresh and local. Do not miss afternoon
tea served at 4.30 pm from silver teapots and fresh
baking from the Aga. Their friendliness and
hospitality is overwhelming. A real find!

    Open all year
🏠 Rooms: 3 en suite
🛏 DB&B £55–£65 B&B £35–£45
SP Special rates available
✗ Residents only
UL Unlicensed – guests welcome to take own wine
✗ Dinner ££
V Vegetarians welcome – by arrangement
ᚾ Children over 10 years welcome
✗ No smoking in dining room + bedrooms

**Seared scallops on rice noodles with mustard seed
dressing. Tenderloin of pork fillet with almond and
apricot stuffing wrapped in smoked bacon, served
on bed of spinach in tomato lochan. Fresh pears
poached in red wine served with a light creme
anglais.**

STB ★★★★★ Guest House
💳 Credit cards: Mastercard/Eurocard, Visa
ᚼ Proprietors: Peter & Helen Stockdale

THE OLD LIBRARY LODGE & RESTAURANT
Sea Front
Arisaig
Inverness-shire PH39 4NH
Tel: 01687 450651
Fax: 01687 450219
E-mail: oldlibrary.arisaig@btinternet.com
Web: www.road-to-the-isles.org

In centre of village on waterfront, next to Post
Office.

Friendly restaurant with imaginative dishes.

- Small cottage-style restaurant with rooms.
- Good, fresh food, seafood a speciality.
- "Where comfort and creativity are rolled into
one."

The Old Library Lodge and Restaurant enjoys an
attractive situation on the waterfront in Arisaig. The
building itself, which is over 200 years old, is a
stone-built stable converted into a restaurant of
character with accommodation attached. The
comfortable accommodation is in a wing of terraced
bedrooms with balconies overlooking the terraced
garden. A cheerful and welcoming atmosphere
prevails not least in the dining room where guests
choose from a table d'hôte menu with a choice of
five of everything – starters, main courses and
puddings. Alan does most of the cooking, and
everthing humanly possible is sourced locally.
Breakfast is something to really look forward to.

    Open 24 Mar to end Oct
    Restaurant open all afternoon in summer
    Closed Tue lunch
🏠 Rooms: 6 en suite
🛏 DB&B from £60 B&B from £37
SP Special rates available
❢ Table licence
✗ Lunch except Tue £-££
✗ Dinner £££
V Vegetarians welcome – prior notice required

**Pan-fried cous cous coated goats cheese. Grilled
local scallops on a celeriac purée. Caramelised
lemon tart with home-made elderflower ice cream.**

STB ★★★ Restaurant with Rooms
💳 Credit cards: Mastercard/Eurocard, American
    Express, Visa, Switch, Delta
ᚼ Proprietors: Alan & Angela Broadhurst

BALCARY BAY HOTEL
Shore Road
Auchencairn
Dumfries & Galloway DG7 1QZ
Tel: 01556 640217/640311
Fax: 01556 640272

A711 Dalbeattie-Kirkcudbright to Auchencairn. Then take 'no through road' signposted Balcary (single track) for 2 miles.

Country house in idyllic setting.

- Superb country house dating back from 1625 standing on the shore of Balcary Bay.
- Modern Scottish cooking.
- "Refreshing modern Scottish cuisine, carefully presented in a uniquely beautiful area."

A carefully modernised and extended country house hotel sitting in its own mature grounds on the edge of picture-postcard pretty Balcary Bay. Standards are consistently high here. The hotel and grounds are very well-kept and all is professional yet welcoming and personal. Take lunch in the delightful conservatory overlooking the bay or sit round an open fire in the cosy drawing room and take afternoon tea. Dinners at Balcary Bay are special and formal. The expectations which arise from the hotel's magnificent setting are more than met by the excellent standards set within.

Open Mar to end Nov
🏨 Rooms: 17 en suite
🛏 DB&B £52–£80   B&B £52–£59
SP Special rates available
✗ Lunch Sun – booking advisable £: Lunch Mon to Sat – by prior reservation only ££
✗ Bar Lunches daily
✗ Dinner £££
Ⓥ Vegetarians welcome
🧒 Children welcome
♿ Facilities for non-resident disabled visitors
🚭 Smoking discouraged in dining areas

Local smoked salmon layered with continental leaves and horseradish potato salad with gherkin and dill dressing. Medallions of Highland venison resting on a red onion marmalade topped with quenelles of haggis. Shortbread hearts layered with fresh strawberries and creme chantilly.

STB ★★★★ Hotel
💳 Credit cards: Mastercard/Eurocard, American Express, Visa, Switch, Delta
🅗 Proprietors: The Lamb Family

AUCHTERARDER HOUSE
Auchterarder
Perthshire PH3 1DZ
Tel: 01764 663646 Fax: 01764 662939
E-mail: auchterarder@wrensgroup.com
Web: www.wrensgroup.com

Take B8062 from Auchterarder towards Crieff. Hotel is 1 mile from village.

A majestic country house hotel.

- Baronial style 19th century mansion.
- Country house cooking with modern influences.
- "A romantic and relaxing country house hotel steeped in history."

Auchterarder House is a magnificent Victorian mansion nestling in the rolling Perthshire hills which has undergone extensive refurbishment whilst retaining many original, priceless features. It is set in 17 acres of beautifully maintained grounds which include herb gardens, of which some of the produce can be found in the magnificent dining room. Menus are created by chef Willie Deans, using only the finest Scottish produce and prepared with great skill and imagination. Service is warm and friendly without being intrusive. *See advert page 23.*

Open all year
🏨 Rooms: 15 en suite
🛏 B&B £90–£200
SP Special rates available
✗ Food available all day £
✗ Lunch ££
✗ Dinner ££££
Ⓥ Vegetarians welcome
🚭 No smoking in dining room
🐂 Member of the Scotch Beef Club

Open chive flower ravioli of lime leaf roast lobster, lemon cous cous, Thai gras and broad bean soup. Loin of Perthshire lamb with organic vegetable terrine, sloe gin and juniper berries. Cranachan iced parfait on oatmeal sponge cake and poached cherry compote.

STB ★★★★ Hotel
💳 Credit cards: Mastercard/Eurocard, American Express, Visa, Diners Club, Switch, Delta
🅗 Owned by The Wrens Hotel Group

COLLEARN HOUSE HOTEL
Auchterarder
Perthshire PH3 1DF
Tel: 01764 663553 Fax: 01764 662376
E-mail: sucollearn@aol.com
Web: www.scotlandshotels

Situated on north side of Auchterarder High Street halfway through village. Turn down private drive to the west side of police station.

Victorian country house hotel offering excellent accommodation and personal attention.

- Victorian mansion set in nine acres of beautiful well-kept grounds.
- Classic Scottish cooking.
- "Personal supervision by the owners ensures good local business and passing trade."

Collearn was built in 1870 as a private house, designed by the distinguished architect William Lieper. Many beautiful stained glass windows and original features enhance the Victorian splendour and in addition to this the owners have lovingly restored and decorated the house to a very high standard. Steve Bjormark, owner/chef, takes time to source all produce as locally as possible and his menus offer classic well-cooked dishes with flair. *See advert page 26.*

Open all year except Boxing Day + New Year's Day
- 🏠 Rooms: 8 en suite
- 🛏 DB&B £75–£85 B&B £70–£80
- SP Special rates available
- ✗ Lunch £-££
- ✗ Dinner ££-£££
- Ⓥ Vegetarians welcome
- ☀ Children welcome
- ✌ No smoking in restaurant
- 🐄 Member of the Scotch Beef Club

Cheesecake of creamy Strathdon Blue on a pool of port and redcurrant sauce. Pan-seared Scotch sirloin beef on a haggis croûton and set on an Arran grain mustard and thyme jus. Banana rolled in filo pastry served with butterscotch sauce and vanilla ice cream.

STB ★★★★ Hotel
- 💳 Credit cards: Mastercard/Eurocard, American Express, Visa, Diners Club, Switch
- 🕴 Owners: Steve & Sue Bjormark

THE DORMY CLUBHOUSE
The Gleneagles Hotel
Auchterarder
Perthshire PH3 1NF
Tel: 01764 694359
Fax: 01764 662134
Web: www.gleneagles.com/

By Auchterarder follow the signs to Gleneagles and the Dormy Clubhouse is on your left on the main driveway to the hotel.

Stylish clubhouse eatery.

- Creamwashed spacious lodge.
- Excellent hearty Scottish.
- "Hearty portions using traditional recipes."

Charming creamwashed building forming part of a clubhouse combination including luxury golf shop and clubhouse restaurant alongside essential locker rooms. The attractive single storey building has generous bay windows encompassing panoramic views of the golf courses. Attractive bar-style of service, excellently staffed in refined surroundings. The aim is to appeal to all, but perhaps to hungry golfers in particular, with top notch bar food – and this is achieved and much much more. The Dormy Clubhouse, as part of the Gleneagles resort, offers honest, traditional and enticing fare as you would expect in such surroundings. Runner-up (Category 2) in The Taste of Scotland Scotch Lamb Challenge Competition 1999.

Open all year
Closed Oct 17 to Mar 15 (dinner)
Closed Christmas Day (dinner) + New Year's Eve (dinner)
Open 7 days a week all day (summer)
- ✗ Food available all day ££
- ✗ Lunch ££
- ✗ Dinner ££
- Ⓥ Vegetarians welcome
- ☀ Children welcome
- ♿ Facilities for disabled visitors
- 🐄 Member of the Scotch Beef Club

Mussel brose. Steak and Guinness pie. Cloutie dumpling.

- 💳 Credit cards: Mastercard/Eurocard, American Express, Visa, Diners Club, Switch, Delta
- 🕴 Restaurant Manager: Karen Sharp

CORROUR HOUSE HOTEL
Inverdruie, by Aviemore
Inverness-shire
PH22 1QH
Tel: 01479 810220
Fax: 01479 811500

Inverdruie is a 1/2 mile from Aviemore, on road to
Coylumbridge, Glenmore and Cairngorms.

**Originally a Victorian dower house, now a country
house hotel in beautiful setting.**

- Victorian house.
- Innovative and imaginative Scottish.
- "A relaxed retreat offering a warm welcome and
  a first class meal."

Corrour House Hotel is an elegant family-run hotel
which offers true Highland hospitality from its hosts
David and Sheana Catto. The house stands in four
acres of garden and woodland, overlooks
Rothiemurchus Forest and enjoys fine views of the
Cairngorm Mountains. The house is attractively
furnished and decorated and is an excellent place
from which to relax and enjoy the surroundings. The
Cattos are friendly and accomplished hosts and the
cooking is excellent making best use of local
produce whether at breakfast or dinner.

Open 27 Dec to 31 Oct
- 🏢 Rooms: 8 en suite
- 🛏 DB&B £60   B&B £37.50
- SP Special rates available
- ✕ Dinner ££
- Ⓥ Vegetarians welcome
- ✦ Children welcome
- ✂ No smoking in dining room + some bedrooms
- 🐄 Member of the Scotch Beef Club

**Asparagus and Mull cheddar tart with hollandaise
sauce. Fillet of wild salmon with pink peppercorns
and green grapes. A terrine of summer fruits with
white chocolate ice cream.**

STB ★★★★ Hotel
- ⊞ Credit cards: Mastercard/Eurocard, Visa
- 🅺 Proprietors: Mr & Mrs Catto

LYNWILG HOUSE
Aviemore
Inverness-shire PH22 1PZ
Tel/Fax: 01479 811685
E-mail: lynwilghouse@tesco.net

A9 Perth-Inverness, take Lynwilg road 1 mile south
of Aviemore.

A beautiful country house built in the 1930s.

- Country house overlooking the Cairngorms.
- Traditional Scottish cooking.
- "A joy of a place – no wonder guests constantly
  return."

Lynwilg is an impressive country house, built by the
Duke of Richmond, standing on high ground looking
out over the Cairngorms. The house is set in four
acres of attractively landscaped gardens with a
well-planned kitchen garden providing much of the
fruit, vegetables and herbs used in the daily
changing menus. Marjorie Cleary presents a set
menu each evening; her inventiveness and flair in
the kitchen mean that every meal is special.
Comfortable, well-furnished bedrooms, roaring log
fires, croquet on the lawn and fishing on a private
loch are all indications of a relaxed country house
style. There is an obvious dedication to Scottish
produce, home produce and cooking in general at
Lynwilg. An extremely enjoyable place to visit. A
private self-catering cottage in the grounds sleeps
four. Winner of The Macallan Taste of Scotland
Special Merit Award for Outstanding Hospitality
1994.

Open New Year to 31 Oct
- 🏢 Rooms: 3 en suite
- 🛏 DB&B £48–£58   B&B £28–£35
- SP Special rates available
- ✕ Residents only
- UL Unlicensed – guests welcome to take own wine
- ✕ Dinner 4 course menu ££-£££
- Ⓥ Vegetarians welcome
- ✦ Children welcome
- ✂ No smoking in restaurant

**Scallop mousse in a courgette flower with beurre
blanc sauce. Duck roasted with rosemary and
honey, with celeriac mash and Lynwilg greens.
Warm pear and almond tart with cinnamon ice
cream.**

STB ★★★★ Guest House
- ⊞ Credit cards: Mastercard/Eurocard, Visa
- 🅺 Proprietors/Owners: Alan & Marjory Cleary

THE OLD BRIDGE INN
Dalfaber Road
Aviemore PH22 1PU
Tel: 01479 811137
Fax: 01479 811372

At south end of Aviemore, take B970 ski road (Cairngorms) for 300 yards then take turning on left for another 300 yards.

A popular Highland pub offering hearty fare.

- Tastefully extended but retaining the country inn feel.
- Hearty pub food.
- "An ideal venue for a guaranteed warm welcome and a very fine meal."

Only minutes on foot from the centre of Aviemore, the Old Bridge Inn has the air of a country pub. This quaint and unpretentious building offers pub food as it should be – freshly prepared and cooked. Innkeeper Iain MacRury and chef Norma Hutton concentrate on fresh local produce for their extensive and imaginative menu. Rightly popular, they even make their own ice cream. There is a special children's menu. In the evenings, the menu is based on food cooked on a large chargrill. In the summer the inn hosts regular Highland ceilidhs, with pipers and Scottish dancing. Bookings accepted. Please note that new owners, Dr William J Cox and Robin Playfair, took over on 1 September 1999. This establishment was inspected whilst under the previous ownership of Nigel Reid.

    Open all year
✗   Lunch £
✗   Dinner ££
Ⓥ   Vegetarians welcome
⚘   Children welcome
♿   Facilities for disabled visitors

Platter of smoked fish, cucumber relish. Seared fillet of beef, shallot and peppercorn sauce. Chocolate and walnut praline.

💳   Credit cards: Mastercard/Eurocard, Visa
☒   Owners: Dr William J Cox & Robin Playfair

THE EISENHOWER APARTMENT, CULZEAN CASTLE
Maybole
Ayrshire KA19 8LE
Tel: 01655 884455
Fax: 01655 884503
E-mail: cardales@bt.internet.com
Web: www.aboutscotland.com   www.nts.org.uk

Culzean Castle is well signposted on Ayr to Turnberry road. Take A77 towards Stranraer then A719 from Maybole to Culzean (signposted).

One of Scotland's most famous castles – a National Trust for Scotland property.

- Listed building designed by Robert Adam.
- Traditional Scottish.
- "A chance to experience a privileged way of life that has effectively passed forever."

Culzean is a captivating 'castle' that is elegant and beautifully proportioned. It has been carefully restored and maintained. To stay in the Apartment is a very special experience, surrounded as one is by real, priceless antiques, paintings, silver and the perfect lines of the Adam-designed details. The apartments are located on the top floor of the castle and all lead off the astoundingly beautiful oval staircase/balcony. The rooms are extremely spacious and have fantastic views. The atmosphere is one of a real Edwardian house party – guests are encouraged to mingle and meet and afternoon tea is served with astonishing antique silver-service. *See advert page 29.*

    Open Apr to Oct
🛏   Rooms: 6 (5 en suite, 1 with private bathroom)
🛌   B&B £100–£210 (incl tea)
SP   Special rates available for group booking of whole apartment
✗   Non-resident dinner parties – by prior notice
Ⓤ   Unlicensed – complimentary drinks cupboard
✗   Dinner ££££
⚘   Children welcome (prior notice for under 10 yrs)
♿   Facilities for disabled visitors
🚭   No smoking in dining room + bedrooms

Seared fresh and smoked salmon topped with crème fraîche on a tartare potato pancake. Roast fillet of Scottish beef with a green peppercorn and whisky sauce served with fresh seasonal vegetables. Poached pears with a fresh raspberry sauce.

💳   Credit cards: Mastercard/Eurocard, American Express, Visa
☒   Administrator: Jonathan Cardale

FOUTERS BISTRO RESTAURANT
2A Academy Street, Ayr
Ayrshire KA7 1HS
Tel: 01292 261391
Fax: 01292 619323
E-mail: laurie_fran@fouters.demon.co.uk

Town centre, opposite Town Hall.

Historic basement restaurant in Ayr.

- Converted bank vaults.
- Modern Scottish cooking.
- "Thoroughly reliable for bringing together superb ingredients in exciting modern cooking, in a charmingly intimate atmosphere."

This year Fouters has an up-to-date new look. The delightful stencils have been changed to a more simple style and modern 'foodie' watercolour prints now add a certain elegance to this restaurant. Table linen is now a bistro-style pale green. The table appointments remain of the highest quality and fresh flowers are a welcoming and tasteful touch on each candlelit table. A bustling, friendly atmosphere makes one feel like a 'regular' and the warm welcome from Laurie and Fran and their team is sincere and palpable. Laurie's food is modelled on the best of French ethics of simplicity married to the very best ingredients and at Fouters, the quality of these really does shine through. With skilful cooking and the best ingredients from around Scotland, no wonder Fouters retains its reputation as one of the best West Coast restaurants with 2 AA Rosettes.

Open all year except 25 to 27 Dec + 1 to 3 Jan
Closed Sun Mon
✗ Lunch except Sun Mon £
✗ Dinner except Sun Mon £££
Ⓥ Vegetarians welcome
✗ Special diets catered for
🕯 Children welcome
🐂 Member of the Scotch Beef Club

Risotto of local seafood, seared scallop and fennel oil dressing. Medallions of local venison, Chianti and chocolate game jus. Steamed lemon and honey sponge, almond custard sauce and orange ice cream.

💳 Credit cards: Mastercard/Eurocard, American Express, Visa, Diners Club, Switch, Solo
Ⓜ Owners: Laurie & Fran Black

NETHER UNDERWOOD
Nr Symington
Ayrshire KA1 5NG
Tel: 01563 830666 Fax: 01563 830777
E-mail: netherund.@aol.com

On A77 from Glasgow, past Hansel Village on left then turn left at signs to Ladykirk and Underwood. Turn left at 'T' junction, turn left at bottom of hill past Wardneuk Farm. Pass Underwood House and immediately turn left up lane.Nether Underwood is first house on left, through gate.

Charming country guest house in large family home.

- Attractive country home.
- Delicious modern Scottish cooking.
- "There is no compromise at Nether Underwood, only the guests total comfort and personal pampering will do!"

A large 1930s style country house lovingly restored and improved by the Thomsons. Their obvious good taste and attention to quality are evident in this house. Meals are candlelit, with the light sparkling in silver and glass, yet despite all this comfort and simple elegance this is still a family home and the place is filled with eclectic and extraordinary collections of, for instance pince-nez and African tribal hunting spears. Felicity Thomson is a talented cook and has no qualms about offering her guests only the very best food, surroundings and above all service. This is a great place from which to escape from the daily routine to the delights of total pampering. *See advert page 262.*

Open all year except 24 Dec to 2 Jan
🛏 Rooms: 4 en suite
🍴 DB&B £65–£75 B&B £40–£50
🆂🅿 Special rates available
✗ Non residents – prior notice required (private dinner parties welcome)
✗ Lunch – prior arrangement for residents
✗ Dinner £££
Ⓥ Vegetarians welcome
🕯 Children over 16 years welcome
🚭 No smoking throughout

Asparagus and mint frittata. Fillet of Scottish salmon with vodka and fresh lime with vegetables in season. Pear and almond tart served with home-made apple sorbet.

STB ★★★★ Guest House
💳 Credit cards: Mastercard/Eurocard, Visa, Switch
Ⓜ Chef/Proprietor: Felicity Thomson

COSSES COUNTRY HOUSE

Ballantrae
Ayrshire KA26 0LR
Tel: 01465 831 363
Fax: 01465 831 598
E-mail: cosses@compuserve.com

From A77 at southern end of Ballantrae, take inland road at Caravan sign. Cosses is c. 2 miles on right.

Luxury bed and breakfast to the highest standards with superb cooking and hospitality to match.

* Converted farmhouse full of character.
* Gourmet country house cooking.
* "Still one of my favourite places after six years!"

Now a country house, dating from 1606, standing in 12 acres of glorious gardens and woodland in a fold in the hills, Cosses was built as a shooting lodge and became the home farm for nearby Glenapp Estate. It is the home of Robin and Susan Crosthwaite, and guests are made to feel they are part of the family. Two cottage suites of the very highest standard are provided within the courtyard and there is a double bedroom en suite within the house itself. At Cosses they grow their own vegetables, herbs and some fruit, and Susan – a Cordon Bleu Chef – creates menus that are unique and moreover quite delicious. She is a sympathetic and delicate cook. Flavours are nurtured and treated with great respect. All breads, rolls even teacakes are home-made as are preserves and yoghurt. Cosses is a treasury of good food.

Open Feb to Nov
🏡 Rooms: 3 en suite
🛏 DB&B £57–£80   B&B £32–£48
SP Special rates available
✗ Dinner £££
✗ Dinner for non-residents – by reservation only
Ⓥ Vegetarians welcome
🕏 Children welcome
🚭 No smoking in dining room

Ballantrae prawns wrapped in Scottish oak-smoked salmon in a piquant mayonnaise with *Cosses* salad leaves. Breast of Gressingham duckling with *Cosses* plum sauce, clapshot and *Cosses* spring cabbage and ginger. Brandy snap cones with *Cosses* rhubarb fool.

🈺 Credit cards: Mastercard/Eurocard, Visa
Ⓝ Proprietors: Susan & Robin Crosthwaite

BALGONIE COUNTRY HOUSE HOTEL

Braemar Place
Ballater AB35 5NQ
Tel/Fax: 013397 55482

Off A93 Aberdeen-Perth, on outskirts of village of Ballater.

A country house hotel in the heart of Deeside.

* Tranquil Edwardian mansion in four acres of mature gardens with views towards hills of Glen Muick.
* Traditional and innovative recipes using fresh local produce.
* "A memorable visit offering first class cuisine, hospitality and scenery."

Balgonie is five minutes walk from Ballater on Royal Deeside, set in spacious gardens overlooking Ballater Golf Course. The resident proprietors, John and Priscilla Finnie, pride themselves on maintaining a friendly but unobtrusive service. The nine en suite bedrooms are very comfortable and tastefully furnished. The dining room is the heart of Balgonie providing an inviting cuisine using locally sourced fish and game. When in season, herbs and soft fruits from the garden are always found on the menu. French and German are spoken. The hotel has 2 AA Rosettes.

Open 12 Feb to 5 Jan
🏡 Rooms: 9 en suite
🛏 DB&B £85–£95   B&B £55–£70
SP Special rates available
✗ Lunch – by reservation only ££
✗ Dinner 4 course menu – non-residents by reservation £££
Ⓥ Vegetarians welcome – prior notice required
🕏 Children over 5 years welcome at dinner
🚭 No smoking in dining room

Warm salad of Arbroath smokies finished with lemon and virgin olive oil. Roast loin of Scotch lamb served with ratatouille and finished with a thyme scented jus. Rich bread and butter pudding served with marmalade ice cream.

STB ★★★★ Hotel
🈺 Credit cards: Mastercard/Eurocard, American Express, Visa, Switch, Delta
Ⓝ Proprietor: John G Finnie

CRAIGENDARROCH HOTEL AND COUNTRY CLUB
Braemar Road, Ballater
Royal Deeside AB35 5XA
Tel: 013397 55858
Fax: 013397 55447
E-mail:
general.manager@craigendarroch.stakis.co.uk
Web: www.stakis.co.uk/

On A93 western end of Ballater, near Balmoral.

A resort hotel with full leisure and sports facilities.

* Victorian country house.
* Modern grand hotel with fine dining and bistro cooking.
* "Craigendarroch offers the complete package of food, sport and leisure facilities."

This house was built in the 19th century for the Keiller family (the inventors of marmalade) and has been converted into a modern resort hotel with time-ownership lodges and every imaginable facility. The food on offer has all the feel of a large hotel with a brigade of chefs working busily to support the restaurants. The Oaks is a classy formal restaurant serving interesting and imaginative dishes prepared by executive chef, Paul Moran, both continental and classic influences are detectable in his beautifully presented dishes. In The Clubhouse Restaurant, which adjoins the pool area in the Leisure Club, the bistro style food is fast, comprehensive and unsophisticated – good grub for all the family, and some dishes may be taken away.

Open all year
🏨 Rooms: 45 en suite
🛏 DB&B £39–£89 B&B £29–£65
SP Special rates available
✕ Lunch (Clubhouse Restaurant) ££
✕ Dinner (Clubhouse Restaurant) from ££-£££
✕ Dinner (The Oaks) from ££-£££
Ⓥ Vegetarians welcome
🕇 Children welcome
🚭 No smoking in The Oaks

Grilled red mullet, creamed cucumber and chives, beetroot purée and vanilla vinaigrette. Roulade of rabbit and corn-fed chicken, morel mousse, Savoy cabbage, potato and green lentil pancake, prune sauce. Apple bavarois with ivory chocolate ice cream and almond biscuit.

STB ★★★★ Hotel
💳 Credit cards: Mastercard/Eurocard, American Express, Visa, Diners Club, Switch, Delta
Ⓜ General Manager: Andrew Murphie

DARROCH LEARG HOTEL
Braemar Road, Ballater
Aberdeenshire AB35 5UX
Tel: 013397 55443 Fax: 013397 55252
E-mail: darroch.learg@exodus.uk.com
Web: www.royal-deeside.org.uk/darroch.htm

½ mile from centre of village of Ballater, off A93.

Country house hotel on Royal Deeside with views of Cairngorms.

* Victorian period house overlooking Ballater and Royal Deeside.
* Modern Scottish cooking.
* "Darroch Learg offers exceptional quality in comfort and fine cuisine, with surroundings to match."

Darroch Learg was built in 1888 as a country residence when Royal Deeside was at its most fashionable. The hotel enjoys a wonderful situation, high up on a rocky hillside, with excellent views. The house has period charm and has retained the comfortable atmosphere of the family home it once was, with two drawing rooms (smoking and non-smoking). The dining room and spacious conservatory allow diners to enjoy the wonderful outlook south to the hills of Glen Muick. The short table d'hôte menu (three main courses) offers top quality local meat from the excellent local dealers confidently and expertly prepared in unusual combinations and sauces. The hotel has 3 AA Rosettes.

Open Feb to Dec closed Christmas
🏨 Rooms: 18 en suite
🛏 DB&B £56–£82   B&B £37.50–£57.50
✕ Food available all day £££
✕ Lunch £££
✕ Dinner ££££
Ⓥ Vegetarians welcome – prior notice required
🕇 Children welcome
♿ Facilities for disabled visitors – ground floor
🚭 No smoking in dining room
🐂 Member of the Scotch Beef Club

Ravioli of foie gras and Parma ham, with onion jam, crispy potatoes and a Parmesan cream. Loin of lamb with a tian of summer vegetables, roast lamb kidney and rosemary sauce. Iced vanilla parfait with langues du chat and spiced red wine pear.

STB ★★★★ Hotel
💳 Credit cards: Mastercard/Eurocard, American Express, Visa, Diners Club, Switch
Ⓜ Proprietors: Nigel & Fiona Franks

DEESIDE HOTEL
Braemar Road
Ballater
Aberdeenshire AB35 5RQ
Tel: 013397 55420
Fax: 013397 55357
E-mail: deesidehotel@talk21.com
Web: www.royal-deeside.org.uk/deeside.htm

On west side of Ballater, set back from A93 Braemar road.

A comfortable family hotel with a relaxed atmosphere.

- Pink granite town house.
- Traditional Scottish cooking with modern twist.
- "A family-run hotel on Royal Deeside offering informal hospitality."

The Deeside is an attractive pink granite building, set back from the main road with an informal well-maintained garden. It is a family-run establishment with nine en suite bedrooms, two of which are situated on the ground floor. The house is welcoming and in the sitting room there is an impressive painted frieze of wild animals; the original Victorian mantelpiece and tiled fireplace have been retained. Through an open archway from the lounge bar is the dining room with its varnished wooden floor and oil paintings of mountain scenery on the walls. In the evening, meals are available in both the restaurant and bar where you can also sample a good selection of Scottish real ales and malt whiskies.

Open 10 Feb to 2 Jan except Christmas Day + Boxing Day
🛏 Rooms: 9 en suite
🍴 DB&B £37.50–41.50   B&B £22–£26
SP Special rates available
✖ Dinner ££
Ⓥ Vegetarians welcome
⸙ Children welcome
♿ Facilities for disabled visitors
🚭 No smoking in restaurant

Goats cheese, spring onion and thyme flan. Roast rack of lamb with a rosemary and honey glaze. Clootie dumpling.

STB ★★★ Hotel
💳 Credit cards: Mastercard/Eurocard, Visa, Switch
🔏 Directors: Donald & Alison Brooker

GLEN LUI HOTEL
Invercauld Road, Ballater
Aberdeenshire AB35 5RP
Tel: 013397 55402 Fax: 013397 55545
E-mail: infos@glen-lui-hotel.co.uk
Web: www.glen-lui-hotel.co.uk

Off A93 at western end of Ballater at end of Invercauld Road.

A town hotel with a country house appeal overlooking the golf course and Lochnagar.

- A country house style hotel standing in two acres of grounds.
- Modern Scottish cooking, with distinct French influences.
- "Excellent food, friendly welcome, and peace and tranquility are offered at the Glen Lui."

At the Glen Lui accommodation is comfortable, service is polite and friendly by well-trained staff, and menus are well-presented and varied. The wrap-around conservatory/restaurant overlooks the golf course and offers an extensive à la carte menu with a distinct French influence. Each dish is presented with confidence and artistry. There is a very comprehensive wine list with vintage wines. The hotel has 1 AA Rosette and is a member of the Certified Aberdeen Angus Scheme. Investor in People Award.

Open all year
🛏 Rooms: 19 en suite
🍴 DB&B £46–£62   B&B £30–£46
SP Special rates available
✖ Lunch £
✖ Dinner £-££
Ⓥ Vegetarians welcome
⸙ Children welcome
♿ Facilities for disabled visitors
🚭 No smoking in restaurant + bedrooms
🐂 Member of the Scotch Beef Club

Isle of Gigha goats cheese wrapped in Parma ham, baked and set on salad leaves. Roasted local venison saddle topped with black pudding parfait on a garlic croûton finished with a red wine jus. Scottish bramble frangipane tart with crème fraîche.

STB ★★★★ Hotel
Green Tourism ⟨PPP⟩ GOLD Award
💳 Credit cards: Mastercard/Eurocard, American Express, Visa, Switch, Delta
🔏 Proprietors: Serge & Lorraine Geraud

THE GREEN INN RESTAURANT
WITH ROOMS
9 Victoria Road, Ballater
Aberdeenshire AB35 5QQ
Tel/Fax: 013397 55701

In centre of Ballater on village green.

A quality restaurant with rooms; Jeffrey and Carol Purves both have a justified reputation for delicious food in intimate and comfortable surroundings.

- A two-storey granite building, once a temperance hotel.
- Modern regional Scottish cooking, with good use of international influences.
- "A truly gastronomic experience!"

Jeff Purves' reputation is well-deserved: his cooking is innovative and imaginative, and he applies this to the excellent local produce available on Deeside. Chef specials change daily, often treating classic Scottish dishes in an unusual way and combining flavours with assured confidence. Jeff uses cream only when necessary, replacing sugar with honey, and so on – and he is also delighted by the challenge of vegetarian cooking, but requests advance warning to do it justice. Service from Carol is friendly and helpful in the intimate dining room. The Green Inn has 2 AA Rosettes. This establishment is consistently excellent and the quality on offer reflects the owners' commitment. Winner of The Macallan Taste of Scotland Restaurant of the Year Award 1995.

Open all year except 2 weeks Oct, Christmas Day + 26 to 28 Dec
Closed Sun Oct to Mar
- 🏠 Rooms: 3 en suite
- 🍴 DB&B £54.50–£59.50
- SP Special rates available
- ✕ Dinner £££
- Ⅴ Vegetarians welcome
- ☆ Children welcome
- ♿ Disabled access only
- ✗ Smoking permitted at coffee stage only
- 🐄 Member of the Scotch Beef Club

Breast of duck on home-made black pudding with crushed apples served with a ginger and soy dressing. Assiette of local and regional fish dishes. Aniseed parfait with bramble coulis and a hint of orange.

STB ★★★★ Restaurant with Rooms
- 💳 Credit cards: Mastercard/Eurocard, American Express, Visa, Diners Club, Switch
- 👤 Proprietors: J J & C A Purves

RAVENSWOOD HOTEL
Braemar Road
Ballater
Aberdeenshire AB35 5RQ
Tel/Fax: 013397 55539
E-mail: ravens.wood@breathemail.net
Web: www.royal.deeside.org.uk.

On the A93, western end of Ballater – a 10 minute walk from centre of village.

Small friendly hotel.

- Converted Victorian villa.
- Traditional Scottish hotel cooking.
- "A Victorian villa where the owners place great store on traditional, welcoming hospitality."

Ravenswood Hotel is a small friendly family-owned Victorian hotel in the pretty village of Ballater which is already renowned as home to some of the best eating places in Scotland. The hotel is a splendid period building which retains many of its original features. The Fyfes offer simple good food; local produce well-cooked. Family-service meals are offered in the dining room, with fireplace, while the lounge bar offers a selection of alternative dishes. Ravenswood offers good value and is a lovely place from which to explore Royal Deeside.

Open all year except 10 Nov to 5 Dec
- 🏠 Rooms: 6, 5 en suite
- 🍴 DB&B £32.50–£47.50   B&B £20–£35
- SP Special rates available
- ✕ Lunch ££
- ✕ Dinner ££
- Ⅴ Vegetarians welcome
- ☆ Children welcome
- ✗ No smoking in dining room

Fan of honeydew melon and raspberry sorbet. Pan-fried fillet of pork with a cider and apple sauce. Forest fruit cheesecake with Glayva cream.

STB ★★★ Hotel
Green Tourism *ϷϷϷ* GOLD Award
- 💳 Credit cards: Mastercard/Eurocard, American Express, Visa
- 👤 Owners: Fraser & Cathy Fyfe

MONACHYLE MHOR
Balquhidder
Lochearnhead
Perthshire FK19 8PQ
Tel: 01877 384 622
Fax: 01877 384 305

11 miles north of Callander on A84. Turn right at Kingshouse Hotel – 6 miles straight along glen road.

A small, award-winning hotel in the Perthshire hills.

- Family-run establishment of great character.
- Modern Scottish cooking.
- "For a real taste of Scotland take the single track road leading here. Food and scenery will surpass your expectations."

In Rob Roy country of mountains and lochs, Monachyle Mhor sits in its own 2,000 acres in the heart of the Braes o' Balquhidder. Proprietors Rob, Jean and Tom Lewis fully deserve their reputation for hospitality. All rooms are comfortable and have bathrooms en suite. Both the restaurant and cosy bar serve imaginative, good food that makes the best of fresh, local produce – offering game from the estate, fish from the West Coast and the finest Scottish meat cooked with a French influence by Chef Tom. Interesting, discerning wine list. There are also two self-catering cottages, equipped and appointed to the same high standards as the hotel. Monachyle Mhor has 2 AA Rosettes. *See advert page 261.*

Open all year
- 🏠 Rooms: 10 en suite
- 🛏 B&B £32.50–£45
- ✗ Food available all day £-£££
- ✗ Lunch ££
- ✗ Dinner £££
- Ⓥ Vegetarians welcome
- ⟋ No smoking in restaurant
- 🐄 Member of the Scotch Beef Club

Pan-fried veal liver and roasted sweetbreads on haricot vert, Balquhidder chanterelles and sage. Seared Mallaig scallops on charred asparagus, balsamic pink grapefruit and a bell pepper dressing. Chocolate and hazelnut fallen cake with home-made banana ice cream and a caramel sauce.

STB ★★★ Hotel
- 💳 Credit cards: Mastercard/Eurocard, Visa, Switch
- 👤 Proprietors: Jean Lewis & Tom Lewis

GLEN LOY LODGE HOTEL
Banavie, Nr Fort William
Inverness-shire PH33 7PD
Tel/Fax: 01397 712 700
E-mail: glenloy.lodge@virgin.net
Web: www.smoothhound.co.uk/hotels/glenloyl.html

4 miles north of Banavie on the B8004.

Artistic country house from the 1920s.

- Country house.
- Quality local produce.
- "Sympathetically restored 1920s house with delicious home cooking."

Glen Loy Lodge Hotel was originally built in the 1920s to cater for shooting parties on the Locheil Estate and has since been refurbished by Pat and Gordon Haynes into a charming country house hotel. It stands in a beautiful, private location bounded by deer forests and with dramatic views across the Great Glen to Ben Nevis. Pat and Gordon are new to the hotel business – they are both designers and have lent their particular style to the house, which works well. The house has been furnished in Arts and Crafts style to recreate the elegance of the era. The cooking here is good with innovative modern twists to traditional items, from dinner menus to interesting choices for breakfast. Excellent quality produce is used to ensure guests enjoy the best possible experience during their stay at Glen Loy.

Open all year except Nov
- 🏠 Rooms: 9 en suite
- 🛏 DB&B £52–£60 B&B £30–£38
- SP Special rates available
- ⚗ Restricted licence
- ✗ Lunch ££
- ✗ Dinner £££
- Ⓥ Vegetarians welcome
- 🧒 Children welcome
- ⟋ No smoking throughout
- 🐕 Dogs welcome

Smoked salmon and Gruyere soufflé flavoured with basil. Fillet of venison in a port and rowanberry sauce on a bed of wilted spinach, served with purée of celeriac and sweet potatoes and seasonal vegetables. Chocolate Cointreau cream.

STB ★★★ Hotel
- 💳 Credit cards: Mastercard/Eurocard, Visa, Switch, Delta
- 👤 Proprietors: Pat & Gordon Haynes

THE MILTON RESTAURANT
North Deeside Road
Crathes
Banchory
Aberdeenshire AB31 5QH
Tel: 01330 844566 Fax: 01330 844474

14 miles from the centre of Aberdeen. 1 mile before Banchory.

Steading opposite the gates of Crathes Castle.

- Tastefully converted steading.
- Modern Scottish cooking.
- "A warm welcome and quality food in surroundings with a Dutch influence."

The Milton Restaurant was originally steadings which have been tastefully converted to form a restaurant, art gallery and various workshops (including pottery), and incorporating a waterwheel and gift shop. The restaurant is on two levels with very modern decor, based on the stonework of the building and iron work. The tables are well-spaced for comfort and privacy of conversation. Food is served throughout the day until about 10 pm and there is a very attractive walkway approach to the restaurant – this is a joy to visit and eat in.

Open all year
✘ Food available all day £-££
✘ Lunch £
✘ Dinner except Sun ££
Ⓥ Vegetarians welcome
ᄎ Children welcome
ᕾ Facilities for disabled visitors

Thai fish cake served with seasonal leaves on a beurre blanc sauce. Best end of Lamb with a citrus and mint salsa and seasonal leaves. Tart of strawberries and kümmel topped with a crème de menthe sorbet.

▣ Credit cards: Mastercard/Eurocard, Visa, Switch
Ⱶ Owners: Eric & Sandra Lupker

THE OLD WEST MANSE
71 Station Road
Banchory
Royal Deeside
Aberdeenshire AB31 5UD
Tel/Fax: 01330 822202

Situated on the A93 Aberdeen to Braemar road. Car park entrance is approx 60 metres past A980 junction on right (travelling from Aberdeen).

Attractive manse in lovely landscaped gardens.

- Former manse.
- Home cooking with flair.
- "An experience of good food and exceptional hospitality in an atmosphere of relaxation."

Jayne and John Taylor have been at the Old West Manse for five years and have now established themselves as offering exceptional quality to their guests. The highest of standards are aimed for here from the quality of the furniture and fittings to the skill and dedication evident in the cooking. You will find some of these extra special touches, often only found in larger establishments, from a turn down service to fresh milk in your room for that bedtime cuppa! However, you are not in a large establishment but a small and intimate family-run house and it is this blend that makes the Old West Manse a very special place indeed.

Open all year
ᛥ Rooms: 3 (2 en suite, 1 private facilities)
ᕤ DB&B from £43.50   B&B from £25
✘ Residents only
ᘻ Packed lunch on request £
✘ Dinner residents only ££
Ⓥ Vegetarians welcome
ᄎ Children welcome
ᶋ No smoking in bedrooms + dining room
ᖯ Dogs by prior arrangement

Creamy smoked haddock ramekins. Herb-crusted loin of Aberdeenshire pork, roasted on the bone and served with an apricot gravy. Bread and butter pudding laced with sultanas soaked in Glenmorangie, and served with a vanilla custard.

STB ★★★★★ B&B
▣ Credit cards: Mastercard/Eurocard, Visa, Switch, Delta
Ⱶ Owners: Jayne & John Taylor

TOR-NA-COILLE HOTEL
Inchmarlo Road
Banchory
Royal Deeside
Aberdeenshire AB31 4AB
Tel: 01330 822242
Fax: 01330 824012
E-mail: tornacoille@btinternet.com

Situated on the A93 Aberdeen to Braemar road, 18 miles from Aberdeen's city centre on the outskirts of Banchory.

Attractive hotel set in pleasant, well-tended gardens.

- Victorian country house hotel.
- Traditional and modern Scottish cooking.
- "A luxury hotel offering hospitality and food to match."

The Tor-Na-Coille Hotel is an attractive, ivy-clad Victorian mansion standing in its own wooded grounds set back from the A93. It is a friendly, professionally-run hotel and is a very suitable base to explore the surrounding Deeside area. All bedrooms are individually furnished with Victorian and Edwardian furniture. The restaurant is attractive where fresh local produce is used, simply presented with good flavour and texture. Menus are well-balanced offering good choice and served by helpful and professional staff. Tor-Na-Coille Hotel has 1 AA Red Rosette. Investor in People Award.

Open all year except 25 to 28 Dec
🏠 Rooms: 23 en suite
🍴 DB&B £95–£167   B&B £69–£115
SP Special rates available
✗ Food available all day ££
✗ Lunch £
✗ Dinner £££
Ⓥ Vegetarians welcome
✮ Children welcome
⟁ Facilities for disabled visitors
🐄 Member of the Scotch Beef Club

Home-cured gravadlax of sea trout served on mixed leaves with dill and Dijon mustard dressing. Medallions of peppered Scotch beef fillet served on braised Puy lentils, finished with Strathdon Blue cheese cream sauce. Glazed lemon tartlet served with raspberry sorbet.

STB ★★★★ Hotel
💳 Credit cards: Mastercard/Eurocard, American Express, Visa, Diners Club, Switch, Delta
🍴 Owner: Roxanne Sloan-Maris

BANFF SPRINGS HOTEL
Golden Knowes Road
Banff
Aberdeenshire AB45 2JE
Tel: 01261 812881
Fax: 01261 815546

On the western outskirts of Banff on the A98 Fraserburgh to Elgin road.

Superb position overlooking the beach of Boyndie Bay.

- Modern hotel.
- Traditional Scottish cooking.
- "A very popular hotel offering good all-round North East hospitality."

Banff Springs has been a very popular hotel for many years as it is warm and friendly offering high quality food and accommodation at a reasonable price. With wonderful views of the Buchan coastline, it is in a superb location to explore the surrounding area. The restaurant is a particularly good place from which to enjoy the views (and is attractively set out for dinner with crisp and co-ordinating linen). The cooking uses only good local fresh ingredients and is presented and prepared well by a chef who obviously cares and understands his subject. There is a pleasant atmosphere in this hotel with staff who are keen to ensure that guests enjoy their stay.

Open all year except Christmas Day
🏠 Rooms: 31 en suite
🍴 DB&B £44–£70.45   B&B £29–£52.50
SP Special rates available
✗ Lunch £
✗ Dinner ££
Ⓥ Vegetarians welcome
✮ Children welcome
⟁ Facilities for disabled visitors
✔ No smoking in restaurant

Arbroath smokies, mayonnaise and cream laced with malt whisky, served with yoghurt dill dressing and oatcakes. Medallions of beef fillet topped with a Stilton soufflé surrounded by Madeira essence and roasted shallots. Baileys and cinnamon brûlée with vanilla shortbread.

STB ★★★ Hotel
💳 Credit cards: Mastercard/Eurocard, American Express, Visa, Switch, Delta
🍴 Proprietor: Nicola Antliff

PERTHSHIRE VISITOR CENTRE
Bankfoot
Perth
PH1 4EB
Tel: 01738 787696
Fax: 01738 787120

8 miles north of Perth on A9. Follow signs for Bankfoot.

Just off the A9, this is a good place to break a journey.

- Waitress service restaurant, plus shop and 'Macbeth Experience'.
- Country kitchen restaurant with good home cooking.
- "A good restaurant and interesting visitor centre offering the ideal journey break for the family."

'The Macbeth Experience', which is the focus of this visitor centre, is a multi-media exploration of Scotland's mis-judged 11th century warrior king. Next door is a well-stocked shop (knitwear, glass, books, foods, whisky, gifts and souvenirs) and a comfortable friendly restaurant, offering freshly made soups, desserts and a varied selection of home baking as well as a selection of freshly cooked meals listed on a blackboard. Good, fresh coffee also available here! There is a large car park adjacent and a children's play area.

Open all year except Christmas Day + New Year's Day
✘ Food available all day £
☟ Table licence
Ⓥ Vegetarians welcome
⚘ Children's play area
♿ Facilities for disabled visitors

Locally made haggis, sauteed with cream and whisky and served on toast. Home-made venison pie cooked in red wine, topped with pastry and served with new potatoes and vegetables. Cloutie dumpling (establishment's own recipe) served hot with custard.

💳 Credit cards: Mastercard/Eurocard, Visa
👤 Proprietors: Wilson & Catriona Girvan

AUCHEN CASTLE HOTEL
Beattock
Moffat
Dumfries DG10 9SH
Tel: 01683 300407
Fax: 01683 300667
E-mail: auchencastle@easynet.co.uk

Leaving M6 at Junction 15. Head 1 mile on the B7076 Abington road for Auchen Castle Hotel.

Traditional country house style with old-fashioned standards and modern facilities.

- Baronial/Victorian mansion.
- Modern/traditional Scottish cuisine.
- "A haven of tranquillity just off the M74 ideally situated for touring the beautiful Border countryside."

The towers, spires, turrets, gilded staircases and shining silver of a magnificent Victorian Mansion. Once the home of Sir William Younger, Auchen Castle now stands proudly amidst 30 acres of exotic woodland with its own trout loch and boats. The Italian terrace with playing fountain and secluded wedding garden are ideal for memorable photographs. Bedrooms are individually furnished and decorated to a high standard. Menus are well-balanced and offer a good selection of dishes comprising many locally-sourced products – Solway salmon, Galloway beef, Annandale lamb and haggis are available every day. An ideal place for enjoying this beautiful and interesting part of Scotland. *See advert page 24.*

Open all year
🛏 Rooms: 15 en suite
🛏 DB&B £40   B&B from £30
SP Special rates available
✘ Food available all day £
✘ Lunch £
✘ Dinner £-££
Ⓥ Vegetarians welcome
⚘ Children welcome
🚬 Smoking permitted in dining room
🐂 Member of the Scotch Beef Club

Mushrooms in a pastry case and a Dunsyre blue cheese topping. Roast saddle of Annandale lamb with apricots and tarragon, red wine sauce. Fresh fruits glazed with a kirsch sabayon.

STB ★★★ Hotel
💳 Credit cards: Mastercard/Eurocard, American Express, Visa, Diners Club, Switch, Delta
👤 Owners: Keith & Tina Parr

LOVAT ARMS HOTEL
Beauly
Inverness-shire IV4 7BS
Tel: 01463 782313
Fax: 01463 782862
E-mail: lovat.arms@cali.co.uk

On A862, 11 miles from Inverness in Beauly centre.

Superior small town hotel.

- Elegant town hotel.
- Modern Scottish cooking.
- "A comfortable hotel, popular with tourists offering sound Scottish food."

The name Beauly derives its name from 'beau lieu' or beautiful place. The Lovat Arms is a stylish family-owned hotel in the centre of a picturesque small market town. The remains of Beauly Priory, built around 1230 and visited by Mary Queen of Scots, makes an ideal picnic location. The food is very well cooked and presented by head chef Donald Munro who uses his skills to present local produce in innovative ways for good value for money. Afternoon Tea and High Tea available. The hotel is an ideal place from which to explore Beauly or Moray Firth with their natural beauty and wide variety of wild life. *See advert page 260.*

Open all year
- ♠ Rooms: 22 en suite
- 🛏 DB&B £40–£75   B&B £35–£55
- SP Special rates available
- ✗ Food available all day £-££
- ✗ Lunch £-££
- ✗ Dinner £-£££
- Ⓥ Vegetarians welcome
- ✝ Children welcome
- ♿ Facilities for disabled visitors – please telephone
- ⌦ No smoking in dining room

Local salmon marinated with dill, fennel and mustard. Medallions of Strathconon venison filled with woodland mushrooms, set on a port wine and rowan jelly sauce. Home-made ice cream flavoured with Glen Ord malt whisky toasted oatmeal and honey and presented on shortbread.

- ⊞ Credit cards: Mastercard/Eurocard, Visa
- Ⅺ Proprietor: William Fraser

HARTREE COUNTRY HOUSE HOTEL
Biggar
Lanarkshire ML12 6JJ
Tel: 01899 221027
Fax: 01899 221259

Just off A702 on western outskirts of Biggar.

Country house hotel which is an ideal touring base.

- Old sandstone baronial mansion.
- Good Scottish cooking.
- "Good home cooking prepared with the best of local produce."

Hartree is an historic country house with parts dating from the 15th century, although it is mainly Victorian and set in seven acres of peaceful wooded countryside. It is not far from Biggar, and offers a good base from which to tour this part of the Borders. The house is charming and has retained many baronial features in its interior – heavy mouldings and panelling, a marble floor in the lobby, and carved fireplaces. The grand dining room offers an interesting menu with daily changing 'specials' and many Scottish specialities. Almost equidistant from Edinburgh and Glasgow. Over 100 whiskies.

Open Mar to Dec
- ♠ Rooms: 12 en suite
- 🛏 DB&B £41–£65   B&B £25–£50
- SP Special rates available
- ✗ Dinner £-££
- Ⓥ Vegetarians welcome
- ✝ Children welcome

Pan-fried pigeon breasts served on a croûton with red wine and balsamic vinegar jus. Local Border lamb cutlets with a rosemary and garlic gravy. Drambuie parfait with red berry coulis and shortbread biscuit.

STB ★★★ Hotel
- ⊞ Credit cards: Mastercard/Eurocard, American Express, Visa, Diners Club, Switch, Delta
- Ⅺ Proprietors: John & Anne Charlton Robert & Susan Reed

SHIELDHILL

Quothquan, Biggar
Lanarkshire ML12 6NA
Tel: 01899 220035
Fax: 01899 221092
E-mail: enquiries@shieldhill.co.uk
Web: www.shieldhill.co.uk

Turn off A702 on to B7016 Biggar to Carnwath road in middle of Biggar. After 2 miles turn left into Shieldhill road, hotel is on right.

An historic castle – family-run.

- Castle country house hotel.
- Modern Scottish.
- "Well executed, imaginative cooking – a real find – I'll be back!"

Dating back to the late 1100s, Shieldhill is a particularly beautiful building set in south Lanarkshire farmland which makes for a particularly peaceful and tranquil setting. This is a true country house hotel , very relaxing with luxurious bedrooms indivdually furnished to the highest specification. The cooking here is completely in keeping with the surrroundings with a team of highly skilled chefs making best use of local produce in an imaginative way. Shieldhill also has a highly acclaimed wine list to complement the excellent cooking of the à la carte dinner menu – truly a very special place. Shieldhill has 2 AA Rosettes.

Open all year
🏨 Rooms: 16 en suite
🛏 B&B £57-£195
SP Special rates available
✗ Food available all day £
✗ Lunch ££
✗ Dinner £££
Ⓥ Vegetarians welcome
🕭 Children welcome
♿ Facilities for disabled visitors
🐕 Dogs welcome

Courgette Charlotte served with a light sauté of chanterelle mushrooms scented with truffle. Braised shank of Shieldhill lamb glazed with heather honey and thyme, set on a wild garlic risotto. Light chocolate pudding complemented with a banana parfait and white chocolate sauce laced with Baileys liqueur.

STB ★★★★ Hotel
💳 Credit cards: Mastercard/Eurocard, Visa, Switch, Delta
👤 Proprietors: Bob & Christina Lamb

SKIRLING HOUSE

Skirling
Biggar
Lanarkshire
ML12 6HD
Tel: 01899 860274
Fax: 01899 860255
E-mail: enquiry@skirlinghouse.com
Web: www.skirlinghouse.com

In Skirling village overlooking the village green. 2 miles from Biggar on A72.

Architecturally unique, this splendid house is also wonderfully hospitable.

- Small deluxe guest house overlooking the village green in Skirling.
- Excellent home cooking.
- "A gem of a place in beautiful surroundings, with excellent food."

Private houses in the Arts and Crafts style are not common in Scotland, and to find one which retains so many of its original features is a great joy. The house was built in 1908 for Lord Gibson Carmichael and is now the home of Bob and Isobel Hunter, for whom nothing is too much trouble if it makes your stay more enjoyable. Skirling House also has two cottages. Bob presents a four course set menu each evening (guests preferences are sought in advance), based upon the fresh produce available locally that day; he cooks with a light touch and his dishes are very well executed. Everything is home-made, including breads, ice cream and preserves. Breakfast here is "wonderful." The house cellar provides a selection of fine wines. Skirling House is a gem of a find – hospitality is very warm and genuine.

Open 1 Mar to 31 Dec
🏨 Rooms: 3 en suite
🛏 DB&B £49–£64 B&B £32–£42
🍷 Restricted hotel licence
✗ Dinner 4 course menu ££
Ⓥ Vegetarians welcome
♿ Restricted access
🚭 No smoking throughout

Smoked venison ravioli in a spiced broth. Rack of Borders lamb with a pecan herb crust. Rhubarb fool and parfait Napoleon.

STB ★★★★★ B&B
💳 No credit cards
👤 Proprietors: Bob & Isobel Hunter

TOFTCOMBS COUNTRY HOUSE HOTEL AND RESTAURANT

Peebles Road, Biggar
Lanarkshire ML12 6QX
Tel: 01899 220142
Fax: 01899 221771
E-mail: toftcombs@aol.com

At junction of A702 (Edinburgh) and A72 (Peebles), ½ mile north side of Biggar.

Attractive red sandstone country house hotel.

- Country house hotel.
- Modern Scottish.
- "Family-run hotel, warm and friendly welcome and good quality cuisine."

Proprietors, the Littles, purchased Toftcombs in December 1997 and spent the next six months renovating the hotel and restoring it to its former glory, before re-opening. Historical records show that it was part of an estate until 1832 and some of its more notable tenants were the four generations of the Gladstone family. Charles and Vivien Little are warm, friendly and hospitable hosts who have between them a great deal of knowledge and experience in the hospitality industry. Food is of the utmost importance to them and guests here are assured of enjoying imaginative skilled cooking in very comfortable surroundings.

Open all year
Closed Mon + Tue Jan to Mar
🏠 Rooms: 4 en suite
🛏 B&B £30–£45
SP Special rates available
✗ Lunch £
✗ Dinner ££
Ⅴ Vegetarians welcome
🕆 Children welcome
♿ Facilities for disabled visitors
🚭 No smoking throughout
🐕 Guide dogs welcome

Smoked garlic mushrooms: locally-smoked garlic, sauted with button mushrooms. Charred suprême of chicken, napped with a creamy Dunsyre Blue cheese sauce. Home-made oyster meringues, married with Famous Grouse whisky, soaked fruits and whipped cream from Quothquan Farms.

STB ★★★★ Hotel
💳 Credit cards: Mastercard/Eurocard, American Express, Visa, Diners Club, Switch, Delta, Electron, Solo
🍴 Proprietor: Mr Charles Little

THE HOUSE OF BRUAR LTD

by Blair Atholl
Perthshire PH18 5TW
Tel: 01796 483236
Fax: 01796 483218

7 miles north of Pitlochry on the side of A9 at Bruar. Restaurant services A9.

An astonishing emporium of the 'best of Scottish'.

- Self-service restaurant.
- Good Scottish cooking.
- "A not to be missed Scottish shopping experience with a good self-service restaurant."

The House of Bruar is a large, splendidly designed (inspired by Victorian hunting lodges) and expensively built (dressed stone, slate roof, astragal windows, etc.) 'emporium' selling the very best of Scottish country products. It includes a cashmere hall, a cloth room, a wildflower nursery, country wear hall, golf shop, mail order, food hall and 350 seater restaurant. Play and picnic areas are also provided. The lengthy blackboard menus offer snacks and full meals, with many classic Scottish dishes; the cooking is fresh and accomplished; breads, cakes and scones are freshly baked. A cheerful place for the whole family to break a journey. *See advert page 16.*

Open all year except Christmas Day, Boxing Day + New Year's Day
✗ Food available all day
Ⅴ Vegetarians welcome
🕆 Children welcome
♿ Facilities for disabled visitors
🚭 No smoking throughout

Fresh salmon, honey roast hams, filled crusty pies and Aberdeen Angus beef. Home-baked cakes and scones.

💳 Credit cards: Mastercard/Eurocard, American Express, Visa, Switch, Delta
🍴 Chef: Hugh Cuthbertson
Restaurant Manager: David Coupar

THE LOFT RESTAURANT
Golf Course Road
Blair Atholl
Perthshire
PH18 5TE
Tel: 01796 481377
Fax: 01796 481511

Take B8079 off A9, 5 miles north of Pitlochry. In village take golf course road by Tilt Hotel, the Loft is 50 yards on right.

Character bistro in historic village.

- A 19th century hay loft converted into a fine restaurant.
- Elegant Scottish.
- "Excellent skilful cuisine in a most attractive restaurant."

Located in a quiet side street off the main road through Blair Atholl is the Loft, a restaurant which is full of surprises and not to be bypassed! Climb the stairs, through the stable-style door and you will see an eaterie retaining all the characteristics of twisted old beams, stone walls and oak flooring. Well thought out and fitted to high standards it forms a delightful setting in which to sample the excellent cuisine of head chef Kevin Graham. The menus, which change throughout the day, are refreshing and appealing to suit all levels of appetite. The Loft has a conservatory bar and roof terrace. Advance bookings, especially for evenings, is strongly advised. The Loft has 2 AA Rosettes.

	Open all year
✘	Morning coffee to late dinner available
✘	Lunch £
✘	Dinner ££
Ⓥ	Vegetarians welcome
⚹	Children welcome
⇚	No smoking in restaurant

Warm roast red pepper salad with tapenade, goats cheese, basil oil dressing. Seared saddle of Perthshire venison, braised red cabbage compote, game and chocolate jus. White chocolate croissant bread and butter pudding with caramelised banana and coconut ice cream.

⊞	Credit cards: Mastercard/Eurocard, American Express, Visa, Diners Club, Switch, Delta, JCB
⋈	Partner: Mrs P M Richardson

ALTAMOUNT HOUSE HOTEL
Coupar Angus Road, Blairgowrie
Perthshire PH10 6JN
Tel: 01250 873512 Fax: 01250 876200
E-mail: althotel@netcomuk.co.uk

Take A923 to Coupar Angus from centre of the town. The hotel is 500 yards on right-hand side and is well-signed.

A comfortable family-run hotel offering an extremely high standard of cuisine.

- A stone-built house within lovely grounds.
- Modern Scottish cooking.
- "This is still a very memorable stay with the emphasis on the creative and innovative cuisine."

Altamount Hotel is a lovely old Georgian house built in 1806 and set in six acres of its own well-tended gardens. Robert Glashan, is an accomplished host and makes every effort to ensure that his guests feel at home in his home. The cooking is in a modern style, well-presented using the best local produce and offering good value for money. Menus are well-balanced, wide-ranging and are seasonally changed. The hotel garden provides an assortment of vegetables and herbs and a comprehensive wine list complements the meal experience. Altamount House Hotel has 1 AA Rosette. Finalist in The Taste of Scotland Scottish Field Black Pudding Competition 1999.

	Open all year
⊞	Rooms: 7 en suite
⊨	DB&B £50–£75 B&B £35–£60
SP	Special rates available + golf packages
✘	Food available all day £
✘	Lunch £-££
✘	Dinner £££
Ⓥ	Vegetarians welcome
⚹	Children welcome
♿	Facilities for disabled visitors
⇚	No smoking in dining room
🐄	Member of the Scotch Beef Club

Compote of chicken liver and black pudding accompanied by roast apples, broad beans and a balsamic reduction. Best end of Perthshire lamb set on creamed Savoy cabbage and bacon. Hot chocolate fondant pudding served with home-churned vanilla ice cream and a strawberry coulis.

STB ★★★ Hotel
⊞	Credit cards: Mastercard/Eurocard, American Express, Visa, Diners Club, Switch, Delta
⋈	Proprietors: Robert & Sally Glashan

CARGILLS RESTAURANT & BISTRO

Lower Mill Street
Blairgowrie
Perthshire PH10 6AQ
Tel: 01250 876735
E-mail: exceed@btconnect.com
Web: www.exceed.co.uk

At the Square in the centre of Blairgowrie, turn left off A93 Perth-Braemar road into Mill Street. Cargills is behind the car park, 200 yards down on the left.

An attractive bistro in a converted grain store, with riverside location.

- Converted mill store of old stone.
- Modern Scottish cooking with some European influence.
- "Friendly staff combined with high culinary skills make Cargills the perfect venue."

The old grain store with original stone exterior has been attractively converted into a modern bistro/restaurant with some original fittings such as metal pillars left as a feature. Well-known accomplished chef/proprietor Willie Little creates an impressive selection of high quality dishes all very reasonably priced. A blackboard shows daily specials in addition to the menu. A concise and carefully chosen wine list complements the food. An ideal venue for a relaxed lunch or dinner followed by a riverside stroll to Cargills Leap – a few hundred yards away! Sunday brunch has also become a firm favourite with guests at Cargills.

 Open all year
 Closed Mon
✕ Lunch ££
✕ Dinner ££
Ⓥ Vegetarians welcome
⚹ Children welcome
⚹ Facilities for disabled visitors

Fresh Glamis asparagus with lime mayonnaise. Seared trout fillets with crispy potatoes and prawn oil. Macademia, ricotta and rhubarb tart with crème fraiche.

⊞ Credit cards: Mastercard/Eurocard, Visa, Switch, Delta
Ⓜ Chef/Proprietor: Willie Little

KINLOCH HOUSE HOTEL

by Blairgowrie, Perthshire PH10 6SG
Tel: 01250 884 237 Fax: 01250 884 333
E-mail: reception@kinlochhouse.com
Web: www.kinlochhouse.com

On A923, 3 miles west of Blairgowrie.

An outstanding country house hotel with sporting facilities.

- Luxury country hotel.
- Outstanding Scottish cuisine.
- "So many guests return time after time to enjoy the finest of Scottish produce cooked with care, and to sample fine wines from the extensive list."

Kinloch House was built in 1840, extended in 1911 and has been in the same ownership since 1981. It is a fine example of a Scottish country house with oak panelling and first floor galleries. The house is set in 25 acres of wooded policies and parkland, grazed by Highland cattle and has delightful views. Service is impeccable yet unobtrusive in an elegant dining room with fine table settings. Menus offer the finest Scottish produce, carefully selected and cooked by head chef Bill McNicoll. During the months of February, March and April, Bill runs cookery courses over two mornings. The hotel also has an excellent health and fitness centre. Nothing is too much trouble for proprietors, the Shentall family. Kinloch House Hotel has 3 AA Rosettes. Shortlisted and Commended for The Macallan Taste of Scotland Awards 1999.

 Open 1 Jan to 18 Dec
🛏 Rooms: 21 en suite
🛏 B&B £74.45–£81.25
✕ Lunch ££
✕ Dinner £££
Ⓥ Vegetarians welcome
⚹ Children welcome – over 7 years only at dinner
⚹ Facilities for disabled visitors
⚹ No smoking in dining room
🐂 Member of the Scotch Beef Club

Finnan haddock mousse placed on woodland mushrooms, with a chive and horseradish sauce. Loin of Perthshire lamb wrapped in a tarragon mousse, with garden vegetables and a rosemary sauce. Raspberry cranachan parfait with a raspberry sauce and shortbread biscuit.

STB ★★★★★ Hotel
⊞ Credit cards: Mastercard/Eurocard, American Express, Visa, Diners Club, Switch, Delta
Ⓜ Proprietors: David & Sarah Shentall

CRAIGARD HOUSE HOTEL
Kinchurdy Road, Boat of Garten
Inverness-shire PH24 3BP
Tel: 01479 831 206
Fax: 01479 831 423
E-mail: craigard@zetnet.co.uk
Web: www.users.zetnet.co.uk/craigard

In the village of Boat of Garten, turn right at village Post Office. Hotel is 300m on left-hand side.

A traditional Highland hotel.

- Scottish baronial-style.
- Contemporary Scottish.
- "An ideal haven to explore Speyside."

Craigard House Hotel was formerly a shooting lodge built for the Countess of Seafield some 100 years ago. It is now a family-run hotel and restaurant set in its own grounds with views over an 18-hole golf course, and to the mountains beyond. The restaurant has been tastefuly refurbished in a modern-style which complements the ambience. Cooking here is skilful with menus offering a blend of traditional Scottish produce and a range of contemporary colours, flavours and textures.

	Open all year except Feb
🏠	Rooms: 18 en suite
🛏	DB&B £38–£65 B&B £20–£40
SP	Special rates available
✕	Food available all day £££
✕	Lunch £
✕	Dinner £££
Ⓥ	Vegetarians welcome
✰	Children welcome
✍	No smoking in restaurant
🐕	Dogs welcome

Speyside smoked salmon and trout roulade presented with a creamy red capsicum and grain mustard sauce. Breast of Guinea fowl set on braised red cabbage and pommes pailles, laced with a rich port and wild berry sauce. Queen Mary tart served with a Drambuie butterscotch sauce.

STB ★★★ Hotel
- 💳 Credit cards: Mastercard/Eurocard, Visa, Switch
- 🕴 General Manager: Lachlan Cunningham

HEATHBANK – THE VICTORIAN HOUSE
Boat of Garten
Inverness-shire PH24 3BD
Tel: 01479 831 234
E-mail: quirky@heathbank32.freeserve.co.uk
Web: www.host.co.uk

Situated in village of Boat of Garten.

Country house set in heather and herb gardens.

- Victorian house with painstakingly designed interiors.
- Skilled, imaginative cookery with fine attention to detail.
- "A comfortable country house with individual charm and excellent food."

Built at the turn-of-the-century, Heathbank retains much of its period charm. Bedrooms, including two with four-poster beds, are beautiful and filled with Victoriana. Attention to detail is paramount. At dinner one can expect fresh soups, roulades and terrines, home-made bread, local game and fish, Scottish beef and lamb, and of course, glorious puddings with little regard to calorie values! Presentation is stylish, surroundings in Charles Rennie Mackintosh style are stunning. Heathbank was inspected under its previous owners. New owners David and Janet Lawton took over in August 1999.

	Open all year
🏠	Rooms: 7 en suite
🛏	DB&B £45–£60 B&B £25–£38
✕	Non-residents – booking essential
⛋	Restricted licence
⛺	Packed lunches available £
✕	Dinner 4 course menu ££-£££
Ⓥ	Vegetarians welcome
✰	Children over 8 years welcome
✍	No smoking throughout

Cream of ginger soup with spiced sultana bread. Escalope of Spey salmon on a bed of crispy Savoy, with a white wine, cream and Scottish grain mustard reduction. Ice cream eclair with hot butterscotch sauce.

STB ★★★★ Hotel
- 💳 No credit cards
- 🕴 Proprietors: David & Janet Lawton

THE GRAPE VINE RESTAURANT
27 Main Street
Bothwell
Lanarkshire G71 8RD
Tel: 01698 852014
Fax: 01698 854405

On main street in conservation village of Bothwell,
½ mile off M74 (East Kilbride exit).

Restaurant/wine bar.

- Restaurant and wine bar.
- Modern Scottish cooking.
- "Informal restaurant offering modern Scottish cooking in a popular meeting place."

The Grape Vine is in the centre of the attractive conservation village of Bothwell. It is run by proprietor Colin Morrison who has developed the style of the business to suit customers particular tastes: for example a wide range of wines are now offered by the glass due to popular demand. Customers can enjoy anything here from an informal light snack to more formal dining where a good choice of menu items is on offer yet still enjoy a relaxed atmosphere.

    Open all year except 1+ 2 Jan
✘ Food available all day £
✘ Lunch £
✘ Dinner ££
Ⓥ Vegetarians welcome
✸ Children welcome
♿ Restricted access for disabled visitors

Steamed queen scallops with walnut and strawberry vinaigrette and smoked bacon. Pan-roast lamb with haggis stuffing and mint relish. Mille-feuilles of chocolate with atholl brose cream.

💳 Credit cards: Mastercard/Eurocard, American Express, Visa, Diners Club, Switch, Delta
🅺 Proprietor: Colin Morrison

BRIDGE OF ORCHY HOTEL
Bridge of Orchy
Argyll PA36 4AD
Tel: 01838 400 208
Fax: 01838 400 313
E-mail: bridgeoforchy@onyxnet.co.uk
Web: www.scottish-selection.co.uk

On main A82 road to Fort William. 6 miles north of Tyndrum.

The imposing Bridge of Orchy Hotel, on the Road to the Isles with spectacular views.

- Attractive, traditional Scottish hotel.
- Modern and stylishly presented Scottish fare.
- "Enjoy skilful use of freshly prepared Scottish dishes in a delightful candlelit dining room."

Dramatic scenery surrounds you here as the Bridge of Orchy Hotel is situated where you can enjoy spectacular views to Glencoe in the north and Rannoch Moor to the east – a stroll from the hotel leads to forestry walks on the banks of the River Orchy. This comfortable hotel, with its warm log fires and delightful candlelit dining room, makes a very enjoyable place from which to explore this stunning part of the Highlands and to relax again after a long day. Equally this is a good spot to stop on your travels and enjoy good Scottish cooking with a modern twist. Bridge of Orchy Hotel has 1 AA Rosette.

    Open all year except Christmas Day + New Year
🛏 Rooms: 10 en suite
🛏 B&B £30–£45
🆂🅿 Special rates available
✘ Food available all day ££
✘ Lunch – by arrangement in dining room: Bar lunches served daily ££
✘ Dinner £££
Ⓥ Vegetarians welcome
✸ Children welcome
🚭 No smoking in dining room

Ballotine of salmon on fine leaves with a citrus dressing. Pan-fried loin of venison on a bed of spinach complemented with a balsamic jus. Orange and passionfruit parfait accompanied with a mixed berry coulis.

STB ★★★★ Hotel
💳 Credit cards: Mastercard/Eurocard, American Express, Visa, Diners Club, Switch, Delta

THE LOCHNAGAR
Main Street
Bridge of Weir
Renfrewshire PA11 3LA
Tel/Fax: 01505 613410

In centre of village of Bridge of Weir. Car parking to rear of building. 5 miles from Glasgow Airport.

Restaurant and coffee shop with adjoining gift shop.

- Whitewashed stone building.
- Modern Scottish cooking.
- "Quality is never compromised in this attractive restaurant offering excellent home cooking."

The Lochnagar is a single-storey painted stone building on the main street beside the Post Office. Enter through the gift shop to the attractively decorated restaurant and coffee room. There is a small indoor children's play area which includes tables for parents to sit and enjoy coffee or lunch if they wish. A wide range of 'designer' coffees is on offer to enjoy with the delicious home baking. The lunch menu is compact which allows the kitchen to concentrate on producing a few dishes extremely well. The quality of the ingredients shines through and the preparation is careful and sensitive. The reputation of this small establishment is spreading fast, therefore it is advisable to reserve a table in advance. Home baking available all day. A conservatory extension is planned by May 2000.

Open 6 Jan to 31 Dec
Closed Sun
- ☗ Licensed
- ✗ Food available all day £
- ✗ Lunch except Sun ££
- ✗ Dinner – party bookings, minimum of 14, welcome by arrangement
- Ⓥ Vegetarians welcome
- ⚲ Children welcome
- ♿ Facilities for disabled visitors
- ✍ No smoking throughout

Fresh carrot and ginger soup. Loch Striven salmon and prawn pie. Lochnagar's home-made apple and lemon tart.

- ⊞ Credit cards: Mastercard/Eurocard, Visa
- ⋈ Partners: John & Mary-Ann Rankin/ Hamish & Kate Rankin

ROYAL MARINE HOTEL
Golf Road
Brora
Sutherland
KW9 6QS
Tel: 01408 621252
Fax: 01408 621181
E-mail: highlandescape@btinternet.com

On the A9 from Golspie to Helmsdale. At Brora cross bridge over River Brora and take Golf Road on right. Follow the road – hotel is on left.

Centrally situated hotel for everyone's needs.

- Sporting hotel.
- Traditional with a modern influence.
- "A consistently reliable haven of good food and wine."

The Royal Marine Hotel was built in 1913 and commands a fine position overlooking the mouth of the River Brora and adjacent to Brora's 18 hole James Braid Links Golf Course. Guests may also fish from the hotel's own boat on Loch Brora. The hotel has a leisure complex which includes an indoor swimming pool, sauna, steam room, gymnasium and Garden Restaurant; conference and meeting facilities are also available. The Royal Marine Hotel is an ideal base for touring the Northern Highlands and Orkney, and exploring nearby visitor attractions. The Royal Marine Hotel has 1 AA Rosette.

Open all year
- 🛏 Rooms: 22 en suite
- 🛏 DB&B £50–£80   B&B £40–£65
- ⓢ Special rates available
- ✗ Food available all day ££
- ✗ Lunch £
- ✗ Dinner £££
- Ⓥ Vegetarians welcome
- ⚲ Children welcome
- ♿ Facilities for disabled visitors
- ✍ No smoking in restaurant
- 🐂 Member of the Scotch Beef Club

Cushion of Brora run salmon set on a bed of leek tagliatelle with pan-seared scallops and saffron fumet. Roast loin of Highland venison with elderberry wine and old fashioned vegetables. Orkney fudge tian with Clynelish malt whisky sauce.

STB ★★★★ Hotel
- ⊞ Credit cards: Mastercard/Eurocard, American Express, Visa, Diners Club, Switch
- ⋈ Managing Director: Robert Powell

SOUTH KINGENNIE HOUSE
Kellas, by Broughty Ferry
Dundee DD5 3PA
Tel: 01382 350 562

From A92 Dundee–Arbroath, take B978 to Kellas then road to Drumsturdy to signpost for South Kingennie, 2 miles.

Converted farmhouse.

- A quiet and formal restaurant in a tranquil country setting.
- Skilful, traditional Scots cooking.
- "A restaurant which uses the best of fresh local produce to tantalise your taste buds."

Originally a farmhouse, South Kingennie deserves its excellent local reputation. Owned and run by Peter and Jill Robinson, it serves inexpensive and imaginative table d'hôte meals in a long, elegant dining room. With the addition of an attractive extension, the room is light and airy with views over the garden and beyond. Peter's stylish and imaginative cooking is matched by Jill's supervision of the front of the house. Atmosphere and service are relaxed and friendly. The wine list is comprehensive. Tasting notes are clear and helpful. Although in the countryside, South Kingennie is within close proximity of Dundee.

Open all year except Boxing Day, 1 Jan, last week Jan + first week Feb
Closed Sun evening + Mon
✕ Lunch except Mon £-££
✕ Dinner except Sun Mon ££-£££
Ⓥ Vegetarians welcome
✦ Children welcome
♿ Facilities for disabled visitors
🚭 No smoking in restaurant

Timbale of local crab and avocado with lemon dressing. Grilled fillet of Shetland salmon, basil crust and white wine sauce. Glazed lemon tart with citrus sorbet.

💳 Credit cards: Mastercard/Eurocard, American Express, Visa, Switch, Delta, Diners Club
🗒 Proprietors: Peter & Jill Robinson

THE OLD MONASTERY RESTAURANT
Drybridge, Buckie
Moray AB56 5JB
Tel: 01542 832660
Fax: 01542 839437

Turn off A98 opposite main Buckie Junction onto Drybridge road. Continue up hill for 2½ miles – do not turn right into Drybridge village. Restaurant on left at top of hill – twisty road – take care!

Converted Benedictine monastery with stunning views and exquisite food.

- A lovingly converted monastery within its own grounds.
- A blend of classical French and Scottish.
- "The best of quality food served in a delightful and unusual building."

Originally built in 1904 as a holiday retreat for the Benedictine monks from Fort Augustus Abbey – The Old Monastery Restaurant was converted in 1980. The views overlook the western mountains and Moray Firth, and stepping into the monastery you enter a world where the eating experience is the harmonisation of body and soul in an atmosphere of comfort and relaxation. It is now under the caring new ownership of Val and Calum Buchanan who are already building on its previously excellent reputation. Menus change seasonally and feature locally-sourced Scottish produce. There is also a well-sourced and representative wine list to complement the menus. The Old Monastery has 2 AA Rosettes.

Open all year except 3 weeks Jan + 2 weeks Nov
Closed 1, 2 Jan + 25, 26 Dec
Closed Sun Mon
✕ Lunch except Sun Mon ££
✕ Dinner except Sun Mon ££££
Ⓥ Vegetarians welcome
✦ Children welcome: (must be) over 8 years in evening
🚭 No smoking in restaurant

Seared local scallops on a fennel purée with fish velouté. Roast loin of wild Highland venison on a potato pancake with wild mushroom sauce. Chocolate trio: dark chocolate tartlet, white chocolate mousse and milk chocolate parfait with vanilla sauce.

💳 Credit cards: Mastercard/Eurocard, American Express, Visa, Switch, Delta
🗒 Proprietors: Calum and Valerie Buchanan

LOCH FYNE OYSTER BAR

Clachan
Cairndow
Argyll PA26 8BL
Tel: 01499 600217/600264
Fax: 01499 600234
E-mail: info@loch-fyne.com
Web: www.lochfyne.com

At head of Loch Fyne on A83 Arrrochar to Inverary Road. Well signposted on right-hand side 10 miles before Inverary.

Renowned seafood restaurant, fish shop and garden centre with craft gift shop.

* Converted farm steading.
* Fresh seafood.
* "Vast choice of local shellfish and seafood carefully prepared - even breakfast is served until 12 noon!"

In 1978 John Noble and Andrew Lane started a business which sets out to make the best possible use of the wonderful fish and shellfish of Loch Fyne, historically the most famous fishing loch on the West Coast. During the mid 19th century 670 boats were based here, and there were extensive oyster beds. Their plan was to re-establish the oyster beds and, as well as offering them for sale generally, to establish an oyster bar on the loch where people could sample a whole range of seafood. The restaurant eschews 'haute cuisine'; dishes are very simply prepared, so the fresh natural flavour of the seafood can be enjoyed. Meals served throughout the day. The adjacent shop features an extensive chilled cabinet displaying all their products in an attractive layout. Permits 'carry-outs'. Winner of The Macallan Taste of Scotland Special Merit Award for Achievement 1995.

Open all year except Christmas Day + New Year's Day
✕ Food served all day ££
Ⅴ Vegetarians welcome

Fresh rock oysters from Loch Fyne. Queen scallops roasted with bacon. Bradan roast (salmon smoked in a hot kiln) served hot with a whisky sauce. Shellfish platter – fresh oysters, langoustines, queen scallops, brown crab and clams.

🖸 Credit cards: Mastercard/Eurocard, Visa, Diners Club, Switch, Delta
🚻 Proprietors: Loch Fyne Oysters Ltd

ROMAN CAMP HOTEL

Off Main Street, Callander
Perthshire FK17 8BG
Tel: 01877 330003
Fax: 01877 331533
E-mail: mail@roman-camp-hotel.co.uk
Web: www.roman-camp-hotel.co.uk.

At the east end of Callander main street from Stirling, turn left down 300 yard drive to hotel.

Designed and built for the Dukes of Perth as an idyllic hunting lodge.

* Close to the town, yet set on the banks of the River Teith.
* Outstanding Scottish cuisine.
* "Comfort, tranquillity and the highest levels of Scottish hospitality – a luxurious country house."

Designed and built for the Dukes of Perth in 1625, the Roman Camp has been a hotel since 1939. Under the guidance of Eric and Marion Brown, it maintains its atmosphere of elegance. With its 20 acres of beautiful gardens, old library and secret chapel, the hotel offers the peace of the past alongside every possible modern convenience. The dining room, hung with tapestries and lit by candles, boasts a particularly fine painted ceiling. The best of fresh local produce is imaginatively used to create the finest Scottish cuisine, complemented by an excellent wine list. Service is unhurried and impeccable, the food is first class. Eric and Marion continue to run this establishment to a consistently high standard. Roman Camp has 2 AA Rosettes. *See advert page 262.*

Open all year
🛏 Rooms: 14 en suite
🍴 DB&B £78.50–£113.50   B&B £44.50–£79.50
ⓢⓟ Special rates available
✕ Lunch ££
✕ Dinner 4 course menu ££££
Ⅴ Vegetarians welcome
⚹ Children welcome
♿ Facilities for disabled visitors
🚭 No smoking in dining room

Cold ratatouille soup with basil oil, melon and cucumber. Red wine-poached turbot with squat lobster and caviar fricassée. Vanilla and passion fruit bavarois with caramelised pineapple syrup.

STB ★★★★ Hotel
🖸 Credit cards: Mastercard/Eurocard, American Express, Visa, Diners Club, Switch, Delta
🚻 Proprietors: Eric & Marion Brown

JEDFOREST HOTEL
Camptown
Jedburgh
Roxburghshire TD8 6PJ
Tel: 01835 840222
Fax: 01835 840226

200 metres from A68, main tourist route from
Newcastle to Edinburgh. 7 miles north of border
and 3 miles south of Jedburgh.

**The first hotel in Scotland – set in the beautiful
border countryside.**

- Small country house.
- French cooking with flair and imagination.
- "Outstanding cuisine – a real find!"

Travelling up the A68 this is actually the first hotel
you reach in Scotland. This is an elegant, small
country house with excellent accommodation,
beautifully furnished and finished to a very high
standard. The hotel is set in landscaped gardens
adjacent to the Jed Water, looking down the 35 acre
valley with Jed Water running through it. The food
here is excellent, professionally executed showing
high levels of skill and attention to detail which is
always a pleasure to find. This hotel also offers
residents and guests a golf driving range, and free
fishing on its own stretch of the River Jed.

   Open all year
🏨 Rooms: 8 en suite
🛏 DB&B £62–£77 B&B £42.50–£57.50
SP Special rates available
✕ Lunch ££
✕ Dinner £££
Ⓥ Vegetarians welcome
🚭 Smoking restricted to residents lounge only

**Grilled haggis on a bed of blanched leeks with
horseradish mousseline and balsamic dressing.
Roast fillet of Borders lamb with grain mustard
served with tapenade courgette. Muscadet
bavarois wrapped in brandy sponge with a tangy
compote of rhubarb.**

STB ★★★★ Hotel
💳 Credit cards: Mastercard/Eurocard, American
   Express, Visa, Diners Club, Switch, Delta
🅝 Proprietor: Mr George Cochrane

LETHAM GRANGE RESORT
MANSION HOUSE HOTEL
Colliston, Angus DD11 4RL
Tel: 01241 890373 Fax: 01241 890725
E-mail: lethamgrange@sol.co.uk
Web: www.lethamgrange.co.uk

From A92, Arbroath, take A933 Brechin road and
turn right at Colliston to Letham Grange.

**A gracious and beautifully restored baronial
mansion and resort with two 18 hole golf courses.**

- A grand country house hotel preserving the best
  of the past.
- Modern/traditional Scottish cuisine.
- "Whether you are golfing or here purely for
  relaxation you can do it all at Letham Grange."

With its period features – original oak panelling,
sculptured ceilings, period paintings – faithfully and
carefully restored to their original splendour of 1884.
Mansion rooms and less expensive golf estate
rooms are offered. Outdoor pursuits vary from golf
on its rolling parkland estate to fishing, shooting,
tennis and indoor curling rink. In its magnificent
Rosehaugh Restaurant the hotel offers both à la
carte and table d'hôte dishes that draw on fresh
local produce, imaginatively cooked by head chef
Gary Cross. Period conservatory open for lunch and
light meals all day in summer months. The menus
are well-balanced and reasonably priced. The wine
list is extensive. The hotel stocks over 90 single malt
whiskies.

   Open all year
🏨 Rooms: 42 en suite
🛏 B&B £50–£95
SP Special rates and golfing packages available
✕ Lunch £
✕ Dinner ££
Ⓥ Vegetarians welcome
🧒 Children welcome
♿ Facilities for disabled visitors

**Smoked Perthshire venison served with a crisp
salad, enhanced with a lime and ginger vinaigrette.
Collops of Angus beef fillet served on a haggis rösti
and drenched with wild mushrooms in a whisky
and cream sauce. Fresh local raspberry
crannachan served in a brandy basket and topped
with a Carse of Gowrie strawberry.**

STB ★★★★ Hotel
💳 Credit cards: Mastercard/Eurocard, American
   Express, Visa, Diners Club, Switch, Delta
🅝 General Manager: Alistair Risk

CARRADALE HOTEL
Carradale
Argyll PA28 6RY
Tel/Fax: 01583 431 223
E-mail: carradaleh@aol.com

From Tarbert (Loch Fyne) 26 miles via A83, B8001 and B842. From Campbeltown about 17 miles on B842.

A country hotel in a pretty garden setting.

- Country hotel in its own grounds.
- Innovative/traditional cooking.
- "Menus feature local produce and modern presentation."

This family hotel attracts golfers and tourists to this pretty village in the heart of Kintyre. A 9-hole golf course is located next door and the hotel has a squash court, table tennis, sauna and mountain bikes. Fresh, local produce in abundance is featured on the menus, and dining can be either formal or informal. Continual refurbishment is taking place with the lounge bar now completed and bedrooms being up-graded. This is an ideal base for exploring Kintyre and the islands. Cyclists and walkers are welcome.

Open all year except 23 to 26 Dec
🏨 Rooms: 9 en suite
🛏 DB&B £41.50–£51.50   B&B £25–£35
SP Special rates available
✕ Lunch £
✕ Dinner ££
Ⓥ Vegetarians welcome
✵ Children welcome
🚭 No smoking in restaurant

Guinea fowl and venison terrine with a tomato and black olive salsa. Bouillabaise of local scallops, langoustines and seafish with grated Parmesan and garlic rouille. Poached Conference pear with cinnamon and red wine syrup, Champagne sorbet and vanilla cream pastry.

STB ★★★ Hotel
💳 Credit cards: Mastercard/Eurocard, Visa
🅗 Proprietors: Marcus & Morag Adams

DALRACHNEY LODGE HOTEL
Carrbridge
Inverness-shire PH23 3AT
Tel: 01479 841252
Fax: 01479 841383
E-mail: eat@dalrachney.co.uk
Web: www.dalrachney.co.uk

The hotel is located at the north side of Carrbridge opposite the golf course, on the A938. The village is signed off the main A9, 23 miles south of Inverness.

Popular country house hotel of wide appeal to locals, tourists and sportsmen alike.

- Country hotel, formerly a hunting lodge of the Countess of Seafield.
- Traditional Scottish cooking.
- "A comfortable hotel with a warm welcome."

Dalrachney Lodge is a traditionally built Highland shooting lodge standing in 16 acres of peaceful grounds on the banks of the River Dulnain. Decor throughout the hotel is of a high standard with comfortable, spacious bedrooms and well-maintained public rooms. There are also two self-contained houses within the grounds which are available on a self-catering or serviced basis. The Lodge Restaurant is a typical period dining room with a bright, open outlook. At lunch a wide-ranging bar menu is presented, augmented by a dish of the day – this can be eaten in the restaurant or in the bar. For dinner, both à la carte and table d'hôte menus are offered. Provision is made for anyone with food allergies and special needs.

Open all year
🏨 Rooms: 11, 10 en suite
🛏 DB&B £45–£70   B&B £25–£50
✕ Lunch £
✕ Dinner ££
Ⓥ Vegetarians welcome
✵ Children welcome
🚭 No smoking in restaurant

Tiger king prawns lightly sauteed in butter with fresh chillies and garlic. Medallions of wild Highland venison served with a crushed juniper berry sauce. Raspberries in Glayva whisky liqueur with crushed meringue and cream.

STB ★★★★ Hotel
💳 Credit cards: Mastercard/Eurocard, American Express, Visa, Switch, Delta
🅗 Proprietor: Helen Swanney

CRAIGADAM

Castle Douglas
Kirkcudbrightshire
DG7 3HU
Tel/Fax: 01556 650233
E-mail: inquiry@craigadam.com
Web: www.craigadam.com

2 miles north of Crocketford on the A712.

A luxury farmhouse set in the Galloway Hills.

* Farmhouse.
* Delightful home cooking.
* "A fine Scottish welcome, exceptional home cooking and congenial surroundings."

Craigadam is a large and elegant farmhouse with strong sporting connections (Mr Pickup organises shoots, stalking and fishing). It is set up a hill and enjoys fabulous views across rural Galloway. Walks begin at the back door! New rooms are situated in the converted farm steading round a courtyard, which features an attracive modern fountain garden. The dining room and drawing room are filled with family treasures, photographs and interesting books. The cooking is carefully balanced, presented with great attention to detail and the flavours are delightful. Dinner is enjoyed en masse in the oak-panelled dining room. Drinks and coffee are served in the drawing room. At Craigadam there is a pervading atmosphere of relaxation, informality and good humour.

Open all year except Christmas Eve to 2 Jan
🏨 Rooms: 6 en suite
🛏 DB&B £36–£39   B&B £22–£25
Ⓤ Unlicensed
✕ Dinner ££
Ⓥ Vegetarians welcome
☀ Children welcome
🚭 No smoking in bedrooms

Smoked haddock mousseline with prawn and hollandaise sauce, and home-made bread. Noisettes of Galloway lamb on a bed of spinach with a mint sauce. Lemon meringue roulade with mango and passion fruit sauce.

STB ★★★★ B&B
💳 Credit cards: Mastercard/Eurocard, Visa, Switch, Delta, JCB, Solo, Visa Electron
👤 Partner: Celia Pickup

CHIRNSIDE HALL COUNTRY HOUSE HOTEL

Chirnside
nr Duns
Berwickshire TD11 3LD
Tel: 01890 818 219
Fax: 01890 818 231
E-mail: jgea@globalnet.co.uk
Web: www.chirnsidehallhotel.com

Between Chirnside and Foulden on A6105. 1 mile east of Chirnside.

A luxury country house hotel.

* Sandstone Victorian mansion house.
* Modern Scottish.
* "Joe and Kathryn Gomez personally ensure that your stay is memorable. Enjoy panoramic views, luxurious surroundings and delicious food."

Relaxing country house situated in the beautiful Scottish Borders. Chirnside Hall has been refurbished with antiques, warm soft furnishings and delightful well-appointed en suite bedrooms. Open log fires, wonderful views, elegant surroundings and an intimate candelit restaurant add to the atmosphere. The hotel is ideally situated for those who enjoy walking, golf, fishing and shooting, or simply relaxing. Chirnside Hall has 2 AA Rosettes.

Open all year
🏨 Rooms: 10 en suite
🛏 DB&B £62.50–£67.50   B&B £45–£50
SP Special rates available
✕ Dinner – booking essential ££
Ⓥ Vegetarians welcome
☀ Children welcome
🚭 No smoking in dining room

Bacon and basil wrapped canon of lamb served with balsamic vinegar and herbs. Rolled fillet of pork stuffed with haggis with a wild berry and apple compote. Pear streusel with raspberry and white chocolate ice cream.

STB ★★★★ Hotel
💳 Credit cards: Mastercard/Eurocard, American Express, Visa, Switch, Delta
👤 Proprietors: Joe and Kathryn Gomez

DUNLAVEROCK COUNTRY HOUSE
Coldingham Bay
Nr Eyemouth
Berwickshire TD14 5PA
Tel/Fax: 018907 71450
E-mail: dunlaverock@lineone.net
Web: www.come.to/dunlaverock

Take A1107 to Coldingham and then follow signs to Coldingham Bay.

Small deluxe country house hotel overlooking the sea-topped sands of Coldingham Bay.

• Late Victorian villa.
• Innovative home cooking.
• "A wonderfully relaxing escape from it all. A warm welcome and good home cooking making an unforgettable stay."

Dunlaverock House has six spacious individually decorated, en suite bedrooms and every effort has been taken to make guests as comfortable as possible. Proprietors Mari and Ronnie Brown are very friendly and attentive – excellent hosts. Scottish produce is evident on the menu, including a range of cheeses from the Scottish Borders. Freshly prepared, the flavours excellent. Standards are high throughout this relaxing hotel.

     Open 1 Feb to 2 Jan except 22 to 26 Dec
🏨   Rooms: 6 en suite
🛏   DB&B £48–£60
SP   Special rates available
✖   Dinner ££
Ⓥ   Vegetarians welcome
✶   Children over 9 years welcome
⚹   Facilities for disabled visitors
⚰   No smoking in dining room

Double-baked smoked salmon soufflé. Roast leg of Border lamb, with mint gremolata sauce. Bread and butter pudding, with apricot compote.

STB ★★★★ Guest House
Ⓔ   Credit cards: Mastercard/Eurocard, Visa, JVC
𝕄   Proprietors: Mari and Ronnie Brown

THE GRANARY
Drummond Street, Comrie
Perthshire PH6 2DW
Tel: 01764 670838
E-mail: mgrieve@sol.co.uk

On main street of Comrie (A85 west of Crieff) – opposite garage.

Award-winning tea room in the centre of Comrie village.

• A charming little tea-room/coffee shop with the comfortable air of an Edwardian coffee shop.
• Good home baking.
• "Skilful home-made dishes and a range of home baking available throughout the day."

The Granary is an old fashioned building in the centre of the bustling village of Comrie. The large windows with sunny, flowered curtains look towards the Perthshire hills and the antique mahogany counter is laden with a mouth-watering display of home baking. A rich collection of home-made jams and chutneys crowd the shelves and there is also a good range of pottery and giftware. Proprietors Liz and Mark Grieve have made the Granary a special place with a warm and welcoming atmosphere, tempting customers with a delicious choice of food such as home-made ice cream and a large selection of cakes, biscuits and puddings. There is a good selection of ground coffees and teas (including fruit and herbal infusions). The full menu is available all day and visitors can purchase cakes, scones, breads and preserves to carry out.

     Open 28 Feb to 28 Oct
     Closed Mon except Bank Holiday Mondays
UL   Unlicensed
✖   Food available all day Tue to Sat: afternoon Sun £
✖   Lunch £
Ⓥ   Vegetarians welcome
✶   Children welcome
⚹   Facilities for disabled visitors
⚰   No smoking throughout

Tomato and basil soup. Smoked salmon salad platter with home-made bread. Lemon meringue ice cream with raspberry coulis.

Ⓔ   No credit cards
𝕄   Proprietors: Mark & Elizabeth Grieve

CRAIGELLACHIE HOTEL
Victoria Street
Craigellachie
Moray AB38 9SR
Tel: 01340 881204
Fax: 01340 881253
E-mail: sales@craigellachie.com
Web: www.craigellachie.com

On A941/A95, 12 miles south of Elgin.

An imposing hotel in its own grounds just off the main square of the village, with the River Spey at the foot of the garden.

- A large 19th century country hotel.
- Modern Scottish cuisine.
- "A delightful welcome, very good food and luxurious Highland hospitality."

Located at the heart of Whisky Country, within the attractive Speyside village of Craigellachie, this imposing hotel is decorated to a high standard and in excellent taste. Welcoming, comfortable and well-run, its elegant interior is matched by attentive and unobtrusive service. The bedrooms, some with four-poster beds, have lovely views over the river and countryside beyond. The kitchen uses fresh produce as far as possible, and carefully sources delicacies from all around Scotland – from Ayrshire smoked bacon to Sheildaig shellfish. The hotel has three dining areas each unique in style but all with a warm, welcoming atmosphere and professional, yet unobtrusive service. Craigellachie has 2 AA Rosettes.

Open all year
- 🏠 Rooms: 26 en suite
- 🛏 B&B £54.50–£65
- SP Special seasonal rates available
- ✗ Lunch £-£££
- ✗ Dinner 4 course menu £-££££
- ⓥ Vegetarians welcome
- 🧍 Children welcome
- ⤢ No smoking in restaurants
- 🐂 Member of the Scotch Beef Club

Terrine of chicken, leek and basil with onion marmalade. Grilled lemon sole with dill mash, fine vegetables and a butter sauce. Red berry brûlée accompanied with fruits of the forest coulis.

STB ★★★★ Hotel
- 💳 Credit cards: Mastercard/Eurocard, American Express, Visa, Diners Club, Switch, Delta
- Ⓜ General Manager: Duncan Elphick

ALLT-CHAORAIN HOUSE
Inverherive
Crianlarich
Perthshire FK20 8RU
Tel: 01838 300283
Fax: 01838 300238

Off A82, 1 mile north of Crianlarich on Tyndrum road.

Small country house in beautiful gardens with dramatic views.

- Informal country house with sweeping driveway.
- Home cooking.
- "A very hospitable host."

Crianlarich is a warm and welcoming house, perched on a hill in its own grounds overlooking the scenic countryside of Benmore and Strathfillan. Its owner, Roger McDonald has a relaxed, hospitable manner with all his guests. Each evening he presents a different dinner menu in the charming wood-panelled dining room where you will share one of three large tables with other guests staying in the hotel. Homely, freshly-prepared set meals with generous portions are provided. A 'trust' bar is available in the attractive drawing room where a log fire burns throughout the year.

Open 17 Mar to 1 Nov
- 🏠 Rooms: 7 en suite
- 🛏 DB&B £48–£53   B&B £30–£35
- SP Special rates available
- ✗ Residents only
- ✗ Dinner ££
- ⓥ Vegetarians welcome
- ♿ Facilities for disabled visitors (3 ground floor rooms)
- ⤢ No smoking throughout

Creamed onion and parsnip soup. Scottish leg of lamb with haggis and mint stuffing with garlic and rosemary fanned potatoes and an assortment of celery, courgettes, red pepper and mushroom stir-fry. Bread and butter pudding made with summer fruits and brandy sauce.

STB ★★★ Guest House
- 💳 Credit cards: Mastercard/Eurocard, American Express, Visa, Switch, Delta
- Ⓜ Proprietor: Roger McDonald

THE BANK RESTAURANT

32 High Street
Crieff
Perthshire
PH7 3BS
Tel/Fax: 01764 656575

In Crieff town centre opposite tourist office and town clock.

A town restaurant offering skilful cuisine cooked to order.

- Listed building c. 1900 – old British Linen Bank.
- Modern Scottish cooking.
- "Creative cooking and friendly service in a tastefully converted bank building."

The Bank has many of the original features from its previous life as a bank cleverly integrated to complement the style of the restaurant. It is run by Bill and Lilias McGuigan. Bill is chef/proprietor, whose cooking is skilful, talented and ambitious, Lilias is very hospitable as front of house. All dishes are cooked to order making the dining experience a leisurely and relaxed one. There are plans to refurbish the restaurant later in the season.

Open all year except 2 weeks Jan
Closed Sun evening + Mon
✗   Lunch £
✗   Dinner ££
Ⓥ   Vegetarians welcome
⚹   Children welcome

Wild mushroom risotto with truffle oil and Parmesan. Char-grilled fillet of salmon with langoustine, mussels and samphire with a shellfish, saffron and dill sauce. Burnt Glayva cream.

▣   Credit cards: Mastercard/Eurocard, American Express, Visa, Switch, Delta
⋈   Proprietors: Bill & Lilias McGuigan

BRASSERIE AT THE HYDRO, CRIEFF HYDRO HOTEL

Ferntower Road, Crieff
Perthshire PH7 3LQ
Tel: 01764 65 1661 (restaurant)
     01764 65 1666 (reservations)
Fax: 01764 65 3087
E-mail: enquiries@crieffhydro.com
Web: www.crieffhydro.com

1 hour from either Edinburgh or Glasgow. Follow A85 from Perth to Crieff (signposted Crianlarich) for 20 minutes. From Crieff town centre - up on the hill overlooking the town.

Independent family-run prestigious resort hotel.

- Victorian splendour set amidst 900 acre estate.
- Scottish produce with modern influences.
- "Fun, warmth, hospitality and excellent food for everyone – from 9 day olds to 90 year olds - a splendid place for a holiday!"

The Brasserie at the Hydro is stylish and designed to an exceptionally high standard. Its lively, informal atmosphere is excellent for the young and young-at-heart who are looked after with compassion. Customer care is second to none, for those requiring extra help. The happy smiling faces in this busy establishment tell the story. The standard of staff is noteworthy. Crieff Hydro Hotel is a unique resort hotel with excellent sporting facilities.

Open all year
🛏   Rooms: 221 en suite (+ 23 self-catering units)
⊨   DB&B £59–£212   B&B £55–£108
ⓈⓅ   Special rates available
✗   Lunch £-££
✗   Dinner ££
Ⓥ   Vegetarians welcome
⚹   Children welcome
♿   Facilities for disabled visitors
⚮   No smoking in brasserie
🐕   Kennels available for dogs of hotel guests

Marinaded strips of beef, pork and chicken on a cushion of tomato and yellow courgette with coriander cream. A ratatouille of lamb with a hint of Madras seasoning topped with roasted baby vegetables. Layered tangerine and strawberry with caramelised raisins.

STB ★★★★ Hotel
▣   Credit cards: Mastercard/Eurocard, American Express, Visa, Switch, Delta
⋈   Food & Beverage Manager: William Lindsay

GLENTURRET DISTILLERY
The Hosh
Crieff
Perthshire PH7 4HA
Tel: 01764 656565
Fax: 01764 654366
E-mail: Glenturret@highlanddistillers.co.uk
Web: glenturret.com

Approx 1 mile outside Crieff on A85 Crieff to Comrie road. Just over 1 hour from Edinburgh (M9) and Glasgow (M8).

Restaurant in a converted distillery building, offering a range of good quality food for both formal and informal occasions.

- An 18th century bonded warehouse in the grounds of Scotland's oldest distillery.
- Traditional Scottish fare.
- "Good freshly cooked dishes available throughout the day."

Glenturret makes a strong claim to being Scotland's oldest distillery. It was established in 1775 although the site was used by illicit distillers and smugglers long before then. The Smugglers Restaurant, with the Kiln Room conversion at one end, is on the first floor of the converted warehouse and is self-service but has high standards of cooking. The Pagoda Room extends from the other end and offers a more formal setting. In good weather visitors can sit at tables on the terrace. The menus feature Highland venison, beef and salmon. Coffee, afternoon tea and home baking are also available during the day. Dinners and parties are welcome at Glenturret by prior arrangement. *See advert page 29.*

Open all year except 25, 26 Dec, 1 + 2 Jan
✗ Food available all day £
✗ Lunch ££
✗ Dinner – by private arrangement only ££££
Ⓥ Vegetarians welcome
🕏 Children welcome
🕭 Facilities for disabled visitors
🚭 Complete facilities are no smoking but a smoking area is provided in Smugglers Restaurant

Glenturret smoked salmon. Local venison in illicit whisky sauce. Cranachan (oatmeal, cream and raspberries flavoured with the Glenturret Original Malt Liqueur).

STB Highly Commended Visitor Attraction
💳 Credit cards: Mastercard/Eurocard, American Express, Visa, Switch
👤 Tourism Manager: Philippa Ireland

CRINAN HOTEL
Crinan, Lochgilphead, Argyll PA31 8SR
Tel: 01546 830261 Fax: 01546 830292
E-mail: nryan@crinanhotel.com
Web: www.crinanhotel.com

A82 Glasgow-Inveraray, then A83 to Lochgilphead. Follow A816 (Oban) for c. 5 miles, then B841 to Crinan.

One of Scotland's most famous and outstanding hotels.

- 1870s baronial style country hotel with a spectacular location.
- Fresh imaginative fine cooking.
- "A very comfortable hotel, run by consummate professionals in surely one of Scotland's most outstanding locations."

One of the most beautiful spots in Scotland with fine fresh produce landed on the doorstep. Uniquely located by the famous Crinan canal, this is yachtsfolks' heaven – and a joy to 'landlubbers'! Fine paintings adorn every wall space and there is an adjacent exhibition (Frances Macdonald is Mrs Ryan). The main restaurant, the Westward, offers a delicious table d'hôte menu and an à la carte lunch is available in the bar. So much does chef Craig Wood rely on the catch of the day that he will often not know until 5 pm what is on the menu, which features prime beef, wild venison and hill lamb, as well as fish. The exclusive and celebrated Lock 16 Restaurant on the top storey enjoys the view to the full and has a bar alongside. Winner of The Macallan Taste of Scotland Hotel of the Year Award 1998.

Open all year
🛏 Rooms: 22 en suite
🛏 DB&B £105–£120   B&B £75–£90
SP Special winter rates available
✗ Lunch £
✗ Dinner (Westward Restaurant) ££££
✗ Dinner (Lock 16 mid Apr to end Sep only) except Sun Mon booking essential ££££
Ⓥ Vegetarians welcome
🕏 Children welcome
🕭 Facilities for disabled visitors

Duck, foie gras and Puy lentil terrine with winter truffle and sweet shallot dressing. Pan-fried tranche of halibut with shellfish risotto, roasted salsify and saffron velouté. Baked fig tarte tatin with vanilla ice cream and marsala wine syrup.

STB ★★★★ Hotel
💳 Credit cards: Mastercard/Eurocard, American Express, Visa, Switch
👤 Proprietors: Nick & Frances Ryan

THE SEAFIELD HOTEL
19 Seafield Street
Cullen
Banffshire AB56 4SG
Tel: 01542 840791
Fax: 01542 840736
E-mail: herbert@theseafieldarms.co.uk
Web: www.theseafieldarms.co.uk

Situated on A98 (main road through Cullen) up from town square.

A charming and well-appointed old town hotel offering comfort and relaxation and value for money.

- A 17th century coaching inn in the heart of Cullen.
- Traditional Scottish cooking with modern influences.
- "Good food, a homely atmosphere and a warm welcome awaits the visitor here."

The Seafield is an impressive former coaching inn, built by the Earl of Seafield in 1822. Hospitality of this hostelry is a key priority whilst retaining the original character of the inn. The staff are smart, polite and attentive; the accommodation comfortable and traditional. The place is popular with local people and the bar offers a range of over 100 whiskies to enjoy before a roaring fire. A wide-ranging menu is available for all ages and preferences and thus caters for a variety of customers.

Open all year
- Rooms: 20 en suite
- B&B £26–£42
- Lunch £
- Dinner £££
- Vegetarians welcome
- Children welcome
- Facilities for disabled visitors
- No smoking in dining room

Haggis bites with a grain mustard mayonnaise. Char-grilled monkfish with baked red pepper dressing and finished with a rocket and basil pesto. Iced banana parfait with a kiwi fruit coulis.

STB ★★★ Hotel
- Credit cards: Mastercard/Eurocard, American Express, Visa, Switch, Delta
- Proprietors: Herbert & Alison Cox

OSTLERS CLOSE RESTAURANT
Bonnygate
Cupar
Fife KY15 4BU
Tel: 01334 655574

Small lane directly off A91 main road through town.

Many years success at consistently high standards are very apparent in this small and friendly restaurant.

- An intimate cottage-style restaurant.
- Elegant Scottish cuisine using fresh Scottish produce.
- "Ostlers Close never fails to offer the best of Scottish produce and hospitality to match."

Nestling in a lane or 'close' just off the market town of Cupar's main street, Ostlers is a simply and unpretentiously decorated small restaurant. Chef/proprietor Jimmy Graham deserves the excellent reputation he has earned for his imaginative cooking over the past 18 years. His treatment of fish and shellfish is outstanding, but he applies the same flair to Scottish meat and game. Organic vegetables, fruit and herbs are used here. Jimmy has a particular passion for wild mushrooms and these are to be sought after if on the menu. Given such quality, a meal here – complemented by a good wine list – is excellent value for money. Amanda Graham looks after guests with courtesy and charm. Ostlers has 3 AA Rosettes. Shortlisted and Commended for The Macallan Taste of Scotland Awards 1999.

Open all year except Christmas Day, Boxing Day, 1 Jan + first 2 weeks Jun
Closed Sun Mon
- Lunch Tue, Fri, Sat only – booking essential
- Dinner except Sun Mon £££
- Vegetarians welcome – please mention at booking
- Children welcome
- Smoking restricted until all diners at coffee stage
- Member of the Scotch Beef Club

Seared West Coast scallops with a smoked haddock risotto. Roast saddle of roe venison with oriental flavoured Puy lentils and wild mushrooms in a red wine sauce. Steamed rhubarb and orange sponge on a cream custard.

- Credit cards: Mastercard/Eurocard, American Express, Visa, Switch, Delta
- Proprietors: Jimmy & Amanda Graham

BRAIDWOODS
Drumastle Mill Cottage
By Dalry KA24 4LN
Tel: 01294 833544
Web: www.braidwoods.co.uk

A737 Kilwinning-Dalry. On southern outskirts of Dalry, take road to Saltcoats for 1 mile and follow signs.

An outstanding restaurant deep in the Ayrshire countryside.

- A converted 18th century miller's cottage, surrounded by rolling farmland.
- Innovative modern Scottish cooking.
- "A meal at Braidwoods shows just how exciting fresh Scottish produce can be when skilfully handled."

Simple but understated elegance is the underlying principle at Braidwoods. The decor is unfussy but stylish and the focus is on the food. This little two roomed restaurant is approached via a track through a field and stands amidst rolling green pastures. The food is highly seasonal with the menu changing daily to take advantage of whatever is best on the market. These Scottish ingredients are put together with real skill and delicacy to create imaginative dishes with great depth of flavour and integrity. This is modern Scottish cooking at its best. Booking is essential as the restaurant is small but once you have a table it is yours for the duration of your meal. Winner of The Macallan Taste of Scotland Special Merit Award for Newcomers 1995.

Open last week Jan to last week Sep + second week Oct to 31 Dec except Christmas Day Closed Sun pm, Mon + Tue lunch
- ♟ Table licence
- ✕ Lunch except Mon Tue ££
- ✕ Dinner except Sun Mon £££
- Ⓥ Vegetarians welcome – prior notice required
- ✠ Children over 12 years welcome
- ⊬ No smoking throughout
- 🐄 Member of the Scotch Beef Club

Crisp roast confit of duck on stir-fried vegetables and an oriental sauce. Baked fillet of turbot with home-made pasta, spinach and a lobster bisque sauce. Warm dark chocolate and maple tart with vanilla anglaise and a rocher of cinnamon ice cream.

- ⊞ Credit cards: Mastercard/Eurocard, American Express, Visa, Switch, Delta
- ⋈ Owners: Keith & Nicola Braidwood

SCORETULLOCH HOUSE HOTEL
Darvel, Ayrshire KA17 0LR
Tel: 01560 323331 Fax: 01560 323441
E-mail: mail@scoretulloch.com
Web: www.scoretulloch.com

Turn off A71 at eastern end of Priestland, near Darvel. Follow signs – approx 1 mile from A71. 20 minutes south of Glasgow.

A restaurant with rooms offering the best of countryside living.

- Converted from 15th century mill.
- Best modern Scottish cooking.
- "A special place of great charm and superb cooking in the rolling Ayrshire countryside."

Set high upon a green Ayrshire hill with stunning views over the wooded river valley, this ancient mill, once a ruin, has been transformed into a delightful hotel in the best modern Scottish tradition. Under the careful guidance of Donald and Annie Smith the pleasant staff bring home one of the greatest assets of Scotland – its friendliness. The cooking by head chef Kevin Dalgleish is highly skilled (as you would expect from someone with his pedigree), giving emphasis to the natural flavours and a real commitment to fresh local produce. Try the home-made bread, sausages or the smoked salmon or beef, smoked on the premises. Scoretulloch House Hotel has 2 AA Rosettes. Shortlisted and Commended for The Macallan Taste of Scotland Awards 1999.

Open all year except Christmas Day + New Year's Day
- ♜ Rooms: 8 en suite
- ⇌ DB&B £63–£93   B&B £44.50–£75
- ⓈⲢ Special rates available
- ✕ Lunch ££
- ✕ Dinner £££
- Ⓥ Vegetarians welcome
- ♿ Limited facilities for disabled visitors
- ⊬ No smoking in restaurant
- 🐄 Member of the Scotch Beef Club

Chilled Scottish lobster, mizuna leaves, aïoli and crab oil. Cutlet of new season lamb topped with basil mousse, complemented by lamb sweetbread summer truffle and rosemary jus. Peach melba: poached peach and vanilla ice set in a tuile basket.

STB ★★★★★ Restaurant with Rooms
Green Tourism 𝒫𝒫𝒫 GOLD Award
- ⊞ Credit cards: Mastercard/Eurocard, American Express, Visa, Diners Club, Switch, Delta, JCB
- ⋈ Proprietor: Donald Smith

DAVIOT MAINS FARM

Daviot
Inverness IV1 2ER
Tel: 01463 772215 Fax: 01463 772099
E-mail: farmhols@globalnet.co.uk

On B851 (B9006) to Culloden/Croy, 5 miles south of Inverness. Ignore signs for Daviot East and Daviot West.

Category B Listed farmhouse on a working farm.

• Early 19th century Highland farmhouse.
• Creative home cooking.
• "Margaret Hutcheson continually endeavours to find the best produce to tempt her guests."

Daviot Mains is a lovely and most unusual farmhouse and steading, in that it is almost completely square and built around a courtyard. One of only three of its type in Scotland, this is the warm and friendly home of Margaret and Alex Hutcheson. The public rooms have log fires. Licensed, guests can enjoy wine with Margaret's excellent home cooking. Ingredients are meticulously sourced to provide only the best of Highland meat and fish. Portions, as one might expect on a working farm, are generous. At 10 pm guests are offered a supper of tea and the day's home baking such as scones, shortbread or sponges. Daviot Mains is a member of the Certified Aberdeen Angus Scheme. **N.B. The Hutcheson family will be re-locating to a new farmhouse, but still at the same address in the autumn of 2000. Contact numbers remain the same.**

Open all year except Christmas Eve + Christmas Day
Note: Dinner served Mon to Fri Apr to Sep incl, thereafter Mon to Sat incl ££
🏠 Rooms: 3, 2 en suite
🛏 DB&B £35–£40   B&B £22–£26
SP Special rates available – Nov to Mar
❢ Licensed
Ⓥ Vegetarians welcome – prior notice required
✕ Special diets on request
ᵏ Children welcome
✏ No smoking throughout

According to season: home-made soups, fresh local salmon and trout, Aberdeen Angus beef, Scotch lamb, vegetables and cheeses. Local fruits and home-made puddings.

STB ★★★★ B&B
💳 Credit cards: Mastercard/Eurocard, Visa
Ⅺ Proprietors: Margaret & Alex Hutcheson

KINKELL HOUSE

Easter Kinkell
by Conon Bridge
Dingwall, Ross-shire IV7 8HY
Tel: 01349 861270
Fax: 01349 865902
E-mail: kinkell@aol.com
Web: www.kinkell-house.co.uk

1 mile from A9 on B9169, 10 miles north of Inverness.

A well-appointed hotel with a reputation for high class cooking.

• Small country house hotel.
• Country house cooking.
• "A culinary gem – a delightful find with true Highland hospitality."

This delightful farmhouse has been tastefully extended and developed to a high standard of homely comfort. It is the home of Marsha and Steve Fraser, who are generous hosts, making guests feel instantly welcome and relaxed. Kinkell retains the atmosphere of a private house, with appropriate period furnishings and log fires. The excellence of Marsha's cooking, which has won Kinkell an AA Rosette, is presented in interesting and well-balanced à la carte menus for lunch and dinner (five main courses; changing daily) featuring fresh local produce with both classic and innovative treatments. The restaurant is popular, and non-residents are asked to book in advance.

Open all year
🏠 Rooms: 9 en suite
🛏 DB&B £55–£65   B&B £35–£45
SP Special rates available
✕ Lunch – by reservation ££
✕ Dinner – by reservation ££
Ⓥ Vegetarians welcome
ᵏ Children welcome
♿ Facilities for disabled visitors
✏ No smoking in dining room + bedrooms

Kinkell game terrine flavoured with sloe gin and served with oatcakes. Mixed grill of Atlantic fish: lemon sole, monkfish and scallops, with a Noilly Prat and sorrel cream. Chocolate and hazelnut roulade filled with wild raspberry cream and garnished with summer berries.

STB ★★★★ Hotel
💳 Credit cards: Mastercard/Eurocard, Visa
Ⅺ Proprietors: Marsha & Steve Fraser

THE OPEN ARMS HOTEL
The Green
Dirleton
East Lothian EH39 5EG
Tel: 01620 850 241
Fax: 01620 850 570
E-mail: openarms@clara.co.uk
Web: www.home.clara.net/openarms

From Edinburgh take coast road to Gullane and
North Berwick. Dirleton is 2 miles between them.

**A traditional country hotel offering fine food and
wines.**

- Late 1800s sandstone building – originally
  farmhouse.
- Modern Scottish.
- "Good food in relaxing and peaceful
  surroundings."

The Open Arms is set in the sleepy hamlet of
Dirleton, opposite Dirleton Castle and village green.
Long a favourite of its Edinburgh neighbours the
Open Arms offers a warm friendly atmosphere in
surroundings reminiscent of a country home in a
renovated farmhouse. There is a fine dining
restaurant open for lunch and dinner and also The
Brasserie which is less formal. Local salmon is a
particular favourite served with East Lothian
vegetables. There is a good accompanying wine list,
with thoughtfully selected vintages, fairly priced.
The Open Arms Hotel has 2 AA Rosettes.

Open all year
🏠 Rooms: 10 en suite
🛏 DB&B £70–£110   B&B £50–£90
ⓈⓅ Special rates available
✕ Lunch £-££
✕ Dinner ££-£££
Ⓥ Vegetarians welcome
🕯 Children welcome
♿ Limited facilities for disabled visitors
🚭 Smoking discouraged: cigars + pipes
   not permitted

**Warm salad of pigeon breast served on an Ayrshire
bacon and Puy lentil broth. Roast turbot and
smoked salmon paupiette with baby vegetable
fondue and garden rhubarb confit. Poached peach
flavoured with rosewater and cinnamon served on
creamed rice and warm raspberry sauce.**

STB ★★★★ Hotel
💳 Credit cards: Mastercard/Eurocard, Visa,
   Switch, Delta
👥 Proprietors: Tom & Emma Hill

MALLIN HOUSE HOTEL
Church Street
Dornoch
Sutherland IV25 3LP
Tel: 01862 810335
Fax: 01862 810810
E-mail: mallin.house.hotel@zetnet.co.uk
Web: www.users.zetnet.co.uk/mallin-house

Down to centre of town, turn right.

Comfortable town hotel, popular with golfers.

- Modern hotel close to historic golf course and
  beach.
- Scottish cooking with seafood a speciality.
- "Centrally located hotel with good hearty food."

The hotel is a mere 200 yards from the Royal
Dornoch Golf Course, one of the finest and oldest
links courses in the world. As you would expect, it is
very popular with golfers: its bar, in particular, is a
refuge from the rigours of the course, with an
exceptionally good range of bar meals including
lobster and a special 'malt of the month'
promotion. An extensive à la carte menu offers a
good choice of local produce with superb, locally
caught seafood as something of a speciality. Food is
imaginatively prepared with unusual sauces and
accompaniments. The restaurant itself has
magnificent views of the Dornoch Firth and the
Struie Hills. Accommodation is very comfortable
including a residents lounge.

Open all year
🏠 Rooms: 10 en suite
🛏 DB&B £48–£55   B&B £30–£35
✕ Lunch ££
✕ Dinner £-££
Ⓥ Vegetarians welcome
🕯 Children welcome
♿ Facilities for disabled visitors

**Trio of smoked fish. Seared sea bass presented on
the skin side served in a pool of fresh lemon, lime
and saffron cream sauce. Linda's crème caramel.**

STB ★★ Hotel
💳 Credit cards: Mastercard/Eurocard, American
   Express, Visa, Switch, Delta
👥 Proprietors: Malcolm & Linda Holden

THE ROYAL GOLF HOTEL
The First Tee
Dornoch
Sutherland IV25 3LG
Tel: 01862 810283
Fax: 01862 810923
E-mail: info@morton-hotels.com
Web: www.morton-hotels.com

From A9, 2 miles into Dornoch town square, straight across crossroads, 200 yards on right.

The hotel is appropriately named, being adjacent to the first tee.

- Country house golfing hotel.
- Innovative Scottish cooking.
- "Beautiful situation, adjacent to first tee."

The Royal Golf Hotel is a traditional Scottish hotel, within yards of the first tee of the world famous Royal Dornoch Golf Course. Meals are served daily in the picture-windowed extension, which overlooks the golf course and the sandy beaches of the Dornoch Firth beyond. Head chef Jeanette Weatheritt creates wonderful dishes using the fresh local produce available. The cooking is first rate with very good presentation.

      Open 1 Mar to 31 Dec
🏠 Rooms: 25 en suite
🛏 DB&B £50–£75   B&B £45–£65
SP Special rates available
✗ Lunch £
✗ Dinner 4 course menu £££
Ⓥ Vegetarians welcome
🕆 Children welcome
🚭 No smoking in restaurant

Gâteau of smoked salmon and prawns, topped with an Arran mustard cream cheese. Duo of pigeon and pheasant wrapped in smoked bacon and set on a herb pancake with a redcurrant and juniper jus. Crisp filo tartlet filled with raspberries and Mascarpone crème.

STB ★★★ Hotel
Green Tourism 🌿🌿 SILVER Award
💳 Credit cards: Mastercard/Eurocard, Visa, Diners Club, Switch
👤 General Manager: Joanne Urquhart

MACKEANSTON HOUSE
Doune
Perthshire FK16 6AX
Tel: 01786 850213
Fax: 01786 850414
E-mail: mackean.house@cwcom.net
Web: www.aboutscotland.com/stirling/mackeanston

Take junction 10 off M9 motorway to Stirling/Perth. Follow A84 to Doune for 5 miles, turn left on to B826 to Thornhill. Take farm road on left after 2 miles then private road before farmyard.

Private home in Braveheart, Rob Roy countryside.

- Modernised 17th century farmhouse.
- Scottish home cooking.
- "Mackeanston offers Scottish hospitality in a relaxed family atmosphere home."

Mackeanston House has all the credentials expected of a small, family-run Taste of Scotland member. On arrival one is aware that this is a real family home where Fiona Graham offers a warm, hospitable welcome combining informality and a relaxing atmosphere with efficient service and food of a high standard. Many of the ingredients used in the kitchen are organically grown in Fiona's garden which may be viewed from the conservatory dining room. Guests may stay in the luxuriously appointed cottage a few minutes from the house or in the house itself.

      Open all year except Christmas Day
🏠 Rooms: 4 – 3 en suite, 1 private facilities (2 in house, 2 in cottage)
🛏 DB&B £50–£57   B&B £30–£35
SP Special rates available
✗ Residents only
UL Unlicensed
✗ Dinner £££
Ⓥ Vegetarians welcome
🕆 Children welcome
♿ Facilities for disabled visitors
🚭 No smoking throughout

Roasted red peppers with basil and Aga-baked Mediterranean loaf. Garden herb roulade with salmon and Ricotta, new potatoes and fresh tomato sauce. Home-made strawberry ice cream with Mackeanston shortbread.

STB ★★★★ Self Catering
💳 No credit cards
👤 Proprietors: Colin & Fiona Graham

A TASTE OF SPEYSIDE
10 Balvenie Street
Dufftown
Banffshire AB55 4AB
Tel/Fax: 01340 820860

50 yards from the Clock Tower on the road to Elgin.

Popular restaurant on the whisky trail.

- Informal town restaurant.
- Good wholesome Scottish fare.
- "Good food and a warm welcome awaits you here."

The restaurant is situated in malt whisky heartland and was originally a whisky tasting centre and restaurant. To this day one of its major attractions is the superb selection of malt whiskies on offer. Situated close to the centre of Dufftown the restaurant revels in its Scottishness, evident in its tartan inspired decor and style of cuisine. You will find simple fare that makes the most of local ingredients, cooked and presented with style. This is home cooking at its best, enhanced by a well-chosen wine list with a predominance of reasonably priced New World wines. A Taste of Speyside has 1 AA Rosette.

Open 1 Mar to 14 Nov
- ✘ Food available all day £
- ✘ Lunch £
- ✘ Dinner ££
- Ⓥ Vegetarians welcome
- ☂ Children welcome

Speyside platter between two as a starter: smoked salmon, whiskied chicken liver pâté, smoked venison, local farmhouse cheese, sweet-cured herring, salad, oatcakes and home-made bread. Lossiemouth scampi in a birch wine sauce. Heather honey and malt whisky cheesecake.

- ☒ Credit cards: Mastercard/Eurocard, Visa
- ☒ Partners: Raymond McLean & Peter Thompson

AUCHENDEAN LODGE HOTEL
Dulnain Bridge, Inverness-shire PH26 3LU
Tel/Fax: 01479 851 347
E-mail: hotel@auchendean.com
Web: www.auchendean.com

On A95, 1 mile south of Dulnain Bridge.

A charming Highland country hotel.

- Edwardian hunting lodge, with a great view over the Spey.
- Original, talented, eclectic cooking.
- "You may arrive as a guest, but leave as a friend. Country house living at its best."

Auchendean was built just after the turn of the century as a sporting lodge and has architectural details from the Arts and Crafts Movements. The present owners, Eric Hart and Ian Kirk, are convivial professionals dedicated to giving their guests a full dining experience. Before dinner you are served drinks in the drawing room, and meet the other diners, and choose from a splendid selection of over 50 malt whiskies. Both Ian and Eric share the cooking; Eric is a keen mycologist and finds over 30 varieties of edible wild mushrooms locally; the hotel's garden also provides vegetables (including 24 varieties of potato!), salads, herbs and honey. Eggs are supplied by the hotel's own hens. Wild berries, mountain hare, rabbit, pigeon, mallard, pheasant and home-cured gravadlax are specialities. As a New Zealander Ian has created an extensive cellar including over 50 special wines from his home country. French spoken.

Open all year except 4 Jan to 10 Feb + 20 Sep to 16 Oct
- 🏠 Rooms: 7 en suite
- 🛏 DB&B £39–£76   B&B £18–£51
- ⓢⓟ Special rates available
- 🍴 Pre-booked packed lunch £
- ✘ Dinner £££
- Ⓥ Vegetarians welcome – advise on booking
- ☂ Children welcome
- ♿ Facilities for non-residents only
- 🚭 No smoking in dining room + one lounge

Roasted aubergine soup with saffron garlic mayonnaise. Wild mountain hare casseroled with wild cep mushrooms. Liquorice and vanilla ripple ice cream.

STB ★★★★ Hotel
- ☒ Credit cards: Mastercard/Eurocard, American Express, Visa, Diners Club
- ☒ Proprietors: Eric Hart & Ian Kirk

LOW KIRKBRIDE FARMHOUSE
Auldgirth
Dumfries DG2 0SP
Tel/Fax: 01387 820258

From Dumfries take A76 Kilmarnock for 2 miles, then B729 to Dunscore. Beyond Dunscore at crossroads go right. After 1½ miles take first left. Farm first on left.

Farmhouse bed and breakfast set amidst rolling Dumfries pastures.

- Farmhouse family-bed and breakfast.
- Good home cooking.
- "This is a true experience of home cooking emanating from home-grown produce, where possible."

This is a working farm with a prize-winning herd of Friesian cattle and lots of sheep, so there is much to entertain those who love the countryside and farming life. The traditional farmhouse has beautiful views and has a lovingly tended garden to the front. The guest rooms are comfortable with a domestic appeal about them. Dinner is provided for residents with substantial helpings of wholesome home-made dishes using home-grown produce wherever possible. Zan and her family cook, serve and entertain you in their friendly and happy home.

Open all year except Christmas Day
- 🏠 Rooms: 2 en suite
- 🛏 DB&B £26   B&B £15
- 🆂🅿 Special rates available
- ✗ Residents only
- 🍷 Unlicensed
- ✗ Dinner ££
- Ⓥ Vegetarians welcome
- ⅄ Children welcome
- ⅄ No smoking in bedrooms

Nettle soup. Low Kirkbride lamb. Local venison casserole. Pecan pie with whisky cream.

STB ★★★ B&B
- 🅔🅔 No credit cards
- 🅗 Proprietors: Joe & Zan Kirk

CROMLIX HOUSE
Kinbuck, by Dunblane (nr Stirling)
Perthshire FK15 9JT
Tel: 01786 822125
Fax: 01786 825450
E-mail: reservations@cromlixhouse.com
Web: www.cromlixhouse.com

5 minutes off the A9. North of Dunblane Exit A9 to Kinbuck (B8033). Through Kinbuck village, cross narrow bridge and drive is 2nd on left.

A baronial mansion recalling the splendours of a bygone age. A unique Chapel is attached to the house for special weddings.

- A highly praised hotel with the atmosphere of a much loved home.
- Outstanding modern Scottish cuisine.
- "Cromlix is unique - for sheer elegance and fine dining, Cromlix will enchant you."

Proprietors David and Ailsa Assenti succeed in exemplifying the true traditions of country house hospitality, treating each of their guests as a cherished individual. This is reflected in the high standard of their accommodation, which includes eight large suites with private sitting rooms. Head chef Paul Devonshire takes only the best of fresh produce procured locally, and produces imaginative meals for the discriminating palate. Menus change daily. The wine list is discerning and extensive. Cromlix has 2 AA Rosettes.

Open mid Jan
- 🏠 Rooms: 14 en suite (incl 8 suites)
- 🛏 DB&B from £131.50   B&B £92–£150
- 🆂🅿 Special rates available – Oct to mid May
- 🍷 Residents + diners licence only
- ✗ Lunch Mon to Fri – Oct to mid May pre-booked only; Sat Sun ££-£££
- ✗ Dinner ££££
- Ⓥ Vegetarians welcome
- ⅄ No smoking in dining room
- 🐕 Dogs in bedrooms only
- 🐄 Member of the Scotch Beef Club

Pan-fried fillet of sea trout set on tempura vegetables with red pepper and pesto. Loin of lamb with a fresh herb crust on a bed of ratatouille, pomme Elizabeth and a rosemary jus. Crème fraîche and vanilla mousse with seasonal fruits.

STB ★★★★★ Hotel
- 🅔🅔 Credit cards: Mastercard/Eurocard, American Express, Visa, Diners Club, Switch
- 🅗 Proprietors: David & Ailsa Assenti

DAVAAR HOUSE HOTEL AND RESTAURANT

126 Grieve Street
Dunfermline
Fife KY12 8DW
Tel: 01383 721886/736463
Fax: 01383 623633

From M90, junction 3, A907 Dunfermline. Straight on through town, over Sinclair Gardens roundabout, right into Chalmers Street at 3rd set of traffic lights, 2nd left into Grieve Street.

Consistently good quality family-run hotel in quiet residential area.

* Large Georgian house.
* Good home cooking.
* "Family run hotel with good home cooking and hospitality in a relaxed and friendly atmosphere."

Davaar House was built at the turn of the century and retains such features as a splendid oak staircase, marble fireplaces and elaborate cornices. It is centrally situated in a residential area of Dunfermline. There is an appealing, chintzy appearance to the hotel which stands in lovely gardens. The food is cooked by Doreen Jarvis and her daughter Karen who create traditional dishes with intuitive flair and, using the best fresh local produce which is abundant in the Fife Valley and coastal East Neuk of Fife.

Open all year except 23 Dec to 6 Jan
Closed Sun
⚑ Rooms: 10 en suite
🛏 DB&B £54–£68   B&B £35–£50
SP Special rates available
❢ Restricted licence
✗ Lunch (Dec only) except Sun ££
✗ Dinner except Sun £££
Ⓥ Vegetarians welcome
✿ Children welcome
♿ Facilities for disabled visitors
✗ No smoking in restaurant + 1st floor bedrooms

Fluffy scrambled eggs with ribbons of smoked salmon. Perthshire rack of lamb presented with parsnip cakes, red wine and rosemary jus. Spring garden rhubarb flavoured with honey and ginger smothered over crème brûlée.

STB ★★★ Hotel
💳 Credit cards: Mastercard/Eurocard, Visa, Switch, Delta
👤 Proprietors: Doreen & Jim Jarvis

GARVOCK HOUSE HOTEL

St John's Drive, Transy
Dunfermline, Fife KY12 7TU
Tel: 01383 621067 Fax: 01383 621168
E-mail: sales@garvock.co.uk
Web: www.garvock.co.uk

Exit junction 3, M90 and follow A907 into Dunfermline. After football stadium turn left into Garvock Hill and first right into St John's Drive. Hotel is 500m on right-hand side.

Elegant Georgian house.

* List B building.
* Modern Scottish cooking.
* "Tranquil surroundings, modern facilities with good food and old fashioned service - the perfect combination."

Garvock House is situated in the Transy district of Dunfermline, which is part of the Transy estate once owned by the West Fife Coal Company. It is an elegant house which dates back over 200 years and retains many of its original features which have been lovingly restored by its present owners. The cooking here is excellent – a blend of Scottish modern innovative-style with traditional and, more recently available, Scottish ingredients. There is much attention to detail evident here – from turndown service to the care and consideration given to the presentation of your meal.

Open all year
Closed Sun evening
⚑ Rooms: 11 en suite
🛏 B&B from £42.50
SP Special rates available
✗ Lunch ££
✗ Dinner £££ except Sunday
Ⓥ Vegetarians welcome
✿ Children welcome
♿ Facilities for disabled visitors
✗ No smoking in dining room
🐕 Small dogs welcome

Seared gravadlax on a warm potato salad, drizzled with parsley oil. Roast rack of Ross-shire lamb with Puy lentils, garlic and balsamic reduction. Caramelised vanilla crème brûlée with home-made raspberry ice cream.

STB ★★★★ Hotel
💳 Credit cards: Mastercard/Eurocard, Visa, Switch, Delta
👤 Proprietors: Rui & Pamela Fernandes

KEAVIL HOUSE HOTEL
Main Street, Crossford
nr Dunfermline, Fife KY12 8QW
Tel: 01383 736258
Fax: 01383 621600
E-mail: keavil@queensferry-hotels.co.uk
Web: www.keavilhouse.co.uk

Crossford lies on the A994 Dunfermline-Kincardine road, 2 miles west of Dunfermline. Hotel is just off main street at western end of village.

Well-established country house with excellent leisure facilities.

- Country hotel with modern additions.
- Modern Scottish cooking.
- "A relaxed country house offering excellent choices for the discerning customer."

Crossford village is just outside Dunfermline and Keavil House is on the Main Street, standing in 12 acres of gardens and woods. As well as having two restaurants to choose from, the hotel also has a swimming pool, gym and sauna/solarium, etc. Staff are smart and well-trained; rooms are very comfortable. There is a choice of à la carte or table d'hôte menus which offer both traditional and more adventurous dishes, all of them well-cooked and presented. Keavil is part of the Best Western group of hotels and has 1 AA Rosette.

Open all year
🏠 Rooms: 47 en suite
🛏 DB&B £52.50–£72.50   B&B £49–£84
SP Special rates available
✗ Food available all day
✗ Lunch £
✗ Dinner £££
V Vegetarians welcome
☀ Children welcome
♿ Facilities for disabled visitors
🚭 No smoking throughout

A clear broth of oyster and crayfish with a chilli and saffron oil. Crown of spring lamb with a lemon, thyme and sweetbread farce. Warm griddle scones with a cinnamon and toffee cream, served with tayberries.

STB ★★★★ Hotel
💳 Credit cards: Mastercard/Eurocard, American Express, Visa, Diners Club, Switch
🍴 General Manager: Mark Simpkins

THE PEND
5 Brae Street, Dunkeld
Perthshire PH8 0BA
Tel: 01350 727586
Fax: 01350 727173
E-mail: react@sol.co.uk
Web: www.thepend.com

In the town centre, on Brae Street, off the High Street. Opposite the turning to the cathedral.

Georgian town house in historic town.

- Delightful town house furnished with antiques.
- Scottish home cooking.
- "Warm and friendly hosts, good food and home comforts."

The Pend is a delightful house with plenty of character, tasteful decorations, antique furniture and ornaments, which enhance the building. Rooms are comfortable and of a good standard and it is obvious that a greal deal of thought has gone into guests' comfort. Dinner is served at a set time, special diets and requests are catered for, and everyone is seated around one table. Owner/chef Marina Braney is eager to provide guests with an optimum level of service.

Open all year
🏠 Rooms: 6
🛏 DB&B £50–£60   B&B £30–£35
SP Special rates available
✗ Residents only
✗ Dinner ££
V Vegetarians welcome
☀ Children welcome
🐕 Dogs welcome

Thai crab cakes with sweet pepper sauce. Roast haunch of Perthshire venison marinaded in red wine, served with home-made redcurrant jelly. Apple pie with home-made cinnamon ice cream.

STB ★★★★ B&B
💳 Credit cards: Mastercard/Eurocard, American Express, Visa, Diners Club, Switch, Delta
🍴 Owner/Chef: Marina Braney

THE ANCHORAGE HOTEL & RESTAURANT
Shore Road, Ardnadam
Holy Loch, Dunoon, Argyll PA23 8QG
Tel/Fax: 01369 705108
E-mail: info@anchorage.co.uk
Web: www.anchorage.co.uk

3 miles out of Dunoon on A815 heading north.

A recently refurbished lochside hotel.

- Very pretty whitewashed Victorian house.
- Scottish food imaginatively cooked.
- "Charming hosts and delightful surroundings in which to enjoy good, fresh modern cuisine."

The Anchorage is a late Victorian villa that has been extended and delightfully modernised to high standards by its proprietors, Tony and Dee Hancock. The large conservatory restaurant is at the back of the hotel and overlooks the immaculate pretty gardens. Dining here, one is given the impression of eating outside. The comfortable lounge and breakfast rooms take in the stunning lochside scenery. This is a marvellous location to enjoy the tranquillity of a very typical west of Scotland scene – and yet only 30 miles (plus ferry ride) from Glasgow! Bedrooms are decorated and equiped to the highest modern standards offering attractive comfort, each with a stunning view over the gardens or the loch. This is a well-presented hotel, and Dee is a charming hostess, thoughtful and thorough.

Open all year
🏠 Rooms: 5 en suite
🛏 DB&B £42.50–£55   B&B £27.50–£40
✗ Lunch £
✗ Dinner £££
Ⓥ Vegetarians welcome
🕇 Children welcome
♿ Facilities for disabled visitors
🚭 No smoking throughout

Roast Isle of Arran king scallops served on a bed of courgette ribbons with a warm orange, ginger and dill sauce, topped with aubergine crisps.
Perthshire pork fillet wrapped in Parma ham and sage sauteed and served with a Marsala wine and pineapple sauce on a pasta ribbon bed. White chocolate and kahlua sponge.

STB ★★★★ Hotel
💳 Credit cards: Mastercard/Eurocard, Visa, Delta
Ⓜ Owners: Dee & Tony Hancock

CHATTERS RESTAURANT
58 John Street
Dunoon
Argyll PA23 8BJ
Tel: 01369 706402
E-mail: oldmill@cwcom.net
Web: www. oldmill.mcmail.com/chatters

Approach John Street from mini-roundabout on the sea front road. Restaurant opposite the cinema.

Delightful modern restaurant near the seafront, displaying local artists work.

- Town restaurant in converted traditional cottage.
- Traditional French-influenced Scottish cooking.
- "Cooking here is perfectly balanced, carefully crafted and presented with flair. Do go!"

In the capable hands of Rosemary MacInnes, a warm and hospitable host, this restaurant has picked up several awards. The chefs are very enthusiastic, original and extremely competent. Credible and well-balanced à la carte menus are presented for lunch and dinner (six starters, six main courses). Dishes are creative with real flavours at the heart. All food is home-made, from oatcakes to ice cream and chocolates (including tablet). The newly added conservatory extension is the perfect place to enjoy pre-meal drinks and after-dinner coffee. In spite of its excellence and distinction, Chatters has a friendly, informal atmosphere and is very popular with locals for morning coffee and home baking. Chatters has 1 AA Rosette. Winner of The Macallan Taste of Scotland Special Merit Award for Enterprise 1994.

Open Mar to mid Jan except Christmas Day,
Boxing Day + New Year's Day
Closed Sun Mon Tue
🍷 Table licence
✗ Lunch except Sun Mon Tue £-££
✗ Dinner except Sun Mon Tue ££-£££
🚭 Smoking in lounge only

Warm roulade of spinach filled with woodland mushrooms on a red pepper and tomato coulis. Loin of local venison with a confit of carrot and celery and a rowan jelly reduction. Chocolate and whisky torte on an elderflower sabayon with a quenelle of Belgian chocolate mousse.

💳 Credit cards: Mastercard/Eurocard, Visa
Ⓜ Proprietor: Rosemary Anne MacInnes

ENMORE HOTEL

Marine Parade
Dunoon
Argyll PA23 8HH
Tel: 01369 702230
Fax: 01369 702148
E-mail: enmorehotel@btinternet.com
Web: www.milford.co.uk/go/enmore.htm

On seafront near Hunters Quay Ferry, approx 1 mile from town centre.

Very comfortable small hotel in its own grounds facing the sea.

- 18th century villa.
- Modern Scottish cooking.
- "An attractive and comfortable hotel in a traditional seaside town."

Enmore is a small, comfortable, peaceful hotel with a family atmosphere. It is set back from the shore-side road within its own neatly-kept pretty gardens and looks out across the Firth of Clyde to Gourock. There is a squash court in the hotel, and a private shingle beach on the shore. Golf and fishing are within easy reach. Chef/proprietor, David Wilson, pays good attention to sourcing local produce and presents a short menu cooked most competently, using home baked bread and preserves. His wife, Angela, offers warm and genuine hospitality. Herbs and vegetables are grown in the hotel's garden. Enmore Hotel has 1 AA Rosette.

Open all year except 22 to 29 Dec
- ⊞ Rooms: 9 en suite
- 🛏 B&B £39–£75
- ⑤ Special rates available
- ✕ Snack food available all day £-£££
- ✕ Lunch – booking preferred ££-£££
- ✕ Dinner – booking preferred £££
- ⓥ Vegetarians welcome
- ⚘ Children welcome
- ⚿ Facilities for disabled visitors – non-residents only
- ⚗ No smoking in dining room

Grilled local goats cheese on a light garlic-flavoured croûton, drizzled with walnut oil and mustard seed. Glen Lean venison fillet, pan-fried and served with a spiced fruit sauce. Drambuie white and dark chocolate trifle.

STB ★★★★ Hotel
- 💳 Credit cards: Mastercard/Eurocard, American Express, Visa, Switch, Delta
- 🄼 Proprietors: Angela & David Wilson

36

36 Great King Street
Edinburgh EH3 6QH
Tel: 0131 556 3636 Fax: 0131 556 3663
E-mail: 36@thehoward.com
Web: www.the howard.com

Great King Street is off Dundas Street, the continuation of Hanover Street – 5 minutes from Princes Street.

Very modern minimalist restaurant in elegant Georgian basement.

- Contemporary interior design within New Town elegance.
- Best contemporary Scottish cooking.
- "Highly accomplished modern Scottish cooking with impeccable service."

A stunningly different modern restaurant. Although in a basement it is light, bright and airy. The minimalist, beautifully designed interior with modern yet comfortable furniture makes for a delightful atmosphere. The staff are all well-trained, professional but with an extra friendly quality which removes any pretentiousness often found in 'better' restaurants. They are rightly proud of their restaurant and this is conveyed in their manner. The cooking is skilful, by Chef Malcolm Warham, who uses the best fresh ingredients and his imagination to come up with inspired dishes.

Open all year
- ✕ Lunch £-££ (Closed Sat lunch)
- ✕ Dinner £££
- ⓥ Vegetarians welcome
- ⚗ No smoking in restaurant
- 🐂 Member of the Scotch Beef Club

Seared scallops with carrot nut butter and an orange and caraway reduction. Breast of Guinea fowl with a ballotine of the leg filled with Stornoway black pudding and bacon on a cider sauce. Fig and white pepper soufflé with blood orange yoghurt ice cream.

- 💳 Credit cards: Mastercard/Eurocard, American Express, Visa, Diners Club, Switch, Delta
- 🄼 Restaurant Manager: Sarah Lock

ATRIUM

10 Cambridge Street
Edinburgh EH1 2ED
Tel: 0131 228 8882
Fax: 0131 228 8808

Within Saltire Court, sharing entrance with Traverse Theatre, adjacent to Usher Hall.

Outstanding and individual modern restaurant of some style.

- Modern building – glass walls to 'Atrium'.
- Outstanding modern Scottish cooking.
- "Inspired and imaginative modern Scottish cuisine in an atmospheric setting."

From its specially-designed oil-lamps to its overall decor, the Atrium is a striking example of modern Scottish design. Appropriately, the imaginative cooking here is as distinctive as the restaurant it serves. The restaurant's talented proprietor, Andrew Radford, has seen his success recognised informally by a devoted clientele. He has won a number of awards, including The Macallan Personality of the Year Award 1994. Neil Forbes, Head Chef, offers an à la carte menu that is based on fresh local produce and changes daily at lunch and daily/weekly at dinner. The Atrium's menus are inspired, creative and well-balanced, as befits its deserved reputation: one of Edinburgh's foremost restaurants. Shortlisted and Commended for The Macallan Taste of Scotland Awards 1999. Shortlisted and Commended for The Macallan Taste of Scotland Awards 1999.

Open all year except 1 week Christmas
Closed Sun
✗ Lunch except Sun ££
✗ Dinner except Sun £££
Ⓥ Vegetarians welcome
✫ Children welcome

Fresh crab and dill hollandaise with rocolla leaves. Breasts of pigeon with celeriac purée, beetroot and braised fennel. Orange chocolate mousse with orange sorbet, chocolate sauce and caramelised oranges.

▣ Credit cards: Mastercard/Eurocard, American Express, Visa, Diners Club, Switch, Delta
Ⓜ Proprietors: Andrew & Lisa Radford

THE BALMORAL HOTEL
WINNER OF THE MACALLAN
TASTE OF SCOTLAND AWARD 1999 –
HOTEL DINING

1 Princes Street, Edinburgh EH2 2EQ
Tel: 0131 556 2414 Fax: 0131 557 3747

Princes Street at the corner of North Bridge at East End of Princes Street.

First class luxury with food to match.

- Sumptuous, elegant and distinguished hotel.
- Variety of impeccable cuisines.
- "Everything a 5 star hotel should be: comfort, quality and service which complements the superb views over the city and its gardens."

Since its opening as the North British Hotel in 1902, the Balmoral has maintained its reputation as the embodiment of hospitality and ease. Executive chef Jeff Bland oversees the hotel's principal restaurant – the spacious and elegant No. 1 Princes St. – offering outstanding classically orientated cooking which is exquisitely presented and served. Alternatively, the hotel's other restaurant Hadrian's offers less formal meals in a contemporary style. Bar lunches are available in NB's Bar. In the Palm Court lounge enjoy afternoon tea whilst a harpist plays. For food, ambience and service, this hotel deserves its reputation for all round excellence. The Balmoral Hotel has 2 AA Rosettes. Winner of The Macallan Taste of Scotland Hotel of the Year Award 1995.

Open all year
🛏 Rooms: 186 en suite
🛌 DB&B £106–£730   B&B £75–£700
Ⓢᴾ Special rates available
✗ Food available all day £££
✗ Lunch £-££££
✗ Dinner ££-££££
Ⓥ Vegetarians welcome
✫ Children welcome
♿ Facilities for disabled visitors
✂ No smoking area in restaurants
🐄 Member of the Scotch Beef Club

Marinated salmon terrine with mustard oil and tomato confit. Roast fillet mignon of beef with grain mustard mash and shallot sauce. Mandarin crème brûlée with blood orange ice cream.

STB ★★★★★ Hotel
▣ Credit cards: Mastercard/Eurocard, American Express, Visa, Diners Club, Switch, Delta
Ⓜ Executive Assistant Manager: Matthew Dixon

BLUE BAR CAFE

10 Cambridge Street
Edinburgh
EH1 2ED
Tel: 0131 221 1222
Fax: 0131 228 8808

Adjacent to the Usher Hall. On the first floor of Saltire Court, above the Atrium and Traverse Theatre box office.

Popular and fashionable cafe bar serving stylish food.

- Modern – part of theatre development.
- Modern fusion bistro style.
- "Modern cafe bar in centre of theatre development. Busy, friendly with plenty of buzz."

Unusually located within this unique theatre venue, this very stylish bar cafe is the brainchild of Andrew and Lisa Radford – proprietors of The Atrium (also located in the same building). 'blue' aims to cater for the discerning diner who is looking for a more informal, whilst still an exceptionally high quality experience. The style of the interior is minimalist with space and light the key features. Well-designed and with some unusual features including oak tables for which the wood was imported from the Dordogne for this specific use. David Haetzman, head chef, is a highly skilled, innovative chef committed to the use of fresh local produce. The menus offer great choice – ranging from innovative soups and sandwiches to main meals. Winner (Category 1) in The Taste of Scotland Scotch Lamb Challenge Competition 1998.

    Open all year except 1 week Christmas
✗ Food available 12 noon –12 pm £
✗ Lunch ££
✗ Dinner ££
Ⓥ Vegetarians welcome
⚘ Children welcome
♿ Facilities for disabled visitors

Crayfish risotto with crab and leek wonton. Roast lamb rump with pea purée and bubble and squeak, with balsamic shallot dressing. Apple fritter with apple crumble sorbet.

▦ Credit cards: Mastercard/Eurocard, American Express, Visa, Diners Club, Switch
⋈ Proprietors: Andrew & Lisa Radford

BOUZY ROUGE

1 Alva Street
Edinburgh
EH2 4PH
Tel: 0131 225 9594 Fax: 0131 225 9593
Web: www.scotscape.com/bouzy-rouge

Corner of Queensferry Street at Alva Street. Located on basement level.

Stylish, vibrant, city centre basement restaurant with quite a buzz.

- Basement restaurant in Edinburgh's West End.
- Modern Scottish.
- "The newest addition to the Bouzy Rouge group - stunning design combined with food to suit all pockets."

Unpretentious steps leads down to Bouzy Rouge's latest restaurant. Open the door and you cannot fail to be impressed by the confident use of colours, tiles and mosaics and the now signature designed wooden and metal handcrafted furniture. All of this creates a very special atmosphere. A surprise find is the inner terrace with canopied ceiling. The cooking is modern Scottish and as with all Bouzy Rouge restaurants, menus are compiled by both Alan Brown and the chef. Prices vary which allows great customer choice – from business lunches and casual dining to a gourmet menu.

    Open all year except New Year's Day
✗ Food available all day £-££
✗ Lunch £-££
✗ Dinner £-££
Ⓥ Vegetarians welcome
⚘ Children welcome

Smoked Finnan haddock poached in a sauce of cream and herbs and served on mash with petits pois. Fillet of pork coated in oatmeal, set on a bed of spicy Lewis haggis with a mature Cheddar sauce. Dark chocolate brandy cake with an orange anglaise.

▦ Credit cards: Mastercard/Eurocard, American Express, Visa, Diners Club, Switch
⋈ Proprietors: Alan & Audrey Brown

CAFE HUB

Castlehill
Edinburgh EH1 2NE
Tel: 0131 473 2067
Fax: 0131 473 2016
E-mail: thehub@eif.co.uk

A landmark church at the top of the Royal Mile, where Castlehill meets the Lawnmarket and Johnston Terrace.

Upbeat venue in newly launched Festival Centre.

- Stunningly restored old Tolbooth Church - reinvented as Edinburgh's Festival Centre.
- Light, innovative and above all fresh.
- "A most worthy addition to the Taste of Scotland Guide and a significant adjunct to Edinburgh's food scene."

This old church has been taken completely in hand - carefully and sensitively redesigned internally and restored externally – to achieve a marvellous venue for Edinburgh's first Festival Centre – The Hub. Under the expert guidance of Andrew Radford (proprietor of Edinburgh's Atrium, and blue bar cafe.) The fine food experience at Cafe Hub is headed up by Steve Hall, to give a light and airy locale for informal eating. Allow time to explore this innovative building, with its exceptional interior design involving many accomplished artists, and its Festival shop. The Hub has two wonderful rooms available for private use; the library and main hall which accommodate up to 600 people.

Open all year except Christmas Day
✕ Food available all day £
✕ Lunch ££
✕ Dinner ££
Ⓥ Vegetarians welcome
ⵉ Children welcome
⅁ Facilities for disabled visitors
⤬ No smoking throughout

Ayrshire ham and poached egg, garlic toast. Slow roast duck, watercress and beetroot. Bread pudding, praline ice cream.

Ⓔ Credit cards: Mastercard/Eurocard, American Express, Visa, Diners Club, Switch, Delta
Ⓜ General Manager: Steve Hall
Chef: Nick Bryan

CALEDONIAN HOTEL

Princes Street
Edinburgh EH1 2AB
Tel: 0131 459 9988
Fax: 0131 225 6632

West end of Princes Street at junction with Lothian Road.

A sumptuous city centre hotel that sacrifices nothing to size.

- Ex grand 'railway' hotel.
- Fresh, lively and world class.
- "A legend in its own time - the Caledonian continues to offer excellent food in stylish surroundings."

The 'Caley' has been a landmark and an Edinburgh institution since it opened its doors in 1903. The Pompadour Restaurant is situated immediately above the hotel's front door, and affords engaging views over the busy West End of Princes Street. The Chef de Cuisine has combed old manuscripts and investigated how international cooks applied and adapted classic methods in order to compose a menu which is described as 'Legends of World Cuisine'. Service is state-of-the-art; the wine list is exceptional; and the flavours are out of this world. Downstairs there is Chisholm's – a modern brasserie-style restaurant. *See advert page 26.*

Open all year
🛏 Rooms: 246 en suite
🍴 B&B £100–£200
ⓢⱷ Special rates available
✕ Lunch (Chisholm's) ££
✕ Dinner (Chisholm's) ££
✕ Lunch (The Pompadour) Tue to Fri ££
✕ Dinner (The Pompadour) Tue to Sat ££££
Ⓥ Vegetarians welcome
ⵉ Children welcome
⅁ Facilities for disabled visitors
⤬ Smoking areas in restaurants
🐂 Member of the Scotch Beef Club

Creamed carrot, honey and coriander soup finished with sour cream. Pan-fried lambs liver with Ayrshire bacon, creamed potato and onion gravy. Bitter chocolate mousse with amaretto.

STB ★★★★★ Hotel
Ⓔ Credit cards: Mastercard/Eurocard, American Express, Visa, Diners Club, Switch, Delta
Ⓜ General Manager: Enda Mullen

CHANNINGS BRASSERIE

South Learmonth Gardens
EH4 1EZ
Tel: 0131 315 2226 Fax: 0131 332 9631
E-mail: brasserie@channings.co.uk
Web: www.channings.co.uk

From Central Edinburgh – Princes Street, West End, cross Dean Bridge into Queensferry Road, then right, just after pedestrian lights, into South Learmonth Avenue and then right at the bottom.

Charming private hotel of character in quiet residential area.

• Edwardian terraced town house.
• Innovative modern Scottish and continental cooking.
• "The perfect base for the visitor to Edinburgh - nothing is too much trouble."

Channings is a very fine establishment offering all the atmosphere of Edinburgh's West End – a much sought after residential area – with a commendable standard of modern facilities. Furniture and fabrics are tasteful; bedrooms are individually designed. The Brasserie, in the basement, has been completely re-styled and extended offering a light and airy space in which to enjoy very fine modern Scottish cooking by Richard Glennie. The atmosphere of the Brasserie and the bar is relaxed and pleasant. Channings has 2 AA Rosettes.

Open all year except 24 to 28 Dec incl
🏠 Rooms: 48 en suite
🛏 DB&B on request   B&B £115–£160
SP Special rates available
✕ Lunch £
✕ Dinner ££
Ⓥ Vegetarians welcome
☆ Children welcome
🚭 No smoking in brasserie

Seared duck breast, beansprout and syboes salad drizzled with hot and sour sauce. Roasted monkfish served on braised chicory, vanilla and caviar beurre sauce. Banana crème brûlée with glazed banana and honey tuilles.

STB ★★★★ Hotel
💳 Credit cards: Mastercard/Eurocard, American Express, Visa, Diners Club, Switch, Delta
Ⓜ Head Chef: Richard Glennie
Restaurant Manager: Liam Bonthrone

CROWNE PLAZA

80 High Street
The Royal Mile
Edinburgh EH1 1TH
Tel: 0131 557 9797
Fax: 0131 557 9789
E-mail: sales@crowneplazaed.co.uk
Web: www.crowneplazaed.co.uk

Centre of the Royal Mile tourist area – just below the Tron Kirk.

Vibrant modern 4 Star hotel offering excellent facilities.

• Large city centre hotel.
• Modern Scottish cuisine with European overtones.
• "City centre hotel with cosmopolitan dining in Edinburgh's Royal Mile."

The Crowne Plaza hotel has been heralded 'the finest example of Scottish medieval architecture built in modern times'. The hotel has one restaurant 'Carrubber's' which takes its name from an ancient Royal Mile Close, preserving the heritage of its Royal Mile setting. The airy village square feel with window boxes and hand-painted murals provides the perfect backdrop to relax with friends in a vibrant and convivial atmosphere. A sumptuous à la carte menu with a daily blackboard selection of speciality dishes captures the unique seasonal characteristics of Scotland's abundant natural larder complemented by a pleasing selection of European and New World wines.

Open all year except 24 to 27 Dec
🏠 Rooms: 238 with private facilities
🛏 B&B from £65
✕ Food available all day ££
✕ Lunch £
✕ Dinner ££
Ⓥ Vegetarians welcome
☆ Children welcome
♿ Facilities for disabled visitors

Borders goats cheese and baby leek terrine with toasted hazelnuts. Collops of wild Highland venison with a parsnip crumble and blueberry jus. Rhubarb and oat crumble with honey ice cream.

STB ★★★★ Hotel
💳 Express, Visa, Diners Club, Switch, Delta, JCB
Ⓜ Director of Food & Beverage: Jean-Michel Gauffre

DUBH PRAIS RESTAURANT
123b High Street
Edinburgh EH1 1SG
Tel: 0131 557 5732
Fax: 0131 557 5263

Edinburgh Royal Mile, opposite Crowne Plaza hotel.

Genuine Scottish cellar restaurant.

- Intimate cellar.
- Contemporary Scottish cooking.
- "The best of Scottish produce cooked with care."

This is a delightful Scottish restaurant, patriotically stencilled with thistles and with pleasant decorative touches of pine. Its imaginative chef/owner, James McWilliams, presents a well-balanced à la carte menu which devotes itself entirely to Scottish seasonal produce and regional recipes – the cooking here is consistently good – and is a testament to the regular customers as well as the visitors to Edinburgh. The dishes offered are described with patriotic fervour and are cooked using simple methods as the freshest produce requires. The impeccable service contributes to the fine dining experience.

Open all year except 2 weeks Christmas +
2 weeks Easter
Closed Sun Mon
✘ Lunch except Sun Mon £
✘ Dinner except Sun Mon £££
Ⓥ Vegetarians welcome
⚐ Children welcome
⚐ Guests are asked not to smoke cigars or pipes

Rabbit and Ayrshire bacon terrine served with a rowanberry and apple compote. Baked smoked haddock coated with an Arran mustard sauce. White chocolate and Drambuie cheesecake.

⊞ Credit cards: Mastercard/Eurocard, American Express, Visa, Switch, Delta, JCB
⋈ Chef/Proprietor: James McWilliams
Proprietor: Heather McWilliams

DUCK'S AT LE MARCHÉ NOIR
2/4 Eyre Place
Edinburgh EH3 5EP
Tel: 0131 558 1608 Fax: 0131 556 0798
E-mail: bookings@ducks.co.uk
Web: www.ducks.co.uk

At the northern end of Dundas Street lies Eyre Place. Duck's lies near the junction of the two.

A relaxed and intimate Scottish restaurant with a hint of 'the garlic'.

- Intimate dining in Edinburgh's New Town.
- Excellent modern French/Scottish cuisine.
- "Very good food with an excellent choice of wines to complement the menu in relaxed and comfortable surroundings."

Proprietor Malcolm Duck established this stylish restaurant which is tucked away in a quiet corner of the New Town. Award-winning chefs produce innovative and excellent Scottish-style cooking from fresh, local ingredients and the exceptional menu is well-presented with French undertones. Malcolm Duck takes justifiable pride in his extensive and spectacular wine list. Duck's at Le Marché Noir is relaxed and restful, with attentive service, fresh flowers, candlelight and crisp linen all contributing to the ambience. Regional food and wine from around the world evenings are held once a month. A private dining room and special menus are available. The restaurant has 2 AA Rosettes.

Open all year except 25 + 26 Dec
✘ Lunch ££
✘ Dinner £££
Ⓥ Vegetarians welcome
⚐ Children welcome
⚐ Facilities for disabled visitors
⚐ No smoking room in restaurant

Boudin of langoustine with mizuna salad and langoustine sauce. Roast loin of lamb coated with a roast garlic mousse, thyme and lentil du Puy sauce. Chocolate tart with a cognac parfait and coffee custard.

⊞ Credit cards: Mastercard/Eurocard, American Express, Visa, Diners Club, Switch, Delta, JCB
⋈ Proprietor: Malcolm Duck

GRAIN STORE RESTAURANT
30 Victoria Street
Old Town
Edinburgh EH1 2JN
Tel/Fax: 0131 225 7635

2 minutes walk from the castle. Victoria Street is between the Grassmarket and George IV Bridge.

Unique city centre restaurant in historic setting near the castle.

- Historic stone store rooms.
- Modern Scottish.
- "Fine service and delectable dining - a truly delightful dining experience."

This is an 'upstairs' vaulted stone cellar – approached from Victoria Street below. The modern staircase opens into a series of rooms or chambers, with attractive bare stone walls, superb arched sash windows, stripped wood floors, all original, tasteful and simply refurbished with 'antique style' wood furniture and fittings. The cooking is accomplished, innovative and delicious and the menu changes according to seasonal availability and the service matches the food. Look out for the cheeseboard as Ian Mellis' (famous local cheesemonger) shop is right next door.

Open all year
Closed Christmas Day + Boxing Day
✘ Lunch £-££
✘ Dinner ££-£££
Ⓥ Vegetarians welcome
大 Children welcome

Velouté of market fresh fish and seafood, vegetables julienne and Pernod. Saddle of venison, roasted chestnuts, rosemary and port. Apple and almond tart, cinnamon ice cream,

⊞ Credit cards: Mastercard/Eurocard, American Express, Visa, Switch, Delta, JCB, Solo
Ⓝ Manager: Paul MacPhail
Chef: Carlo Coxon

THE GRANGE HOTEL
8 Whitehouse Terrace
Edinburgh EH9 2EU
Tel: 0131 667 5681
Fax: 0131 668 3300
E-mail: grange-hotel@edinburgh.co.uk
Web: www.grange-hotel-edinburgh.co.uk

From Princes Street (West End), travel up Lothian Road onto Melville Drive. Turn right into Marchmont Road, continue up through Kilgraston Road then right into Whitehouse Terrace.

Victorian mansion in landscaped gardens in leafy suburb.

- Victorian mansion.
- Contemporary Scottish.
- "A great little Edinburgh hotel, minutes from the city centre."

A relaxed atmosphere with comfort and style awaits at the Grange which stands in its own gardens in this select residential part of Edinburgh. It is really only a few minutes by car from the centre and is thus able to offer a country house atmosphere with real fires and comfort to the weary visitor. Lunch and dinner are served in the conservatory which overlooks the gardens to the rear. Menus are modern, innovative and seasonally changing, cooked sympathetically by the chef.

Open all year
⊞ Rooms: 15 en suite
⇔ B&B £60–£75
ⓈⓅ Special rates available
✘ Food available all day ££
✘ Lunch ££
✘ Dinner ££
Ⓥ Vegetarians welcome
大 Children welcome
✍ No smoking in restaurant

Salmon and tiger prawn kebab with grilled courgette and chunky tomato stew. Smoked haddock fishcakes served on char-grilled courgettes with tomato broth. The Grange banoffi pie.

STB ★★★ Hotel
⊞ Credit cards: Mastercard/Eurocard, American Express, Visa, Switch, Delta
Ⓝ General Manager: Garry Field

HALDANES RESTAURANT
39A Albany Street
Edinburgh
EH1 3QY
Tel: 0131 556 8407
E-mail: haldanes39@currantbun.com

At the east end of the city centre – off Broughton Street on the corner of Albany Street and York Lane.

Stylish restaurant in elegant Georgian New Town basement.

- Basement restaurant.
- Innovative Scottish cuisine.
- "Excellent Scottish cuisine and comfortable surroundings combine to make this a superb culinary experience."

Run by George and Michelle Kelso, Haldanes has established itself as one of the foremost Edinburgh restaurants. The basement has a light and airy feel and has been tastefully furnished and decorated in keeping with the style of the building. George and Michelle are an excellent team with George creating Scottish cuisine in his own unique style while Michelle, as front of house, gives excellent service to diners – a truly professional combination. In summer diners may enjoy the terraced garden to the rear, in winter an open fire greets guests upon arrival.

Open all year
Closed lunch Sun Sat
✗ Lunch except Sun Sat ££
✗ Dinner £££
Ⓥ Vegetarians welcome
♣ Children welcome
⚊ No smoking in restaurant
⬛ Member of the Scotch Beef Club

Seared West Coast scallops with crispy bacon, leeks and balsamic dressing. Saddle of Highland venison with a wild mushroom mousse and red wine and celeriac sauce. Caramelised lemon tart with berry compote and crème fraîche.

💳 Credit cards: Mastercard/Eurocard, American Express, Visa, Switch, Delta
⬛ Proprietor/Chef: George Kelso

HENDERSON'S SALAD TABLE
94 Hanover Street
Edinburgh EH2 1DR
Tel: 0131 225 2131
Fax: 0131 220 3542

2 minutes from Princes Street under Henderson's wholefood shop, at the junction with Thistle Street.

Busy informal, city centre wholefood eaterie.

- Lively, informal, cosmopolitan basement bistro in New Town.
- Innovative and interesting vegetarian cuisine.
- "Proof, if proof were needed, that healthy eating can be interesting and very tasty."

Henderson's was an established institution long before wholefoods became popular and its enviable reputation for excellent and inexpensive fare is as well-deserved now as in Janet Henderson's day. The restaurant has now been extensively re-furbished. The atmosphere here is always congenial and the counter-served helpings generous. Vegetarian salads, savouries, quiches and puddings are freshly prepared and eagerly consumed throughout the day with an unusual selection of real ales and wines, some Scottish and many organic also on offer. Henderson's, still actively run by the family, appeals to all ages proving that wholefoods can be fun, especially Monday to Saturday nights when 'real' musicians enliven the wine bar.

Open all year except Christmas Day, Boxing Day, 1 + 2 Jan
Closed Sun except during Edinburgh Festival
✗ Food available all day except Sun £
✗ Lunch except Sun £
✗ Dinner except Sun £-££
Ⓥ Vegans welcome
♣ Children welcome
⚊ No smoking in main restaurant + wine bar areas

Broccoli and Dunsyre Blue cheese soup with freshly baked nutty malt bread. Vegetarian haggis filo parcels with honey and Drambuie sauce. Walnut pie with crème fraîche.

💳 Credit cards: Mastercard/Eurocard, American Express, Visa, Switch, Delta, JCB
⬛ Proprietors: The Henderson Family

HOWIES STOCKBRIDGE
4-6 Glanville Place
Edinburgh
EH3 6SZ
Tel/Fax: 0131 225 5553

Located by the Stockbridge, on the corner of Hamilton Place.

Clean-cut design in this bustling Stockbridge bistro - ideal for informal dining.

- Corner site bistro in the heart of Stockbridge.
- Modern Scottish with Thai influences.
- "An exciting blend of fusion cooking using the best of Scottish produce."

Howie's latest addition is a welcome entrant to this Guide. Situated in the heart of Stockbridge this is a lively, buzzing bistro where great attention has been given to design. Having chosen the art of Feng Shui to create an ambivalent atmosphere, the finished result is one of a minimalist haven. Pale ochre walls offset the dark slate floor tiles and Italian light fittings. The two or three course menus represent excellent value for money as do the house wines. The food here is exciting and delicious with the best of Scottish produce being used innovatively.

Open all year except 25, 26 Dec + New Year's Day
- ✗ Food available all day Sat Sun £
- ✗ Lunch £
- ✗ Dinner ££
- Ⅴ Vegetarians welcome
- ✝ Children welcome
- ♿ Facilities for disabled visitors
- ✂ No smoking room in restaurant
- 🐕 Guide dogs only

Smoked haddock and crab timbale wrapped in spinach, dressed with wasabi and ginger. Noisette of lamb on warm butter bean purée flavoured with garlic and rosemary, served with a minted Asian pear and ginger sauce. Howies banoffie pie.

- 💳 Credit cards: Mastercard/Eurocard, American Express, Visa, Diners Club, Switch, Delta, JCB

HOWIES RESTAURANT
63 Dalry Road
Edinburgh
EH11 2BZ
Tel: 0131 313 3334

On the south side of Dalry Road, between Richmond Terrace and Caledonian Road, 2 minutes from Haymarket.

Small, informal restaurant offering smart bistro food.

- Bistro within old commercial and residential buildings.
- Modern Scottish with Mediterranean influences.
- "Interesting food combinations cooked with a light touch, served in friendly informal surroundings."

Howies has successfully gained a niche in the market with its innovative menu at reasonable prices. Much of its success lies in its idiosyncratic nature: off-beat location, eclectic selection of tables, chairs and even cutlery! Great care, however, is taken over the daily changing menus to create appealing choices. Howies now offer a limited, but good quality, and very fairly priced wine list. The option to take your own wine is still available (£2 corkage charge).

Open all year except 25, 26 Dec + 1, 2 Jan
Closed Mon lunch only
- ✗ Lunch except Mon £
- ✗ Dinner ££
- Ⅴ Vegetarians welcome
- ✝ Children welcome
- ♿ Facilities for disabled visitors

Cappuccino of wild mushrooms. Rump of lamb on roast olive polenta with a shallot confit, basil oil and Parmesan crackling. Caramelised lemon tartlet.

- 💳 Credit cards: Mastercard/Eurocard, American Express, Visa, Diners Club, Switch, Delta

IGG'S RESTAURANT
15 Jeffrey Street
Edinburgh EH1 1DR
Tel: 0131 557 8184
Fax: 0131 441 7111

Jeffrey Street lies between the Royal Mile and
Market Street, behind Waverley Station.

**Lively, stylish restaurant with a continental
atmosphere.**

- Elegant L-shaped restaurant.
- Many authentic Spanish dishes.
- "The best of Scottish produce beautifully cooked
  with a Spanish influence."

Igg's is a small, friendly, owner-run restaurant in the
heart of Edinburgh's Old Town which has recently
been extended into the premises next door and has
been completely refurbished. It is an attractive and
comfortable restaurant, decorated with taste. It is
difficult to know whether to describe it as a Scottish
restaurant with Spanish influences or vice versa.
Tables are attractively dressed with linen; lighting is
subtle. Iggy Campos, is enthusiastic, generous and
laid back – an excellent host who sets a relaxed
tone in his stylish restaurant. At lunchtime a tapas
menu is available as well as a good priced three/
four course table d'hôte and à la carte evening
menu. Igg's has 2 AA Rosettes.

Open all year except 1 to 3 Jan
Closed Sun
✕ Lunch except Sun ££
✕ Dinner except Sun £££
Ⓥ Vegetarians welcome
🛉 Children welcome
♿ Wheelchair access
🐄 Member of the Scotch Beef Club

**Warm tart tatin of beetroot topped with a quenelle
of Mascarpone and a tomato chive dressing. Fillet
of Stobo Estate beef topped with a blue cheese
crust on a rösti potato with a whisky sauce. Hot
chocolate pudding with a warm chocolate sauce
and vanilla ice cream.**

💳 Credit cards: Mastercard/Eurocard, American
    Express, Visa, Diners Club, Switch, Delta, JCB
🎊 Owner: Iggy Campos

JACKSON'S RESTAURANT
209 High Street
Royal Mile, Edinburgh
EH1 1PZ
Tel: 0131 225 1793
Fax: 0131 220 0620

On the north side of the upper Royal Mile near to
Cockburn Street.

**Atmospheric cellar restaurant in Edinburgh's Old
Town.**

- Cellar restaurant with separate dining upstairs.
- Modern Scottish cooking.
- "A restaurant with old world charm and excellent
  modern Scottish cuisine."

Now in its 16th year, Jackson's is on the High Street
the original thoroughfare and market place of the
ancient city of Edinburgh. The restaurant is open for
both lunch and dinner, offering table d'hôte and à la
carte menus, and its central location attracts both
visitors and locals. There is a cosy feel to the cellar
with alcoves, stone walls, tapestries, discreet
lighting and, at dinner, white linen. Upstairs there is
a second dining room with a tented ceiling, which
can also be hired for private dinners. The 'business'
lunch is creative and very well-priced; the à la carte
majors on Scottish ingredients, treated in unusual
and original ways. The menu also features well-
planned wine and whisky lists.

Open all year except Christmas Day +
Boxing Day
✕ Lunch £
✕ Dinner £££
🎊 Extended hours during Edinburgh Festival
Ⓥ Vegetarians welcome

**King prawns, flash-fried with lime essence set on a
spaghetti of seasonal vegetables. Marinated wild
venison haunch, sauteed in rosemary butter and
sloe gin with plum and red onion confit. Drambuie
spiked crème brûlée served with a cinnamon
shortbread.**

💳 Credit cards: Mastercard/Eurocard, American
    Express, Visa, Switch, Delta, JCB
🎊 Proprietor: Lyn MacKinnon

KEEPERS RESTAURANT

13B Dundas Street
Edinburgh EH3 6QG
Tel/Fax: 0131 556 5707
Mobile: 0410 434812
E-mail: keepers@compuserve.com

At the southern end of Dundas Street, near the junction with Abercromby Place.

Elegant cellar restaurant with friendly atmosphere.

- Series of three adjoining cellar rooms.
- Traditional Scottish cooking.
- "Classic Scottish cuisine in an intimate cellar atmosphere."

As its name suggests, this well-established restaurant specialises in game – supported by fish, shellfish and prime meat. The cooking is traditional, with good sauces and rich jus; the menus are both table d'hôte (five starters, five main courses) and à la carte and the dishes are naturally presented. Although centrally located, just down the hill from George Street, Keepers has an attractive intimacy. The wine list is well-chosen and reasonably priced. The restaurant serves lunch and dinner on a table d'hôte and à la carte basis. Individual rooms (or, indeed, the entire place) can be booked for private or business functions.

Open all year
Closed Sun Mon + Sat lunch unless by prior arrangement
৸ Note: Parties by prior arrangement
✗ Lunch except Sun Mon Sat £
✗ Dinner except Sun Mon ££
Ⓥ Vegetarians welcome
⭑ Children welcome
⤲ No smoking area by request

Creamed smoked haddock on a green peppercorn oatcake. Breast of duck with a cider and pear sauce on a bed of garlic mash. Home-made Cointreau and ginger ice cream with a cinnamon and lemon syrup.

⊞ Credit cards: Mastercard/Eurocard, American Express, Visa, Switch
Ⓝ Proprietors: Keith & Mairi Cowie

LE CAFÉ SAINT-HONORÉ

34 North West Thistle Street Lane
Edinburgh
EH2 1EA
Tel: 0131 226 2211

Centre of Edinburgh, just off Frederick Street, 3 minutes from Princes Street. At Frederick Street end of lane.

A bistro with strong French influences both in design, atmosphere and food.

- Small relaxed restaurant.
- Scottish produce with French influence .
- "Le Café continues to hold its place as one of Edinburgh's favourites."

Café St-Honoré is located in a service street parallel to George Street. It was formerly an authentic French Restaurant, was decorated accordingly and still has a Gallic charm. Its owner favours a more Scottish style of cooking, making good use of the produce available although there are French influences in the preparation. The lunch and dinner menus change daily and are à la carte – realistically limited to about half a dozen starters and the same number of main courses, and very reasonably priced. The cooking is adventurous and highly professional; interesting combinations and fresh, innovative sauces appear regularly. Chef/proprietor Chris Colverson is an outstanding vegetarian cook and is delighted to prepare vegetarian dishes.

Open all year except Christmas Day, Boxing Day, 2 weeks Easter and 1 week Oct
Closed Sun (except during Edinburgh Festival) + Sat Lunch
✗ Lunch ££
✗ Pre + Apres Theatre Suppers
✗ Dinner £££
Ⓥ Vegetarians welcome
⭑ Children welcome
⤲ 2 non-smoking dining areas + 1 smoking dining area
𝄕 No parking

Gratinée of oysters, crispy squid, hollandaise. Shank of lamb, garlic confit and spinach. Crème brûleé.

⊞ Credit cards: Mastercard/Eurocard, American Express, Visa, Diners Club, Switch, Delta, JCB
Ⓝ Chef/Proprietor: Chris Colverson

THE MARQUE

19-21 Causewayside
Edinburgh EH9 1QF
Tel: 0131 466 6660
Fax: 0131 466 6661
E-mail: themarque@claramail.com

100 yards from the Dick Vet and the Meadows.

Stunning restaurant run by a totally professional young team.

- Converted antique shop.
- Modern Scottish with European influences.
- "A superb experience in every sense."

The Marque restaurant opened in August 1998 in the heart of Edinburgh's antiques haven. It is jointly owned and run by Lara Kearney, John Rutter and Glyn Stevens (all of whom previously worked at the Atrium and blue bar cafe). John and Glyn are previous winners of The Taste of Scotland Scotch Lamb Challenge Competition. The Marque is ideally situated for the theatre – pre-theatre suppers are available in addition to the usual menus at lunch and dinner. The Marque's reputation is growing quickly, and deservedly so, as the cooking and hospitality served here is of the highest quality.

Open 7 Jan to 31 Dec
Closed 25, 26 Dec, New Year's Day + 1st week in Jan
Closed Mon
✗ Lunch except Mon ££
✗ Dinner except Mon £££
Ⓥ Vegetarians welcome – prior notice advised
☆ Children welcome
✔ Smoking in lounge only

Duck breast, sweet potato and chilli mash, spinach and tomato jus. Olive oil-roasted halibut, baba ganouj, prawn dumpling, miso noodle broth. White, dark and milk chocolate terrine with caramel ice cream.

🏧 Credit cards: Mastercard/Eurocard, American Express, Visa, Switch, Delta
Ⓜ Restaurant Manager/Partner: Lara Kearney

MARTINS RESTAURANT

70 Rose Street North Lane
Edinburgh EH2 3DX
Tel: 0131 225 3106

In the north lane off Rose Street between Frederick Street and Castle Street.

A first class restaurant tucked away in a back street.

- Small city centre restaurant.
- Creative contemporary Scottish cooking.
- "What a find - perfection is the order of the day, using the very best of Scottish ingredients both wild and organic."

Generally regarded as one of the best places to eat in Edinburgh, Martin and Gay Irons are proud of their restaurant. It is small and discreet, tucked away in a cobbled service lane parallel to Princes Street, in the very heart of the city. Its modest exterior gives no clue to the excellence within: the interior is bright, fresh and pastel-hued, decorated with fresh flowers and good contemporary pictures, and cleverly lit; the dining room is a pleasure to behold. David Romanis continues, in his position as head chef, to create innovative dishes which allow the true flavours of the essential ingredients to come through (the produce is carefully purchased, mainly from small producers). His menus are healthy and well-balanced, his style light; organic and wild foods are favoured. The exceptional cheeseboard, which is famous in its own right, features farmhouse unpasteurised Scottish and Irish cheeses. Service is good. Martins sets out to provide a 'total gourmet experience' – and succeeds. Martins has 3 AA Rosettes.

Open all year except 23 Dec to 20 Jan, 1 week May/June + 1 week Sep/Oct
Closed Sun Mon
✗ Lunch except Sun Mon Sat ££-££££
✗ Dinner except Sun Mon £££-££££
Ⓥ Vegetarians welcome – prior notice required
✔ No smoking in dining areas

Pan-fried crab cake with baby spinach. Roast breast of Barbary duck with roast carrot, broccoli and rosemary jus. Caramel mousse with chilled praline parfait and almond biscuit.

🏧 Credit cards: Mastercard/Eurocard, American Express, Visa, Diners Club, Switch, Delta, JCB
Ⓜ Proprietors: Martin & Gay Irons

THE POTTING SHED RESTAURANT
AT THE BRUNTSFIELD HOTEL
69 Bruntsfield Place
Edinburgh EH10 4HH
Tel: 0131 229 1393 Fax: 0131 229 5634
E-mail: bruntsfield@queensferry-hotels.co.uk
Web: www.thebruntsfield.co.uk

1 mile south of Edinburgh city centre on A702,
overlooking Bruntsfield Links.

Town house hotel, close to city centre.

* Stone-built town house hotel.
* Traditional cooking with modern influences.
* "Close to Edinburgh city centre, the Potting Shed
  offers good quality food."

The Bruntsfield Hotel is a town house hotel located
opposite Bruntsfield Golf Links and incorporates the
Potting Shed Restaurant which offers good food in a
friendly, relaxed atmosphere. The Potting Shed
takes its theme from the walnut floor in the dining
area to the original stone floor in the conservatory
with rich fabrics and terracotta pots completing the
finish. Food prepared by chef Glen Smith offers two
and three course lunch menus which are very good
value for money.

     Open all year
🏠 Rooms: 76 en suite
🛏 DB&B £45–£69.50 B&B £42.50–£98
SP Special rates available
✗ Food available all day (Kings Bar) £
✗ Lunch £
✗ Dinner (Kings Bar) £
✗ Dinner (Potting Shed) ££
Ⓥ Vegetarians welcome
� Children welcome
♿ Facilities for disabled visitors
🚭 Smoking in bar area of restaurant only

**Smoked Scottish salmon and dill cheesecake with
oak leaf salad and an Arran mustard dressing.
Saddle of venison roast with juniper berries and
garlic. Trio of chocolate desserts: white chocolate
ice cream, dark chocolate mousse, milk chocolate
cheesecake.**

STB ★★★★ Hotel
💳 Credit cards: Mastercard/Eurocard, American
     Express, Visa, Diners Club, Switch, Delta
👤 Hotel Manager: Andrea Whigham

THE REFORM RESTAURANT
267 Canongate
Royal Mile
Edinburgh EH8 8BQ
Tel: 0131 558 9992
Fax: 0131 558 1718

Located just up from the New Scottish Parliament
building, on the left-hand side as you go down the
Royal Mile.

Relaxed city centre restaurant.

* Restaurant in one of the oldest parts of
  Edinburgh.
* Modern Scottish.
* "A modern Scottish eating experience which is
  innovative and relaxing."

The Reform Restaurant is situated in the centre of
Edinburgh's Old Town on the famous Royal Mile.
Reform has captured the old town setting with its
decor of red and gold giving an elegant but relaxed
atmosphere. Here you will find the best of Scottish
produce, presented in an innovative style – a truly
modern dining experience in the Old Town. When
dining by candlelight you may enjoy the hub of
activity on the Royal Mile. The Reform also has a
small private dining room for up to ten people.

     Open all year except 24 to 26 Dec
     Closed Sun Mon
✗ Lunch except Sun Mon Tue Wed £
✗ Dinner ££
Ⓥ Vegetarians welcome
� Children welcome
🚭 Smoking in private dining room
🐕 Guide dogs only

**Gâteau of crab, smoked salmon and red pepper
drizzled with a sun-dried tomato dressing. Rump of
Pentland lamb resting on honey roasted root
vegetables, garnished with a glazed shallot sauce.
Raspberry crème brûlée with fresh cream.**

💳 Credit cards: Mastercard/Eurocard, Visa,
     Switch, Delta
👤 Manager: Timothy C Devaney

RESTAURANT AT THE BONHAM

35 Drumsheugh Gardens
Edinburgh EH3 7RN
Tel: 0131 623 9319
Fax: 0131 226 6080
E-mail: reserve@thebonham.com
Web: www.thebonham.com

Drumsheugh Gardens is in the heart of the West End. The Bonham lies at the junction with Rothesay Place.

Contemporary and stylish new hotel.

• A unique and contemporary conversion of three Victorian town houses.
• Modern Scottish/new Californian cooking.
• "Modern Scottish cooking amidst stylish mix of old and new decor."

Seriously trendy, minimalist and striking – in stunning contrast with the Victorian building, the Bonham is a very spacious and chic hotel using the highest standards of fabric and furnishings. There is no clutter here yet many of the original features remain – huge sash windows, ornate cornice and plasterwork and wooden staircases. Modern art, and amazing mirrors decorate the walls. Lighting is hi-tech and makes a statement of its own. This is 'heavy duty' modernism whose quality will last. With chef Pelham Hill in the kitchen the blend between surroundings and quality dining experience is complete.

Open all year except 24 to 28 Dec incl
🏠 Rooms: 48 en suite
🛏 B&B from £135–£185
SP Special rates available
✗ Food served all day £
✗ Lunch ££
✗ Dinner £££
Ⓥ Vegetarians welcome
☆ Children welcome
♿ Facilities for disabled visitors
🚭 Smoking area in restaurant

Salad of tea-smoked lamb, Parmesan biscuits and baby leeks, balsamic reduction. Medallions of venison, chocolate cous cous, blueberry jus. White chocolate and amaretto brûlée.

STB ★★★★ Hotel
💳 Credit cards: Mastercard/Eurocard, American Express, Visa, Diners Club, Switch, Delta
🍴 Restaurant Manager: Jodie Hannan

THE ROCK RESTAURANT

78 Commercial Street
Commercial Quay
Leith
Edinburgh EH6 6LX
Tel: 0131 555 2225
Fax: 0131 555 1116

From city centre follow signs to Leith. At bottom of Leith Walk take left into Junction Street, right at traffic lights to Commercial Street. Turn first left to Dock Place then left into Commercial Quay.

Stylish city restaurant in renovated docks area.

• Modern stylish restaurant.
• Modern Scottish cooking.
• "Exceptional dining – frequented by locals and rock stars – a very popular eating place."

The Rock Restaurant is situated in probably the most fashionable area of Edinburgh, in a new development. It is run by John Mackay, who is an accomplished chef. The Rock Restaurant offers exceptionally good food, all freshly prepared and presented in a modern style. The menu offers delights for the gourmet using interesting combinations of spices and influences from other corners of the world. The restaurant is elegant, tasteful and modern in decor and the staff are friendly, polite and efficient. Finalist in The Taste of Scotland Scottish Field Black Pudding Competition 1999.

Open all year
Closed Sun lunch
✗ Lunch except Sun £-££
✗ Dinner ££-£££
Ⓥ Vegetarians welcome

Open ravioli of seared sea bass with salsa. Rump of Scottish lamb on garlic and goats cheese, flageolet beans with roast shallots and garlic, and a rosemary-scented jus. Strawberry and green peppercorn parfait served with Champagne-poached strawberries.

💳 Credit cards: Mastercard/Eurocard, American Express, Visa, Switch
🍴 Owner & Head Chef: John Mackay
Manager: Craig Drummond

SHERATON GRAND HOTEL

1 Festival Square
Edinburgh EH3 9SR
Tel: 0131 229 9131 Fax: 0131 229 6254
E-mail: rachel_williamson@sheraton.com
Web: www.sheratongrand.co.uk

Vehicle access adjacent to the EICC on Morrison Street. Pedestrian entrance off Festival Square, Lothian Road.

Central luxury hotel offering first class service.

- Modern yet stylish.
- Scottish/international.
- "From the moment you walk through the door the service is impeccable, staff are charming and well-trained and the food is excellent."

The Sheraton Grand Hotel is a modern hotel; and no expense has been spared in its furnishing and decoration; there is a 'Leisure Club' with pool, sauna, solarium and gym. The staff are extremely professional and well-trained, but they are also helpful and friendly. The hotel has two restaurants; The Grill Room and The Terrace. The latter overlooks Festival Square and offers a sophisticated brasserie style menu. The former is formal and intimate: Executive Chef, Nicolas Laurent, is ex-Waldorf, London, and brings international expertise to the finest raw ingredients available. The Grill Room has 3 AA Rosettes.

Open all year
- 🛏 Rooms: 261 en suite
- 🛎 DB&B £95–£186   B&B £75–£151
- ✕ Lunch (The Terrace) ££ (The Grill Room) ££
- ✕ Dinner (The Terrace) ££ (The Grill Room) ££££
- Ⓥ Vegetarian menus available in both restaurants
- 🧒 Children welcome with special menu available
- ♿ Facilities for disabled visitors
- 🚬 Pipes and cigars after 9 pm in The Grill Room
- 🚭 No smoking area in both restaurants
- 🐂 Member of the Scotch Beef Club

Caramelised scallops with spring vegetables, orange and vanilla scented oil. Roast rack of lamb with Provençale crust, black olive sauce. Almond macaroon with Mascarpone cream, roasted pineapple and pina colada parfait.

STB ★★★★★ Hotel
Green Tourism 🏵🏵 SILVER Award
- 💳 Credit cards: Mastercard/Eurocard, American Express, Visa, Diners Club, Switch
- 🏠 Executive Chef: Nicolas Laurent
  Restaurant Manager: Jean-Philippe Maurer

STAC POLLY

29-33 Dublin Street
Edinburgh
EH3 6NL
Tel: 0131 556 2231
Fax: 0131 557 9779

At the east end of Queen Street, Dublin Street runs down hill off Queen Street.

A predominantly Scottish cuisine establishment with European influences.

- Ground and cellar restaurant.
- Modern/Scottish cuisine.
- "Stac Polly has a charming Celtic style, with enticing menus that will delight the taste buds."

Stac Polly, from which this restaurant takes its name, is a magnificent mountain on Scotland's West Coast. The strength of Stac Polly's menu is its originality and its charm. Chef Steven Harvey compiles menus which take full advantage of Scotland's glorious larder to provide exciting interpretations of modern and traditional Scottish cuisine. There is good reference to provenance of produce, which will be of interest to diners. From a full to a light meal, choice and service are excellent. The wine list is small but selective and moderately priced and is complemented by a comprehensive malt whisky and Scottish beer list. Private rooms available by arrangement.

Open all year incl Sun
- ✕ Lunch £
- ✕ Dinner ££
- Ⓥ Vegetarians welcome
- 🚭 Smoking area in restaurant

A duet of warm flaky smoked salmon and West Coast scallops served on freshly prepared spinach tagliatelle, topped with a garlic and basil-scented butter sauce. Dry-seared breast of wild duck served with a timbale of red pepper and tomato risotto, topped with crispy cured ham and a green peppercorn and red jelly reduction. Home-made bramble and mascarpone crème brûlée with vanilla shortbread.

- 💳 Credit cards: Mastercard/Eurocard, American Express, Visa
- 🏠 Proprietor: Roger Coulthard

TOWER RESTAURANT
Museum of Scotland
Chambers Street
Edinburgh EH1 1JF
Tel: 0131 225 3003
Fax: 0131 247 4220

Museum of Scotland, level 5.

Modernist restaurant within stunning addition to museum.

- Innovative creation of significant architectural interest.
- Stylish cuisine.
- "The skilled innovative cooking complements the fine surroundings to make a memorable eating experience."

This latest addition of James Thomson's is a real delight. Stylish and appointed to the highest standards, it cleverly blends a modernist building with bold metals and rich drapes, all the while looking out over the rooftops of Old Edinburgh. Al fresco seating is most appealing, weather permitting. A very fine menu is on offer here with skilled and well-trained staff on hand to ensure that your experience is a memorable one. Everything is cooked with great care and attention to detail and the food is complemented with a well-balanced wine list to suit all tastes.

Open all year except Christmas Day + Boxing Day
✘ Food available all day ££
✘ Lunch ££
✘ Dinner £££
Ⓥ Vegetarians welcome
🕇 Children welcome
♿ Facilities for disabled visitors
🚭 No Smoking throughout

Duck liver parfait with toasted brioche. Scallops with a ragoût of haricot beans and wild mushroom with a butternut squach sauce. Elderflower and pickled ginger crème brûlée.

💳 Credit cards: Mastercard/Eurocard, American Express, Visa, Diners Club, Switch
👤 General Manager: Stuart Thom
Head Chef: Steven Adair

THE WITCHERY BY THE CASTLE
Castlehill
Royal Mile
Edinburgh EH1 1NE
Tel: 0131 225 5613
Fax: 0131 220 4392

At the Castle end of the Royal Mile, just a few feet from the castle entrance, opposite Camera Obscura.

Two restaurants together – The Witchery and The Secret Garden both serving the same menu.

- Historic and highly atmospheric building.
- Stylish modern Scottish cuisine.
- "A superb experience – excellent service, food and atmosphere - another of Edinburgh's special places."

The Witchery is situated right by the entrance to Edinburgh Castle on a site that was once the centre of witchcraft in the Old Town. It has been decorated with immense style and taste creating a warm, rich and jewel-like interior. The Secret Garden, converted from a former school playground, is one of the most romantic dining spots in the city. An à la carte menu is available in the evening as well as a theatre supper menu, all with a choice of stylish and interesting dishes. James Thomson's wine list is spectacular with a large selection of excellent wines from all the wine-growing countries. The Inner Sanctum and Old Rectory are luxurious suites available for guests to stay. Reservations advisable.

Open all year except Christmas Day + Boxing Day
🛏 Rooms: 2 en suite
✘ Lunch ££
✘ Theatre Supper £
✘ Dinner £££

Lobster salad with a new potato and dill remoulade. Fillet of Aberdeen Angus with grilled celeriac and foie gras. Almond sable with Grampian raspberries.

💳 Credit cards: Mastercard/Eurocard, American Express, Visa, Diners Club, Switch
👤 Proprietor: James Thomson

DALHOUSIE CASTLE

Bonnyrigg, nr Edinburgh
Midlothian EH19 3JB
Tel: 01875 820153
Fax: 01875 821936
E-mail: enquiries@dalhousiecastle.co.uk
Web: www.dalhousiecastle.co.uk

A7, Edinburgh-Galashiels, 7 miles south of Edinburgh. Signposted from traffic lights on A7 at B704 junction. ½ mile journey.

Historic castle hotel dating from 13th century, family seat of Ramsays of Dalhousie.

- Historical building with superb features.
- Traditional Scottish and French cooking.
- "A romantic blend of old and new Scottish hospitality."

Splendour and history surrounds this 13th century castle, built over 700 years ago by the Ramsays of Dalhousie. Set amongst acres of forest, parkland and pasture yet close to Edinburgh and gateway to the north. A unique dungeon restaurant; the cooking is traditional Scottish with French influences serving local produce at its best. An Orangery Conservatory dining area is planned for summer 2000, serving 'modern' Scottish cooking. Extensive classical function and conference rooms.

Open all year except 2 weeks Jan
🏨 Rooms: 34 en suite (inc 5 in lodge)
🛏 DB&B £67–£154.50   B&B £40–£127.50
SP Special rates available
✗ Food available all day ££
✗ Lunch from ££
✗ Dinner £££
Ⓥ Vegetarians welcome
🕏 Children welcome
🚭 No smoking in dining room or bedrooms

Arbroath smokie tart resting on an artichoke and asparagus salad with a keta butter. Guinea fowl breast stuffed Stornoway black pudding with roasted pancetta, baby turnips, green lentils and a thyme jus. Warm fruit filo parcels with Blairgowrie fruit compote and a whisky ice cream.

STB ★★★★ Hotel
💳 Credit cards: Mastercard/Eurocard, American Express, Visa, Diners Club, Switch, Delta
🗓 Managing Director: Neville Petts

HOUSTOUN HOUSE HOTEL

Uphall
West Lothian EH52 6JS
Tel: 01506 853831 Fax: 01506 854220

Just off M8 motorway at Junction 3.

A sophisticated baronial house, extended and modernised to include a fine leisure centre.

- 16th century tower house in ancient grounds.
- Country house cuisine.
- "A good example of country house cooking and unpretentious Scottish hospitality."

The core of the house is a substantial, early 16th century tower, built by Sir John Shairp, advocate to Mary Queen of Scots, and lived in by his descendants for 350 years. Its gardens were laid out in the 18th century, and include a 20 foot high yew hedge planted in 1722 and a cedar tree which is even older. Extensions and additions to the house – including the Houstoun Suite for banqueting and conferences – have been done sympathetically. The restaurant is situated in the former drawing room, library and great hall on the first floor – each of them delightful rooms, with 17th and 18th century panelling and plasterwork, beautifully furnished with antiques and pictures. The chef presents a sophisticated and well-balanced table d'hôte menu at lunch and an à la carte menu at dinner – his cooking is first class. *See advert page 258.*

Open all year
🏨 Rooms: 72 en suite
🛏 DB&B £75–£95 B&B £50–£70
SP Special rates available
✗ Lunch except Sat ££
✗ Dinner ££££
Ⓥ Vegetarians welcome
🕏 Children welcome
♿ Facilities for disabled visitors
🚭 No smoking dining room available
🐄 Member of the Scotch Beef Club

Caramelised goats cheese crowning a caraway scone and accompanied by rhubarb chutney. Suprême of chicken centred with straw vegetables on a carrot and ginger purée, pomme noisette and a lemon and herb essence. Delicate pear délice sitting in refreshing fig cream.

STB ★★★★ Hotel
💳 Credit cards: Mastercard/Eurocard, Visa, Diners Club, Switch
🗓 General Manager: Ann Yuille

JOHNSTOUNBURN HOUSE HOTEL
Humbie, nr Edinburgh
East Lothian EH36 5PL
Tel: 01875 833696
Fax: 01875 833626

Turn off A68 at the village of Fala (B6457). Humbie and Johnstounburn House signposted. After ½ mile turn right at T junction then left into hotel.

Peaceful country house in its own grounds, only 15 miles from Edinburgh.

- A beautifully restored and maintained Scottish baronial mansion.
- Traditional/classical cooking.
- "Good food in a wonderfully relaxing, charming hotel."

Built below the rolling Lammermuir Hills in 1625, Johnstounburn House stands in its own extensive, lovely grounds. The staff are welcoming and friendly, as is the ambience – open log fires, panelled and comfortable rooms – in this country house hotel. The table d'hôte dishes are excellent, making the most of good, local produce. The wine list is large – 70 bins – and concentrates on French and European wines.

Open all year
🏨 Rooms: 20, 19 en suite
🛏 DB&B £70–£159   B&B £45–£120
SP Special rates available
✕ Lunch – reservation required ££
✕ Dinner – reservation required £££
Ⓥ Vegetarians welcome
🕆 Children welcome
🚭 No smoking in dining room

Chicken pâté with plum jelly. Lemon sole with leek and mushroom cream and seasonal vegetables. Raspberry Romanov.

STB ★★★ Hotel
💳 Credit cards: Mastercard/Eurocard, American Express, Visa, Diners Club
👤 General Manager: David Flanagan

NORTON HOUSE HOTEL
Ingliston, Edinburgh, Midlothian EH28 8LX
Tel: 0131 333 1275 Fax: 0131 333 5305
E-mail: hotel.reservations@virgin.co.uk
Web: www.virgin.com

Take A8 west from Edinburgh – 6 miles from city centre – signposted on A8 just after airport turn-off.

Relaxed, yet efficient country house hotel with very high standards.

- Victorian mansion set in its own 55 acres of parkland.
- Gourmet/Scottish cooking.
- "Stylish country house hotel offering formal and informal dining."

Norton House is part of the Virgin Hotel Collection. Built in 1840, this country house set in 55 acres of parkland has been refurbished in luxurious style. The hotel has two restaurants: the Conservatory restaurant, open for both lunch and dinner, offers an extensive à la carte menu complemented by a daily dinner menu. The dishes are imaginative – a combination of the unusual and the traditional, but even the latter are given a creative twist. Within the grounds of the hotel you will find the Gathering Bistro and Bar. An informal, friendly atmosphere makes the bistro an ideal meeting place where you can enjoy anything from a light snack to a complete meal. The menu is varied offering the latest food trends as well as family favourites.

Open all year
🏨 Rooms: 47 en suite
🛏 DB&B £65   B&B £110–£175
SP Special rates available
✕ Food available all day £-£££
✕ Lunch except Saturday ££
✕ Dinner from £££
Ⓥ Vegetarians welcome
🕆 Children welcome
♿ Facilities for disabled visitors
🚭 No smoking area in restaurant
🐂 Member of the Scotch Beef Club

A salad of smoked trout, spring onions and tomato served in a pastry basket. Roast loin of Perthshire pork with a sherry and thyme cream sauce. Roast apple with an Earl Grey tea scented apricot compote.

STB ★★★★ Hotel
💳 Credit cards: Mastercard/Eurocard, American Express, Visa, Diners Club, Switch
👤 General Manager: Jonathan Dawson

MANSEFIELD HOUSE HOTEL
Mayne Road, Elgin
Moray IV30 1NY
Tel: 01343 540883
Fax: 01343 552491

Just off A96 in Elgin. From Inverness, drive towards town centre and turn right at first roundabout. At mini-roundabout, hotel on right.

A popular family-run hotel and restaurant.

* Elegant town house.
* Traditional Scottish cooking, with some French influences.
* "A high degree of comfort, charming staff and very good food."

Close to the centre of Elgin, this completely refurbished and restored former manse provides a comfortable retreat. It has excellent facilities to suit the commercial and private guest and the restaurant is especially popular with the local business community. The head chef, Craig Halliday, presents a well-priced à la carte menu made up of classic Scottish dishes, using market available fish, meat and vegetables. The quality of his cooking has been recognised by an AA Rosette.

Open all year
🏨 Rooms: 21 en suite
🛏 DB&B £55–£85   B&B £55–£65
SP Special rates available
✗ Lunch £
✗ Dinner £££
Ⅴ Vegetarians welcome
🕏 Children welcome
🕭 Facilities for disabled visitors
🚭 No smoking in restaurant

Chicken lightly smoked to perfection, served with an avocado pear and accompanying raspberry and walnut dressing. Fine seafood including sole, halibut, scampi tails and monkfish served with either parsley or garlic butter. Sticky toffee pudding with toffee sauce.

STB ★★★★ Hotel
💳 Credit cards: Mastercard/Eurocard, American Express, Visa, Switch
🛏 Owners: Mr & Mrs T R Murray

BOUQUET GARNI RESTAURANT
51 High Street, Elie
Fife KY9 1BZ
Tel: 01333 330374

15 miles from St Andrews. Head south round the coastline via Anstruther, Pittenweem and St Monans, then onto Elie. Restaurant in centre of town.

A delightful little restaurant in charming East Neuk town.

* Town centre restaurant.
* Scottish modern with French influence.
* "Lovely food in a charming, intimate setting."

Bouquet Garni is an attractive little restaurant in the centre of this quaint East Neuk town. With supplies of fresh fish and seafood literally on the doorstep it specialises in seafood dishes but offers seasonal alternatives. The restaurant has good table appointments, and the addition of candlelight in the evening adds an intimacy to the atmosphere. Coffee and pre-and post-dinner drinks can be enjoyed in the small, cosy lounge.

Open all year except Christmas Day + Boxing Day
Closed Sun Mon
✗ Lunch except Sun Mon ££
✗ Dinner except Sun Mon £££
Ⅴ Vegetarians welcome
🕏 Children welcome
🕭 Facilities for disabled visitors
🚭 No smoking in restaurant

Pan-fried breast of duck set on a collade of wilted green leaves and topped with a warm medallion of goats cheese, finished with a red wine and rosemary jus. Roast fillet of monkfish and pan-fried West Coast scallops set on a panaché of roast peppers and spinach, surrounded with a light lemon and thyme infusion. Cold tiramisu soufflé served with a warm, dark chocolate sauce.

💳 Credit cards: Mastercard/Eurocard, Visa, Switch, Delta
🛏 Owner: Mrs Norah Keracher

THE OLD SCHOOLHOUSE RESTAURANT
"Tigh Fasgaidh," Erbusaig, Kyle
Ross-shire IV40 8BB
Tel/Fax: 01599 534369
E-mail: cuminecandj@lineone.net

Outskirts of Erbusaig on Kyle-Plockton road.

Delightful restaurant with three en suite bedrooms.

• A charming 19th century schoolhouse in its own grounds on the picturesque road between Kyle and Plockton.
• Imaginative modern cooking.
• "Here you will find imaginative cooking with the best of Highland hospitality."

This old school has been tastefully converted by the owners Calum and Joanne Cumine into a small restaurant with three bedrooms, each of which is restfully decorated. The conversion has been sensitively done, and retains the character of the place and the feel of the past, while providing the level of comfort required by today's guests. The cooking is imaginative and versatile, and makes good use of the wonderful fish, shellfish, meat and game so readily available in this unspoiled corner of the West Highlands. The menu is reasonably priced and the owners are delighted to cater for vegetarians. It is no wonder that this small restaurant has such a big reputation locally.

Open Easter to end Oct
🛏 Rooms: 3 en suite
🍴 B&B £23–£28
SP Special rates available
✕ Dinner ££–£££
V Vegetarians welcome
🏃 Children welcome
♿ Facilities for disabled visitors – restaurant only
🚭 No smoking in restaurant

Peat-smoked salmon with quails eggs in a sherry-dressed salad. Duck breast simmered in an aromatic ginger wine sauce. Cardamom-scented crème caramel.

STB ★★★★ Restaurant with Rooms
💳 Credit cards: Mastercard/Eurocard, American Express, Visa, Switch, Delta
👤 Proprietors: Calum & Joanne Cumine

FINS SEAFOOD RESTAURANT
Fairlie, Largs, Ayrshire KA29 0EG
Tel: 01475 568989 Fax: 01475 568921
E-mail: fencebay@aol.com
Web: www.fencebay.co.uk

On A78, 1 mile south of Fairlie near Largs.

Fish farm, smokehouse, farm shop, cookshop and bistro/seafood restaurant.

• Renovated farm bistro.
• Imaginative, modern fish cookery.
• "Fun and friendly restaurant cooking its own seafood produce to perfection."

Fins, and Fencebay Fisheries, is now quite a complex set in a traditional Ayrshire steading. The restaurant is situated conveniently between the cookshop and wine cellar in the stable next door. The fish shop smokery is across the court. Those in the know make frequent pilgrimages to enjoy the deft, light cooking of Gillian Dick, head chef. This bistro-style country restaurant is bright, welcoming and unpretentious. Painted concrete floors and old stone walls are decorated with intriguing old photographs and colourful artwork. The menu is extensive and enticing. You may enjoy the fruits of the sea plainly cooked to perfection or presented with creative ingenuity. Try oysters, squat lobsters, bass, sole, langoustines and fresh trout in many delicious guises. Throughout there is attention to detail and a real integrity in the quality of the food produced.

Open all year except Christmas Day,
Boxing Day + New Year's Day
Closed Mon
🛏 Rooms: 2
✕ Lunch except Mon ££
✕ Dinner except Mon £££
V Vegetarians welcome
🏃 Children welcome – lunch only
♿ Facilities for disabled visitors
🚭 No smoking in restaurant

Baked Cumbrae oysters with spinach, garlic and crème fraîche, with goats cheese topping. Warm salad of king scallops and wild mushrooms with pesto and balsamic dressing. Chocolate, hazelnut and rum truffle.

💳 Credit cards: Mastercard/Eurocard, American Express, Visa, Diners Club, Switch, Delta
👤 Owner: Jill Thain

THE GRANGE MANOR

Glensburgh Road
Grangemouth
Stirlingshire FK3 8XJ
Tel : 01324 474836   Fax : 01324 665861
E-mail: info@grangemanor.co.uk
Web: www.grangemanor.co.uk

Just off M9. To Stirling – exit at junction 5, follow A905 for 2 miles (to Kincardine Bridge). To Edinburgh – exit at junction 6, turn right, 200 metres on right.

Stately hotel on the outskirts of Grangemouth.

* Old manor with tasteful modernisation.
* Modern Scottish cooking.
* "Stately old manor hotel, family-run yet with modern facilities."

The Grange Manor is a stately old manor run by the Wallace family. Bill Wallace, an experienced and charming hotelier, enjoys personally greeting his guests and ensures that they feel at home in this comfortable hotel. The hotel has recently undergone a substantial upgrading renovation. Chef Ken Wilson offers complex Scottish cooking of high modern standards. Both à la carte and table d'hôte eating is provided where game and fish feature with light and imaginative sauces, alongside traditional meats and poultry. The Grange Manor has 1 AA Rosette.

Open all year
🛏 Rooms: 37 en suite
🛏 DB&B £83.50–£98.50   B&B £60–£75
SP Special rates available
✖ Food available all day £££
✖ Lunch ££
✖ Dinner £££
Ⓥ Vegetarians welcome
🏃 Children welcome
♿ Facilities for disabled visitors

Saladette of Puy lentil and foie gras with truffle and Muscat wine dressing. Red mullet on a cepe and tomato tart, spiced tapenade and roasted chilli oil. Pear William parfait, sesame seed lacy tuile with hazelnut caramel and a quenelle of rice pudding.

STB ★★★ Hotel
💳 Credit cards: Mastercard/Eurocard, American Express, Visa, Diners Club, Switch, Delta
🙎 Proprietors: Bill & Jane Wallace

INCHYRA GRANGE HOTEL

Grange Road, Polmont
Falkirk FK2 0YB
Tel: 01324 711911 Fax: 01324 716134

Junction 5, M9. Take B9143 to Grangemouth. Right turn at mini-roundabout to Polmont/Wholeflats Road. 400 yards right turn. Hotel is 400 yards on right.

Extended country house hotel with function rooms and leisure facilities.

* Fully modernised and extended country house.
* Choice of Italian Bistro and fine dining restaurant.
* "Good food, and excellent facilities for business or leisure stays are offered here."

Inchyra Grange traces its origins to the 12th century, but its internal lay-out and furnishings are modern. It stands in five acres of garden and park, and has a popular leisure club with swimming pool, sauna and steam baths, multi-gym, solarium and resident beautician. There are two restaurants: the Priory Restaurant with a daily changing menu based on the availability of local produce - dinner is à la carte, and Peligrino's Italian Bistro for a light meal. Bar meals are available in the Earl lounge. The hotel's central situation near Falkirk makes it popular as a business venue, for meetings and conferences, not to mention business lunches. It also does a good trade in functions, as there is a function room for 450. *See advert page 258.*

Open all year
🛏 Rooms: 109 en suite
🛏 DB&B £59.50–£62.50   B&B £30–£55
✖ Food available all day £££
✖ Lunch except Sat ££
✖ Dinner £££
Ⓥ Vegetarians welcome
🏃 Children welcome
♿ Facilities for disabled visitors
🚭 No smoking in restaurant
🐄 Member of the Scotch Beef Club

Warm tartlet of creamed leek and Finnan haddock. Roast rib of Donald Russell beef with Yorkshire puddings and classic chasseur sauce. Chocolate and Cointreau torte served with a chantilly cream and a sauce anglaise.

STB ★★★★ Hotel
💳 Credit cards: Mastercard/Eurocard, American Express, Visa, Diners Club, Switch
🙎 General Manager: Mr Andy Burgess

QUENELLES RESTAURANT
4 Weir Street, Falkirk
Stirlingshire FK1 1RA
Tel: 01324 877411
Fax: 01324 632035

North side of town centre. Visible from roundabout at main post office). From High St, (pedestrian only) turn into Kirk Wynd at Steeple, continue to far end of Vicar Street, restaurant is on right.

200 year old house converted to restaurant.

- 200 year old stone house.
- Modern Scottish cooking.
- "Fresh Scottish produce cooked in an imaginative style."

Quenelles is situated in a 200 year old converted duelling house and has been carefully decorated to give a stylish and relaxed atmosphere. Quenelles offers only the best Scottish produce cooked with flair and imagination by chef/proprietor Andy Bell. This is a family-run restaurant whose policy is to use good raw materials from local producers including hand-picked mushrooms by joint partner Julia Thomas, who looks after the front of house. There is an extended lunchtime menu and a chef 's specials board.

Open all year except first 2 weeks Jul
Closed Sun Mon
✗   Lunch except Sun Mon £
✗   Dinner except Sun Mon ££
Ⓥ   Vegetarians welcome
⚘   Children welcome

Grilled Loch Fyne oysters, topped with goats cheese and lemon. Guinea fowl breast stuffed with pigeon breast surrounded by a Drambuie jus. Home-made sticky toffee pudding served with cream and crème anglaise, drizzled with port.

💷   Credit cards: Mastercard/Eurocard, Visa, Switch, Delta, Solo, JCB
Ⓝ   Chef/Proprietor: Andy Bell

KIND KYTTOCK'S KITCHEN
Cross Wynd, Falkland
Fife KY15 7BE
Tel: 01337 857477

A912 to Falkland. Centre of Falkland near the Palace, turn up at the Square into Cross Wynd.

Bustling cottage tea-room in a uniquely historic village.

- Traditional Scottish tea-room in terraced cottage.
- Excellent home baking.
- "Everything a tea-room should be - the very best of home-baking in charming surroundings."

Kind Kyttock's is situated in a charming 17th century terraced cottage overlooking the cobbled square in one of Scotland's most picturesque villages. Its two rooms are most attractive – comfortable, informal and cheerful, with a 'country tea-room' feel. And this is precisely what Kind Kyttock's is, a tea-room of outstanding quality, which has frequently won the Tea Council's Award for Excellence. Bert Dalrymple is its owner/cook, his baking is divine – including scones, oatcakes, pancakes and other Scottish delicacies – and as well as this he preserves his own fruits, jams, pickles and chutneys, roasts his own meats for sandwiches, makes his own soups, etc. No wonder the place is so popular with locals, and you can buy baking to take away when it is available. Winner of The Macallan Taste of Scotland Special Merit Award for Best Tea-Room 1997.

Open all year except Christmas Eve to 5 Jan
Closed Mon
✗   Food available all day except Mon £
Ⓥ   Vegetarians welcome
⚘   Children welcome
🚭   No smoking throughout

Kind Kyttock's scotch broth or vegetarian soup. Choice of freshly prepared salads. Cloutie dumpling and cream.

💷   Credit cards: Mastercard/Eurocard, American Express, Visa, Switch
Ⓝ   Owner: Bert Dalrymple

MALT BARN INN
Main Street
Newton of Falkland
Fife KY15 7RZ
Tel/Fax: 01337 857589

Half a mile outside Falkland which is off Junction 8 on M90. 20 Minutes south of St Andrews.

A delightful old inn serving the best of Scottish produce, prepared by Swedish chefs.

- 200 year old cottage.
- Scottish produce, Scandinavian-style!
- "Great atmosphere, charming hosts, delicious smoked produce smoked on the premises."

Set in the attractive hamlet of Newton of Falkland, the Malt Barn is a small roadside inn which was originally home to the workers of the brewery next door. Scottish produce is presented Scandinavian-style, using in-house smoked produce as a speciality. Gravlax, cured herring and hot smoked salmon may be supplied in the warm and friendly cottage atmosphere where your hosts, Mark and Monica Henderson, ensure that your every need is catered for. Summer barbeques and buffets are held each Sunday in the Beer Garden – when weather permits! If you don't have time to stop and sample the fayre here then you can always *takeaway* – all the produce can be either vacuum-packed or bottled for you.

Open all year except 1 to 5 Jan
✖ Food available all day £-££
✖ Lunch £-££
✖ Dinner except ££-£££
Ⓥ Vegetarians welcome
⚥ Children welcome- lunchtime only + up to 8pm
♿ Facilities for disabled visitors
⚬ Smoking area

Malt Barn's own vodka and ginger cured gravlax served on pumpernickel. Sweet vanilla and chilli marinated pork fillet medallion served with creamy citrus sauce. Vanilla ice cream topped with 'hot' tangy raspberries.

💳 Credit cards: Mastercard/Eurocard, Visa, Switch, Delta
⚙ Proprietors: Mark & Monica Henderson

CHAPELBANK HOUSE HOTEL & RESTAURANT
69 East High Street, Forfar
Angus DD8 2EP
Tel: 01307 463151
Fax: 01307 461922
E-mail: ewenallardyce@btconnect.com

Just off the High Street – Forfar. 15 miles north of Dundee on A90.

A family-run hotel with an emphasis on service.

- Small, town centre hotel.
- Modern Scottish cooking.
- "A dedicated team is waiting for you at Chapelbank to make your visit a memorable one."

Built in 1865 on the main road leading through the market town of Forfar, Chapelbank was once the home of the town's doctor. Accommodation is spacious and well-apointed. The dining room is popular with local non-residents. Dishes are attractively presented with a good balance of flavours. The Staff here are well-organised and friendly.

Open 21 Jan to 4 Oct + 14 Oct to 31 Dec
Closed Sun evening + Mon
🛏 Rooms: 4 en suite
🛏 B&B £55–£82
🍷 Restricted hotel licence
✖ Lunch except Mon £
✖ Dinner except Sun Mon ££
Ⓥ Vegetarians welcome
⚥ Children welcome
♿ Facilities for disabled visitors
⚬ No smoking in dining room + bedrooms

Grilled fillet of trout presented on a red onion salsa with mustard seed and tarragon dressing. Pan-fried slices of marinated venison finished with black cherries on a juniper and Madeira sauce. Raspberry and vanilla fool with crushed amaretto biscuits.

STB ★★★★ Hotel
💳 Credit cards: Mastercard/Eurocard, American Express, Visa, Switch, Delta, JCB
⚙ Owners: Ewen Allardyce & Bryan Graham

KNOCKOMIE HOTEL

Grantown Road, Forres, Moray IV36 2SG
Tel: 01309 673146
Fax: 01309 673290
E-mail: knockomie.hotel@bt.internet.com

1 mile south of Forres on A940. 26 miles east of
Inverness.

**A timeless and elegant hotel overlooking the Royal
Burgh of Forres.**

- A rare example of Arts and Crafts Movement
  architecture – an elegant villa built in 1914
  around an earlier building.
- The best of Scottish cooking with French
  influences.
- "A stylish small hotel, with a big heart and
  excellent cuisine – a delightful stay."

Knockomie Hotel offers guests first-rate
accommodation and dining facilities. Part of the
hotel's landscaped gardens are set aside to supply
herbs and salad leaves; vegetables are grown
locally, to order. Gavin Ellis is knowledgeable,
courteous and hospitable, and his staff are smart
and well-trained. The daily changing table d'hôte
menu is carefully selected; the food is all local and
fresh; cooking is 'modern classic'. Dining is proving
to be popular in The Bistro which offers a more
casual approach to eating than the traditional dining
room. The wine list is of especial interest – very
well-priced, with some wonderful rarities.
Knockomie Hotel has 2 AA Rosettes.

   Open all year except Christmas Day
🏠 Rooms: 15 en suite
SP Special rates available
✗ Lunch £
✗ Dinner 5 course menu £££
Ⓥ Vegetarians welcome
✯ Children welcome
♿ Facilities for disabled visitors
✍ No smoking in dining room
🐂 Member of the Scotch Beef Club

**Tournedos of rabbit and hare with fondant potato,
cabbage and bacon and a white truffle and
vegetable jus. Grilled fillet of red mullet with a red
pepper coulis and a pasta rösti. Roast peach served
with a nougatine glace and a raspberry sauce.**

STB ★★★★ Hotel
Green Tourism 🌿🌿 SILVER Award
🅮 Credit cards: Mastercard/Eurocard, American
Express, Visa, Diners Club, Switch, Delta, JCB
🄽 Resident Director: Gavin Ellis

RAMNEE HOTEL

Victoria Road, Forres, Moray IV36 0BN
Tel: 01309 672410 Fax: 01309 673392
E-mail: tartan@tartan-collection.co.uk
Web: www.tartancollection.co.uk

A96 Inverness-Aberdeen, off bypass at roundabout
at eastern side of Forres – 500 yards on right.

**An attractive 'country house in town' conveniently
close to the centre of Forres.**

- Edwardian private house with a high standard of
  accommodation and hospitality.
- Fresh local produce well-presented in modern
  style.
- "Tipplings Lounge – where style and quality is
  brought to pub grub."

The Ramnee Hotel is a lively and bustling town hotel
set in two acres of beautiful gardens. It is well-
appointed and offers a high degree of comfort. The
hotel's 20 bedrooms are tastefully furnished and
fitted with all the extras you would expect in a first
rate establishment. Food in Hamblin's Restaurant is
characterised by generous portions imaginatively
presented. A table d'hôte menu is available at
lunchtime and there is a choice of excellent value
table d'hôte and steak menus at dinner. The
accompanying wine list is extensive and well-
chosen. Lighter, more informal meals are
available in 'Tipplings' cocktail lounge. Staff are
friendly and helpful. Ramnee has 1 AA Rosette.

   Open all year except Christmas Day +
   1 to 3 Jan
🏠 Rooms: 20 en suite
🛏 DB&B £55–£99.50   B&B £32.50–£75
SP Special rates available
✗ Lunch £
✗ Dinner £££
Ⓥ Vegetarians welcome
✯ Children welcome
✍ No smoking in restaurant

**Chowder of Moray Firth mussels presented with a
lobster ravioli. Char-grilled Angus beef served with
a parsnip mash, roasted shallot, bacon and
tarragon butter. Scottish summer berries served
with a lemon, and basil sorbet.**

STB ★★★★ Hotel
🅮 Credit cards: Mastercard/Eurocard, American
Express, Visa, Diners Club, Switch, Delta
🄽 Director: Garry W Dinnes

AN CRANN

Banavie
Fort William
Inverness-shire PH33 7PB
Tel: 01397 772 077

10 minutes drive from Fort William. Take A82 north, then at lights take A830 for Mallaig. Turn right towards Banavie B8004, 2 miles to An Crann.

A tastefully and imaginatively restored barn, converted to form a restaurant full of character.

- Converted steading.
- Imaginative Scottish cooking.
- "Take time out to enjoy Sine's delicious home cooking."

Located in an attractive and impressive barn conversion full of character and rustic charm offering unique views of Ben Nevis and the surrounding Braveheart country. Here the emphasis is very much on good food, creatively prepared, high quality local produce. The atmosphere is friendly and relaxed and popular with tourists and locals alike. An ideal stopping off point for a family. Home-made daily specials, soups, vegetarian dishes and fresh seafood are always on the menu. Food available from 5pm – 9pm.

Open 25 Mar to mid Oct
Closed Sun
✗ Dinner except Sun ££
Ⓥ Vegetarians welcome
✝ Children welcome
♿ Facilities for disabled visitors

Scottish smoked salmon pâté served with seasonal salad with a lime and coriander dressing and oatcakes. Highland lamb cutlets with apricot, ginger and elderflower wine. Home-made cloutie dumpling with Drambuie cream.

💳 Credit cards: Mastercard/Eurocard, Visa
Ⓝ Owner/Chef: Sine Marie Ross

CRANNOG SEAFOOD RESTAURANT

Town Pier, Fort William
PH33 7NG
Tel: 01397 705589
Fax: 01397 705026
E-mail: crannogallan@msn.com

Fort William town pier – off A82 Fort William town centre bypass.

Founded by fishermen, this restaurant serves the finest Scottish seafood.

- Converted bait store on town pier.
- Fresh seafood, cooked simply.
- "Crannog retains the original concept of simply fresh, quality seafood."

Crannog is a small, octagonal, red-roofed building on the end of a short pier in Fort William. An unpretentious, informal restaurant with a 'mixture' of chairs and tables, whitewashed walls and rough exposed timber, with paintings and prints adding colour. When they are not admiring the splendid views over Loch Linnhe diners can sometimes watch the catch being landed direct into the kitchen – and soon afterwards enjoy the freshest imaginable seafood. This is Crannog's philosophy: very fresh seafood in friendly surroundings. It works, and the restaurant is very popular, so it is advisable to book. There is a small reception area for pre-dinner drinks. Crannog has 1 AA Rosette.

Open all year except Christmas Day + 1 Jan
✗ Lunch £
✗ Dinner ££
Ⓥ Vegetarians welcome
✝ Children welcome
♿ Facilities for disabled visitors
✂ Smoking area in restaurant

Crannog's own smoked mussels in the half shell served with aïoli. West Coast monkfish in a cream saffron sauce. Heather Liqueur Highland Cream cake.

💳 Credit cards: Mastercard/Eurocard, Visa, Switch
Ⓝ Managing Director: Finlay Finlayson

THE MOORINGS HOTEL
Banavie, Fort William
Inverness-shire PH33 7LY
Tel: 01397 772797
Fax: 01397 772441
E-mail: moorings@lochaberhotels.freeserve.co.uk

On the outskirts of Fort William. From Fort William, take A830 Mallaig road for approx 1 mile. Cross the Caledonian Canal and take first right into the village of Banavie.

Coaching-style inn with grounds leading to 'Neptune's Staircase'.

- Newly re-opened and renovated coaching inn.
- Bold and imaginative Scottish cooking.
- "Friendly and attentive service is always at hand to guests."

The Moorings is a coaching inn run by managing director Stewart Leitch. Located as it is beside the newly renovated 'Neptune's Staircase', part of the Caledonian Canal, it is in an ideal location for visitors to the area. The hotel has floodlit grounds and has been attractively renovated. The cooking here is bold, using good local produce, and the chefs are keen to innovate and experiment. There is a commitment here to quality, equally to be found in the service, surroundings and the cooking.

Open all year except Christmas week
- 🏮 Rooms: 21 en suite
- 🛏 DB&B £62–£78   B&B £36–£52
- SP Special rates available
- ✗ Food available all day ££
- ✗ Lunch ££
- ✗ Dinner £££
- Ⅴ Vegetarians welcome
- 🏃 Children welcome
- ♿ Facilities for disabled visitors
- 🚭 No smoking in dining room
- 🐕 Dogs welcome

Soufflé of West Coast seafood on a pool of saffron sauce with pan-seared scallops. Noisette of Mamore lamb in a wild garlic coat set on a shallot and rhubarb marmalade. Home-made nougat truffle ice cream parfait set on a butterscotch sauce.

STB ★★★★ Hotel
- 💳 Credit cards: Mastercard/Eurocard, American Express, Visa, Diners Club, Switch, Delta, JCB
- ⋈ Managing Director: Stewart Leitch

NO 4 CAMERON SQUARE
Cameron Square, Fort William
Inverness-shire PH33 6AJ
Tel: 01397 704222
Fax: 01397 704888

> As the guide was going to press, Taste of Scotland learned that this establishment has ceased trading.

Centrally located in Fort William, Cameron Square is just off the pedestrianised High Street. *No 4* is next to the Tourist Information Office.

Fine town restaurant in bustling Fort William.

- Fashionable town restaurant.
- Artistic cooking.
- "Where pictures are built with the finest cuisine."

No 4 Cameron Square is a refreshing change, both with its decor and its food. It provides morning coffee, delicious lunches and afternoon teas and wonderful dinners. Whether you are a connoisseur of fine wines and food or just looking for something simple – No 4 will be delighted to welcome you. The kitchen team take great pride in their dishes and some look just too good to eat. The staff are all very friendly and knowledgeable.

Open all year except Christmas Day + New Year's Day
Closed Sun
- ✗ Afternoon Tea available except Sun £
- ✗ Lunch except Sun £
- ✗ Dinner except Sun £££
- Ⅴ Vegetarians welcome
- 🏃 Children welcome
- ♿ Facilities for disabled visitors

Pan-fried Mallaig scallops, salad rocket, tomato and olive oil coulis. Roast breast of Gressingham duck, glazed shitake mushrooms, green beans and oriental juice. Iced passion fruit soufflé, mixed berry compote.

- 💳 Credit cards: Mastercard/Eurocard, Visa, Switch, Delta
- ⋈ Manager: Jonathon McLeod

BIRCHWOOD

Charleston, Gairloch
Ross-shire IV21 2AH
Tel/Fax: 01445 712011

Inverness 70 miles, Inverewe Gardens 5 miles. Located in Charleston, Gairloch's harbour off the A832.

Highland house in elevated position.

- Attractive Highland house.
- Local fresh fish and seafood skilfully prepared.
- "Enjoy a beautiful home with elevated views over Gairloch harbour and settle down to the 'catch of the day' for supper."

Birchwood is the home of Bill and Ruth Swann who offer excellent hospitality. It is richly furnished in the Scottish Arts and Crafts style with period decoration and antique furniture. There are delightful gardens with a small patio which have rambling surroundings and delightful sea views. Bill has recently started his own vegetable garden. Bill and Ruth's aim is to offer dinner party-style entertaining – and it works. Reservations required.

Open Mar to Nov incl
🛏 Rooms: 5 en suite
🍴 DB&B £60–£70 B&B £35–£45
SP Special rates available
❢ Restricted hotel licence
✗ Dinner £££
Ⓥ Vegetarians by arrangement
✔ No smoking throughout

Gairloch scallops with organic spaghetti en papillotte. Fresh Gairloch hake baked with a confit of onion, lemon and bay served with oven-roasted vine tomatoes. Home-made lemon meringue tart.

💳 Credit cards: Mastercard/Eurocard, Visa, Switch, Delta, JCB
👤 Proprietors: Ruth & Bill Swann

LITTLE LODGE

North Erradale, Gairloch
Wester Ross IV21 2DS
Tel: 01445 771237

Take B8021 from Gairloch towards Melvaig for 6 miles, situated 1/4 mile beyond turning to North Erradale.

A charming converted crofthouse.

- Whitewashed crofthouse.
- Innovative menus with excellent local and home-made produce.
- "Simply exceptional!"

Little Lodge stands on a heather-clad peninsula with splendid views towards the Torridon Mountains and Skye. The commitment of Di Johnson and Inge Ford just gets better and better. Their hospitality is second to none. The food is sourced locally with exceptional flavours. Outside, their own hens, sheep and goats roam; their garden provides vegetables and herbs. Di's imaginative marinades and sauces enhance the excellent seasonal local produce (especially freshly-landed fish from Gairloch itself), while Inge's home-made bread, oatcakes, yoghurt and preserves make breakfast a special treat. Little Lodge is an idyllic retreat with superb cuisine which has earned Di and Inge much praise. An absolutely charming experience. Winner of The Macallan Taste of Scotland Special Merit Award for Hospitality 1996.

Open Apr to Oct
🛏 Rooms: 3 en suite
🍴 DB&B £50–£55
SP Special rates available
Ⓤ Unlicensed – guests welcome to take own wine + spirits
✗ Dinner £££
Ⓥ Vegetarians welcome – by prior arrangement
🧒 No children
✔ No smoking throughout

Smoked lamb terrine with pear and rosemary glaze on garden lettuce leaves with raspberry vinaigrette. Pan-fried halibut fillets with a citrus and dill reduction. Sorbet of garden rhubarb infused with cardamom seeds, home-made ginger ice cream and ratafias.

💳 No credit cards
👤 Proprietors: Di Johnson & Inge Ford

MYRTLE BANK HOTEL
Low Road, Gairloch
Ross-shire IV21 2BS
Tel: 01445 712004
Fax: 01445 712214

Close to the centre of Gairloch, just off B2081.

Seafront hotel in spectacular setting, nestling in quiet spot on the bay.

- Modern village hotel.
- Traditional Scottish cooking.
- "Enjoy hearty Scottish cooking while watching porpoises, seals and otters in the bay."

Myrtle Bank Hotel is a modern village hotel set in a quiet cul-de-sac amongst spectacular scenery in the centre of Gairloch. Its location makes it an ideal exploring base. The hotel is popular with both locals and visitors to the area. Local produce and home-made cooking are the basis of the menu which is balanced and well-priced. Guests have the choice between bar and dining room eating. Seafood is particularly tasty given the local catch! The hotel can accommodate up to 140 for weddings and other functions.

Open all year except New Year's Day
- 🏠 Rooms: 12 en suite
- 🛏 DB&B £51–£59   B&B £36–£44
- SP Special rates available
- ✗ Lunch £
- ✗ Dinner £££
- V Vegetarians welcome
- ✶ Children welcome
- ♿ Facilities for disabled visitors
- 🚭 No smoking in dining room

Mixed herb crêpes stuffed with fresh asparagus and cream cheese. Lemon sole lined with smoked salmon, glazed with a hollandaise sauce. Orange and Drambuie parfait.

STB ★★★ Hotel
- 💳 Credit cards: Mastercard/Eurocard, Visa, Switch
- 🅝 Proprietors: Iain & Dorothy MacLean

BABBITY BOWSTER
16-18 Blackfriars Street
Glasgow G1 1PE
Tel: 0141 552 5055
Fax: 0141 552 7774

In the heart of Glasgow's Merchant City – at the East End of city centre.

An atmospheric inn serving traditional food.

- An Adam building c. 1790.
- Scottish cooking.
- "A lively inn, in the heart of the Merchant City."

This Adam building, c.1790, was saved from demolition in 1985 by the present owner and plays a major contribution to the vibrant Merchant City area of Glasgow. Babbity Bowster is described as a cafe/bar/hotel/restaurant and it performs all of these functions with an atmosphere of excitement and is known as one of the 'in places' in Glasgow's city centre. The hotel today has a lively bar on the ground floor, with overflow to the garden outside; the Schottische Restaurant for more formal dining and private parties. There are seven en suite rooms upstairs. Menu items are traditional and reasonably priced. Quality food, good drink and intellectual conversation is the key to the success of this place together with Fraser Laurie's personal supervision.

Open all year except Christmas Day +
New Year's Day
Note: Restaurant closed Sun evening/ Sat lunch
- 🏠 Rooms: 7 en suite
- 🛏 DB&B £60–£85   B&B £50–£70
- ✗ Food available all day £
- ✗ Lunch £
- ✗ Dinner ££–£££
- V Vegetarians welcome
- ✶ Children welcome

Scottish oysters poached with fish stock and vermouth and topped with breadcrumbs. Fillet of beef on a croûton with a rich port and foie gras sauce. Black and white chocolate terrine with more than a hint of Glayva.

- 💳 Credit cards: Mastercard/Eurocard, American Express, Visa
- 🅝 Owner: Fraser Laurie

BOUZY ROUGE

111 West Regent Street
Glasgow
G2 2RU
Tel: 0141 221 8804 Fax: 0141 221 6941
Web: www.scotscape.com/bouzy-rouge

City centre location on corner of West Regent and Wellington Street. Approach via M8 from Charing Cross and follow one-way system from Sauchiehall Street.

A vibrant city centre restaurant for casual and gourmet dining.

- Semi-basement corner site in heart of city centre.
- Scottish with international influence.
- "A unique and effervescent place."

Bouzy Rouge is one of the 'trendy' places in Glasgow. Unique designer furniture specially made to set the scene accentuates the atmosphere of rich-coloured walls, stone floors, bright tiles and mosaics with complementary table settings and glassware centred round a superb horseshoe bar constructed from the same magnificently built woodwork. The menu offers loads of options for both special occasions and day-to-day business and whilst using the best Scottish produce introduces international dishes and themes. Also look out for the speciality nights. Despite being open all day and evening - booking essential. Bouzy Rouge has 2 AA Rosettes.

Open all year except New Year's Day
✘ Food available all day ££
✘ Lunch £-££
✘ Dinner ££
Ⓥ Vegetarians welcome
☂ Children welcome
♿ Facilities for non-wheelchair visitors only

Trio of spicy haggis, white and black puddings served with an Orkney cheese sabayon and whisky jus. Rack of Scottish lamb with a herb crust set on mash with a rich lamb gravy. Warm chocolate bread and butter pudding with sauce anglaise.

⊞ Credit cards: Mastercard/Eurocard, American Express, Visa, Diners Club, Switch, Delta, Solo, Electron
☒ Proprietors: Alan & Audrey Brown

THE BRASSERIE

176 West Regent Street
Glasgow G2 4RL
Tel: 0141 248 3801 Fax: 0141 248 8197

Approach via Bath Street from city centre; turn left into Blythswood Street then left into West Regent Street. From outwith city, follow one way systems via Blythswood Square to West Regent Street.

City centre restaurant and brasserie.

- Restaurant in the heart of Glasgow.
- Modern Scottish cooking.
- "A traditional restaurant serving good food in an easy atmosphere."

This elegant brasserie lies close to both Glasgow's theatreland and its mercantile centre and is popular both with businessmen at lunchtime and theatre goers in the evening. The Brasserie has an impressive pillared facade, and inside the experience is very relaxing, discreet and refined. The à la carte menu reflects this, with skilful use of quality produce, both brasserie-style and more substantial. Flair, continental influences and modern cooking styles are evident, and the service is excellent. The Brasserie is scheduled to receive a full refurbishment late in 1999.

Open all year except Christmas Day, Boxing Day, New Year's Day + 2 Jan Closed Sun
✘ Food available all day except Sun ££
✘ Lunch except Sun ££
✘ Dinner except Sun ££
Ⓥ Vegetarians welcome
☂ Children welcome

Sauteed chicken livers in a Madeira cream sauce with a puff pastry lid. Saddle of lamb crowned with a mustard and herb crust raised on Puy lentils. Hot caramelised bananas in a filo basket surrounded by a coffee crème anglaise.

⊞ Credit cards: Mastercard/Eurocard, American Express, Visa, Diners Club, Switch
☒ Manager: Fraser Campbell

BUDDA
142 St Vincent Street, Glasgow G2 5LA
Tel: 0141 243 2212
Fax: 0141 243 2707

From George Square travel up St Vincent Street for
¹/₄ mile. After crossing over Hope Street Budda is
situated in the first basement on the right-hand side.

**A lively youthful restaurant for casual and
sophisticated dining, with Moroccan-style decor.**

- City centre basement with its own nightclub.
- International cuisine using Scottish produce.
- "Leave your camel at the door and enter the
  casbah to sample good cuisine."

Budda is an exciting and innovative little restaurant
full of dark niches lit by candles in wrought iron
sconces. It is reminiscent of a Moroccan casbah
with its terracotta walls and velvet curtains – East
meets West. The atmosphere is intimate and
romantic. This is a vibrant place for the young and
'young at heart'! This is a place to enjoy good food
where the atmosphere is mellow – not for the
hurried among us. The evening à la carte menu is
changed every four weeks. Budda is available for
private hire.

Open all year except Sun lunch
✖ Food available all day ££
✖ Lunch except Sun £
✖ Dinner £££
Ⓥ Vegetarians welcome
♿ Facilities for disabled visitors

**Seared Oban scallops with a smoked fish risotto.
Oven-roast loin of Borders lamb, onion potato cake
and an Arran mustard jus. Amaretto and almond tart
with a coffee bean sauce.**

Ⓔ Credit cards: Mastercard/Eurocard, American
Express, Visa, Diners Club, Switch
Ⓝ Head Chef: Garry Gill

THE BUTTERY
652 Argyle Street, Glasgow G3 8UF
Tel: 0141 221 8188
Fax: 0141 204 4639

Argyle Street, just below M8 overpass – Westside.
Take Elderslie Street, turn left at mini-roundabout at
southern end of street. Restaurant at bottom of
street on left.

Gourmet restaurant in secluded street.

- Converted tenement building.
- Gourmet, Scottish, contemporary.
- "The chef presents fresh Scottish produce with
  flair."

The Buttery dates back to 1869 when it was
Scotland's first premier restaurant. Entry to the
restaurant is through impressive stained glass
doors, which lead to the Victorian interior of the
wood-panelled dining room. The staff are efficient,
attentive, but not intrusive. Service is impressive.
Scottish dishes are treated in a novel way with
unusual combinations, exquisitely presented and
with lots of interesting textures and flavours. The
luncheon menu is excellent value. The Buttery has 2
AA Rosettes. Winner (Category 2), and Overall
Winner in The Taste of Scotland Scotch Lamb
Challenge Competition 1998. *See advert page 25.*

Open all year except Christmas Day +
New Year's Day
Closed Sun
✖ Lunch except Sun Sat ££
✖ Dinner except Sun £££
Ⓥ Vegetarians welcome
⚟ Smoking of pipes + cigars is preferred in
the bar
🐂 Member of the Scotch Beef Club

**Seared scallops with fettuccini and scallions, and
langoustine essence. Scottish fillet of beef with a
marinated tomato, shallot purée and a sprinkling of
Madeira reduction, topped with foie gras. Hazelnut
tart with a warm poached baby pear and crème
anglaise.**

Ⓔ Credit cards: Mastercard/Eurocard, American
Express, Visa, Diners Club, Switch, Delta
Ⓝ Manager: Kenny Finlayson

THE CABIN RESTAURANT
996-998 Dumbarton Road
Whiteinch, Glasgow G14 9RR
Tel: 0141 569 1036

From Glasgow city take Clyde expressway, pass Scottish Exhibition & Conference Centre to Thornwood Roundabout. Follow sign to Whiteinch (1/2 mile). Restaurant on right-hand side at junction with Haylynn Street.

Informal 'neighbourhood' restaurant in parade of shops.

- Small city restaurant.
- Modern Scottish with Irish influences.
- "Commitment to fresh produce comes through in the superb flavours."

The restaurant is the original front room of an Edwardian tenement building, and is decorated accordingly, with original Art Deco features, a sideboard with china ornaments, old pictures and mirrors. The atmosphere is informal and cheerful. Dishes from the table d'hôte menu (five starters, seven main courses) are cooked to order; the cooking technique is creative, confident and to a very high standard; menus change daily, according to what is available in the market. About 9 pm, Wilma arrives to hostess and to sing one hour later. She is larger than life, first visited the restaurant shortly after it opened, and now returns nightly to encourage guests to sing along and let their hair down. The BBC made a half hour TV programme about her in Las Vegas! Chef/proprietor Denis Dwyer is in charge of the kitchen. A very friendly, fun restaurant where the quality of the food shines through.

Open all year except 1 to 14 Jan + 15 to 30 Jul
Closed Sun Mon
✗ Lunch except Sun Mon Sat £
✗ Dinner except Sun Mon £££
Ⅴ Vegetarians welcome
⚹ Children welcome
♿ Facilities for disabled visitors
✁ Pipes and cigars not permitted

Pan-seared woodpigeon breast on puréed beetroot and orange with game jus. Grilled turbot with fresh herb crust on a bed of braised summer vegetables. Mixed fresh Blairgowrie berries set in red wine jelly accompanied by a mango coulis.

💳 Credit cards: Mastercard/Eurocard, Visa
Ⅺ Proprietors: Mohammad Abdulla
    & Denis Dwyer

CITY MERCHANT
97 Candleriggs
Glasgow G1 1NP
Tel: 0141 553 1577
Fax: 0141 553 1588
E-mail: l.matteo@btinternet.com
Web: www.citymerchant.co.uk

Facing City Halls in Candleriggs, in Glasgow's Merchant City. Candleriggs on right going east along Ingram Street.

Seafood brasserie style restaurant in city centre.

- City centre restaurant.
- Modern Scottish.
- "You will find a wide range of Scottish seafood served in a modern style in a relaxed and friendly atmosphere."

Candleriggs has been upgraded, the City Halls renovated and now opposite the City Merchant Restaurant has expanded, doubling its capacity to cope with demand. This restaurant is not only popular with the business community but also shoppers and visitors. The restaurant specialises in seafood, but also offers game, prime Scottish steaks and vegetarian dishes. Daily fish market 'extras' are offered on the blackboard: Loch Etive mussels and oysters, king scallops, lobster and turbot as well as exotics such as red snapper. Lots of other fish and shellfish on offer on any day. The wine list is extensive with a choice of over 60 bins, but a 'bin-end' blackboard offers excellent value. Gallery area and function room available for private parties. Booking advisable.

Open all year except Christmas Day, 1 + 2 Jan
✗ Food available all day £-££
✗ Lunch £-££
✗ Dinner ££-£££
Ⅴ Vegetarians welcome
⚹ Children over 6 years welcome
♿ Facilities for disabled visitors
✁ No smoking area in restaurant

West Coast seafood terrine with a pesto mayonnaise. Escalope of venison with black pudding mousse and smoked garlic jus. Crannachan ice cream with home-made shortbread biscuit.

💳 Credit cards: Mastercard/Eurocard, American Express, Visa, Diners Club, Switch
Ⅺ Executive Head Chef: Andrew Cumming
    Proprietors: Tony & Linda Matteo

THE DRUM AND MONKEY

93-95 St Vincent Street
Glasgow
G2 5TL
Tel: 0141 221 6636
Fax: 0141 229 5902

On corner of St Vincent and Renfield Street –
approx 100 yards from Central Station.

A very vibrant pub fronts this casual and relaxing restaurant.

- Bank building.
- Modern Scottish.
- "Hidden behind this busy city centre pub is a relaxing restaurant with good Scottish food."

The Drum and Monkey was originally a downtown bank but today it has a warm and comfortable ambience where shoppers rest on wicker chairs and leather couches. A fine selection of beers especially real ales and continental lagers can be obtained. Bar food is available, with a simpler menu of freshly prepared-to-order sandwiches and wholesome salads. But for the real food experience the adjoining bistro provides more elaborate lunches and dinners in the most intimate of settings. Menus are carefully balanced and produced from locally sourced ingredients, highlighting our finest Highland beef, Border lamb and Scottish seafood.

Open all year except 25, 26 Dec, 1 + 2 Jan
✘ Food available all day ££
✘ Sun brunch available in bar
✘ Lunch except Sun ££
✘ Dinner ££
Ⓥ Vegetarians welcome
♿ Facilities for disabled visitors

Warm tartlet of wild Scottish mushrooms and Mozarella cheese on fine herb leaves. Seared Guinea fowl stuffed with crab, pickled ginger and coriander, shitake mushrooms, and fine herbs, with oven-roasted vegetables and chervil jus. Clootie dumpling with ice cream.

▣ Credit cards: Mastercard/Eurocard, American Express, Visa, Diners Club, Switch, Delta
▨ Manager: Kevin D F Dow

GLASGOW HILTON INTERNATIONAL

Camerons Restaurant, 1 William Street
Glasgow G3 8HT
Tel: 0141 204 5555 Fax: 0141 204 5004
Web: www.hilton.com

Access from M8 to hotel, or via Waterloo Street and Bishop Street from city centre.

20-storey landmark in central Glasgow.

- International hotel with a leisure centre, shopping mall and beauty salon.
- Exquisite international cuisine.
- "Cameron's reputation for excellent cuisine and utmost comfort is well deserved."

The Hilton chain is synonymous with style and luxury living and the Glasgow Hilton International is no exception. The standard of service and attention to detail is second to none. In Camerons Restaurant one enters a different world where style, elegance and luxury surround the diner who can experience some of the finest cuisine in the city. In nearby Minsky's New York Brasserie the flavours of New York can be experienced in less formal but equally attractive surroundings. The breakfast here is a culinary marathon! Raffles Bar transports you to the Far East where the culture is reflected in the laid-back style – sip cocktails and listen to jazz. Staff are formal yet happy and friendly, catering for the international guest's every whim. Camerons Restaurant has 2 AA Rosettes.

Open all year
🛏 Rooms: 319 en suite
🛏 B&B from £115
✘ Lunch (Camerons) except Sun Sat ££–£££: (Minsky's) from £
✘ Dinner (Camerons) except Sun ££-£££: (Minsky's) from £
Ⓥ Vegetarians welcome
🧒 Children welcome
♿ Facilities for disabled visitors
🐂 Member of the Scotch Beef Club

Timbale of smoked halibut served with Sevryga caviar and a lobster gazpacho. Suprême of Magret duck served with a roasted parsnip tian on a cider and cinnamon jus. Warm cherry and almond tart with Guinettes ice cream.

STB ★★★★★ Hotel
▣ Credit cards: Mastercard/Eurocard, American Express, Visa, Switch
▨ General Manager: Klaus Zsilla

GLASGOW MOAT HOUSE
Congress Road
Glasgow G3 8QT
Tel: 0141 306 9988 Fax: 0141 221 2022
E-mail: glasgowmoathouse@cwcom.net

Situated on the banks of the River Clyde, next to the SECC and Clyde Auditorium (Armadillo).

A luxurious ultra-modern skyscraper hotel in the city centre on the banks of the River Clyde.

• Well-appointed conference hotel - a Glasgow landmark on the banks of the Clyde.
• Modern international cuisine.
• "Soak up the atmosphere of the riverside and enjoy good food in this busy hotel."

The Glasgow Moat House takes its theme from its splendid position on a former wharf, on the banks of the River Clyde. It has a fully equipped leisure area and two restaurants. Both restaurants provide standards not often encountered in large international hotels. The Mariner which has 1 AA Rosette is a fine dining experience, the style of cooking is modern, fresh and elegant with a Scottish and international feel. No 1 Dockside is a bright, modern, relaxed restaurant with extensive buffet and à la carte menus prepared by executive chef James Murphy. The Moat House also boasts the Quarterdeck, a central bar with a continental feel about it. Winner of The Taste of Scotland Scottish Field Black Pudding Competition 1999.

Open all year
🍴 Rooms: 283 with private facilities
🛏 DB&B from £65 B&B £53–£125
✕ Food available all day (Quarterdeck)
✕ Note: Extensive buffet available at dinner ££
✕ Lunch (No 1 Dockside) ££
✕ Dinner (Mariner) except Sun ££
Ⓥ Vegetarians welcome
🕆 Children welcome
🕭 Facilities for disabled visitors
🚭 No smoking areas in restaurants

Chicken soup, spiced dumplings, beansprouts and five spice glaze. Salt cod, tarragon polenta, wilted greens. Fresh plum clafoutis, armagnac sauce.

STB ★★★★ Hotel
💳 Credit cards: Mastercard/Eurocard, American Express, Visa
👤 General Manager: Mrs Jela Stewart

LA BONNE AUBERGE
Holiday Inn
161 West Nile Street
Glasgow G1 2RL
Tel: 0141 352 8310
Fax: 0141 332 7447
E-mail: labonne@chardonleisure.com
Web: www.chardonleisure.com

At the top of West Nile Street, near the Royal Concert Hall and opposite the multi-storey car park.

French brasserie within international city centre hotel.

• French brasserie in modern building.
• Accomplished French cooking.
• "Hand-crafted exquisite dishes in vibrant French atmosphere."

La Bonne Auberge is privately franchised within the Holiday Inn in Glasgow's city centre. Independently managed, it is an experience not to be missed. The brasserie offers French flair in Parisian style and comfortable surroundings. Guests are invited to relax in L'Orangerie Conservatory – a haven in a busy city. Master Chef Gerry Sharkey demonstrates great skill and intrigue in his hand-crafted dishes, where the use of Scottish produce is evident.

Open all year except Christmas Day + New Year's Day
🍴 Rooms: 201 en suite
🛏 DB&B £45–£95 B&B £29–£82
SP Special rates available
✕ Food available all day ££
✕ Lunch £
✕ Dinner £
Ⓥ Vegetarians welcome
🕆 Children welcome
🕭 Facilities for disabled visitors

Light chicken essence with Strathspey mushrooms and herb ravioli and Thai spices. Char-grilled entrecote steak from the Scottish Borders with horseradish mash, Madeira jus and onion marmalade. Rich white chocolate delicé with a basket of summer fruits.

STB ★★★★ Hotel
💳 Credit cards: Mastercard/Eurocard, American Express, Visa, Diners Club, Switch, Delta
👤 General Manager: Tony Wright

LUX

Great Western Road
Glasgow G12 0XP
Tel: 0141 576 7576 Fax: 0141 576 0162
E-mail: info@luxstazione.com
Web: www.luxstazione.com

2 miles from city centre at entrance to Gartnavel Hospital.

Inventive and stylish city restaurant.

* Former 19th century ticketing hall for railway station.
* Modern Scottish.
* "Top quality Scottish dishes carefully created with imagination."

Situated in a quiet corner of the leafy West End of Glasgow, this restaurant reflects the simplicity of modern London establishments but retains the atmosphere of JJ Burnet's 19th century architecture. Menus are carefully chosen and composed by chef Stephen Johnson who adds his own special touches and secret ingredients to create memorable dishes. This experience is enhanced by a well-balanced and comprehensive wine list. The staff here are very professional. Regular tasting dinners take place at Lux, phone for details.

Open all year except 25, 26 Dec
Closed Sun Mon
✗ Lunch by arrangement only
✗ Dinner except Sun Mon £££
Ⓥ Vegetarians welcome
⚘ Children welcome

Salad of grilled Scottish black pudding, roasted shallots, mustard seed and strawberry dressing. Mignons of Highland venison, mixed berry chutney. Crème brûlée 'Lux', shortbread.

⊞ Credit cards: Mastercard/Eurocard, Visa, Switch, Delta
Ⅺ Manager: Julia Hutton

NAIRNS

13 Woodside Crescent
Glasgow G3 7UP
Tel: 0141 353 0707 Fax: 0141 331 1684
E-mail: info@nairns.co.uk
Web: www.nairns.co.uk

At Charing Cross. Woodlands Crescent is off Sauchiehall Street.

Interestingly designed city centre restaurant with rooms.

* Converted town residence on Georgian crescent.
* Innovative fusion food.
* "Carefully contrived menus of exceptional quality."

This converted town house has been cleverly converted into Nick Nairn's flagship. The established exterior hides a plethora of innovative features and visual impacts of colour and design within. The restaurant is on two floors with the upstairs dining room more classically formal and the downstairs modern with charcoal washed walls, nearly-black bench seating and monochrome food photography on the walls. Menus are carefully inspired and changed daily dependent on produce availability. All dishes are cooked to order and created under the watchful eye of Scotland's best known celebrity chef. The whole menu is a testament to his energy and dedication. Staff are well-informed of ingredients and dish compilation.

Open all year except 25, 26 Dec + 1, 2 Jan
🛏 Rooms: 4 en suite
🛏 Room rate £115–£140
✗ Lunch Tue to Sat ££
✗ Dinner £££
Ⓥ Vegetarians welcome
⚘ Children welcome (if they can eat from menu)
⚞ Diners requested to refrain from smoking until coffee. Cigar and pipe smoking are not permitted.
🐄 Member of the Scotch Beef Club

Glazed confit duck on Puy lentil salad, plum sauce. Fillet of halibut with grain mustard and new potatoes, bok choi and citrus vinaigrette. Caramel parfait, brandy snap basket.

STB ★★★★★ Restaurant with Rooms
⊞ Credit cards: Mastercard/Eurocard, American Express, Visa, Diners Club, Switch, Delta
Ⅺ General Manager: Jim Kerr

Nº SIXTEEN

16 Byres Road
Glasgow G11 5JY
Tel: 0141 339 2544

Byres Road runs from Great Western Road to Dumbarton Road. *NºSixteen* is at the Dumbarton Road end.

Restaurant/bistro in Glasgow University district of the city.

- Converted part of tenement building.
- Modern Scottish cooking.
- "Relaxed bistro atmosphere, modern Scottish cooking with style and a gourmet experience to be found here."

Nº Sixteen is simple in style and decor with white-painted walls and sanded tables and floors. In many ways this acts as a palate for the food served here which is far from simple. Chef Rupert Staniforth's kitchen prepares modern style Scottish dishes in an innovative style. His wife Aisla, assisted by a small team, looks after the front of house. There is a real commitment to an excellent dining experience in this busy west end restaurant.

Open all year except Christmas Day +
Boxing Day
Closed Sun
✘ Lunch Sat only £
✘ Dinner except Sun ££
Ⓥ Vegetarians welcome
✱ Children 12 years and over welcome

Seared marinated salmon with scallop and vegetable tempura with a sweet honey and dill dressing. Braised shank of lamb with a fresh breadcrumb and grain mustard crust and caper hollandaise, served with a choice of potatoes. Warm pear and frangipane tart.

⊞ Credit cards: Mastercard/Eurocard, Visa, Switch, Delta
Ⓜ Proprietors: Rupert & Aisla Staniforth

THE PUPPET THEATRE

Ruthven Lane
Hillhead, Glasgow
G12 9BG
Tel: 0141 339 8444 Fax: 0141 339 7666
E-mail: info@bigbeat.co.uk
Web: www.bigbeat.co.uk

In Ruthven Lane – off Byres Road in Glasgow's West End. Ruthven Lane opposite Hillhead underground station.

Excellent cuisine in a restaurant of individuality.

- Converted mews house.
- Modern Scottish cooking.
- "Impeccable service in this fascinating restaurant contributed to a very special gourmet experience."

In converted mews premises behind Byres Road, this little restaurant is made up of little rooms providing intimate dining in a Victorian setting with the modern addition of a stylistic conservatory bringing the restaurant into the 1990s. The furnishings in the 'old' room are Victorian whilst the conservatory is 'modern' with a 'designer' feel to it. The Puppet Theatre has become one of the best restaurants in Glasgow with booking required weeks in advance for the weekends. The cooking is described by our Inspector as "produced with great skill" with best Scottish produce presented in modern Scottish style which looks great and with tastes that match expectation! A unique restaurant.

Open all year except Boxing Day, New Year's
Day + 2 Jan
Closed Mon
✘ Lunch except Mon Sat £-££
✘ Dinner except Mon £££
Ⓥ Vegetarians welcome
✱ Children 12 years and over welcome
♿ Facilities for disabled visitors
✄ Smoking area, if requested

Seared pave of tuna with baby onion and Parma ham galette, pink peppercorn and coriander jus. Roast pigeon, ail en chemise, and maux mustard sauce, pak choi, apricot and fig chutney. Bitter dark chocolate fondant layered with a white truffle and lychee sorbet.

⊞ Credit cards: Mastercard/Eurocard, American Express, Visa, Switch, Delta
Ⓜ General Manager: Geraldine McDonald
Head Chef: Herve Martin

STRAVAIGIN
WINNER OF THE MACALLAN
TASTE OF SCOTLAND AWARD
1999 – CITY RESTAURANT
28 Gibson Street, Hillhead
Glasgow G12 8NX
Tel: 0141 334 2665 Fax: 0141 334 4099

From M8 junction 17. From city centre take A82, Great Western Road. Turn left down Park Road, right onto Gibson Street. 200 yards on right hand side.

Informal city restaurant in Glasgow's West End.

- Informal bar on street level and basement restaurant.
- Inspired Scottish eclectic menus.
- "A fine artist's palette on a plate – skilful and tasty, Stravaigin is a delightful venue for any discerning palate!"

Stravaigin is situated in the basement beneath its busy bar, popular with locals and students. The name 'Stravaigin' means to wander, gather, and this is the philosophy of proprietor Colin Clydesdale who has collected new ideas and ingredients and adds them to naturally produced local ones. The decor is bistro style using bright shades on walls and wooden table partitions round walls. There is interesting culinary art on the walls in the form of framed dried chilli peppers. There is a vibrant atmosphere and cheerful and informal service. The menus are eclectic and offer good value for money. The cooking is highly-skilled and dishes are presented with flair. Colin contributes to published regular features. Stravaigin has 3 AA Rosettes.

Open all year except Christmas Day,
Boxing Day, 31 Dec + 1 Jan
Closed Mon
✗ Food available all day, 7 days (Cafe bar) ££
✗ Lunch (restaurant) Fri + Sat only £
✗ Dinner (restaurant) except Mon ££
Ⓥ Vegetarians welcome
⚹ Children welcome

Asparagus, Parmesan and roast pumpkin seed tart with Stilton-dressed wild mushrooms. Char-grilled breast of poulet noir on a mound of mint pea mash with cumin almond sauce and home-made mango chutney. Strawberry shortcake with brandied peach coulis and fresh berry yoghurt.

▱ Credit cards: Mastercard/Eurocard, American Express, Visa, Diners Club, Switch, Delta
◧ General Manager: Carol S Wright

UBIQUITOUS CHIP
12 Ashton Lane
Glasgow G12 8SJ
Tel: 0141 334 5007
Fax: 0141 337 1302

Behind Hillhead underground station, in a secluded lane off Byres Road in the heart of Glasgow's West End.

Now in its 28th year – a sure sign of a winning formula.

- Mews courtyard restaurant.
- Modern Scottish cooking.
- "A restaurant where the integrity of the fresh Scottish ingredients is only matched by the skills of the chef."

The Ubiquitous Chip, known affectionately by its regulars as 'The Chip', was established in 1971 by Ronnie Clydesdale – it has been described as a 'legend in its own lunchtime'. The Chip is situated in a cobbled mews in Glasgow's West End. It has a spectacularly green and vinous courtyard area with a trickling pool and a more traditional dining room. The cuisine marries the traditional and original in innovative recipes and this variety is complemented by a wine list rated among the top ten in Britain for quality and value.

Open all year except Christmas Day,
31 Dec + 1 Jan
✗ Food available all day
✗ Lunch ££
✗ Dinner £££
Ⓥ Vegetarians welcome
⚹ Children welcome
♿ Facilities for disabled visitors

Ayrshire Guinea fowl terrine studded with pistachio and peppers, with Blairgowrie raspberry vinaigrette. Free-range Perthshire pork wrapped in Ayrshire bacon, fondant potato, Rothesay black pudding and apple strudel. Blairgowrie raspberry parfait with raspberry tuille and eau de vie de framboise sabayon (as served at the Scottish Parliament opening banquet).

▱ Credit cards: Mastercard/Eurocard, American Express, Visa, Diners Club, Delta
◧ Proprietor: Ronnie Clydesdale

BEARDMORE HOTEL
Beardmore Street, Clydebank
Glasgow G81 4SA
Tel: 0141 951 6000 Fax: 0141 951 6018
E-mail: beardmore.hotel@hci.co.uk
Web: www.beardmore.hotel.co.uk

Between Glasgow and Loch Lomond. Off A82, 8 miles from M8 Junction 19 over Erskine Bridge or approach from Glasgow along Dumbarton Road.

A stunning modern conference hotel offering luxury, and the latest IT for the professional traveller and gourmet alike.

* Recently built within its own grounds, with views over the River Clyde.
* Imaginative cuisine in an imaginative setting.
* "Amazing style and comfort, yet informal and relaxed, offering superb food."

The Beardmore Hotel is ideally situated only 15 minutes from Glasgow city centre. The hotel has two dining areas: Citrus which is unique with 'funky' retro furnishing and presents a combination of well-cooked produce, and B Bar Café, an all-day dining area with fresh food served quickly from 10 am - 10 pm in bright surroundings with river view. Service is impressive with a professional attitude. This is a busy and exciting hotel that makes time for the individual guest. Investor in People Award. Winner of The Macallan Taste of Scotland Restaurant of the Year Award 1996.

Open all year
🏠 Rooms: 168 en suite
🛏 DB&B £50–£135   B&B £35–£120
SP Special rates available
✕ Food available all day from £
✕ Lunch from ££
✕ Dinner from ££
Ⓥ Vegetarians welcome
🕏 Children welcome
♿ Facilities for disabled visitors
🚭 Smoking area in lounge bar

Terrine of smoked salmon and crab, yellow and green pepper dressings. Fillet of beef, roasted shallots, baby vegetables, ham haugh mash. Peach brûlée tower, Darjeeling custard, peach juice.

STB ★★★★ Hotel
💳 Credit cards: Mastercard/Eurocard, American Express, Visa, Diners Club, Switch
🍴 Director & General Manager: David Clarke

THE COOK'S ROOM
205 Fenwick Road
Giffnock
Glasgow G46 6JD
Tel/Fax: 0141 621 1903

Tiny shop front in the middle of terrace on main A77 road between Shawlands and Newton Mearns. Ample free parking at rear in Giffnock Station car park.

Converted shop front restaurant in suburban area on outskirts of Glasgow.

* Converted shop with Arts and Crafts decor.
* Modern Scottish cooking.
* "Great food, relaxed homely atmosphere - a delightful place to spend a Sunday or any evening!"

On the outskirts as you head south from Glasgow, you will find this gastronomic gem. The Cook's Room was converted into a restaurant by Tom and Helen Battersby who have been joined in the business by an enthusiastic young team and are gaining a reputation as one of 'the' places to eat in Glasgow. Together they have embarked on a business in which their passion for food and cooking can be fulfilled in full measure. The menus, offering the finest of Scottish ingredients, are colourful, imaginative and confident and the wonderful description of each dish is guaranteed to make mouths water. This is one of the friendliest restaurants in the friendliest of cities.

Open all year except Christmas Day, Boxing Day, New Year's Day + 2 Jan
Closed Mon
✕ Sun Brunch ££
✕ Dinner except Mon £££
Ⓥ Vegetarians welcome
🕏 Children welcome

Chicken livers with garlicky green beans and Dunsyre Blue cream dressing. Sea bream fillet on mussel and tarragon salad. Steamed date pudding with butterscotch sauce and home-made vanilla ice cream.

💳 Credit cards: Mastercard/Eurocard, Visa, Switch, Delta
🍴 Cook: Tom Battersby

EAST LOCHHEAD
Largs Road, Lochwinnoch
Renfrewshire PA12 4DX
Tel/Fax: 01505 842 610
E-mail: winnoch@aol.com
Web: www.selfcatering-accommodation.co.uk

Exit junction 28a from M8 (A737 Irvine). Turn right on A760. East Lochead is situated 2 miles on left-hand side.

Luxury period farmhouse in beautiful rural landscape.

- 100 year old Scottish farmhouse.
- Accomplished Scottish cooking.
- "Talented, modern, Scottish cooking enjoyed in charming comfort amid genuine hospitality."

East Lochhead is a traditional Scottish stone-built farmhouse, built over 100 years ago. The steading has been renovated to form three self-catering cottages all done to the highest modern standards. There are many delightful touches – fresh flowers, good quality fabrics and furnishings and quality antiques. This is an elegant family home with a pleasant, welcoming atmosphere. Proprietors Janet and Ross Anderson are knowledgable hosts. Janet is an accomplished cook making full use of locally-sourced produce as well as fruit and vegetables from her own garden and honey from her own bees. This is the place to find the breakfast of your dreams! As well as fabulous home cooking.

- Open all year
- 🛏 Rooms: 6, 5 en suite
- 🛏 DB&B £50–£52.50   B&B £30–£32.50
- SP Special rates available
- ✕ Residents only
- UL Unlicensed
- ✕ Food available all day ££
- ✕ Lunch ££
- ✕ Dinner ££
- V Vegetarians welcome
- ⃰ Children welcome
- ⤰ No smoking throughout

Aubergine, red pepper and goats cheese parcels with fresh herb dressing. Grilled chicken breast with braised pearl barley, lemon, thyme and honey-glazed carrots and green beans. Iced cranachan parfait with red berries.

STB ★★★★ B&B
💳 Credit cards: Mastercard, American Express, Visa
👤 Proprietor: Janet Anderson

FIFTY FIVE BC
128 Drymen Road
Bearsden
Glasgow G71 3RB
Tel: 0141 942 7272
Fax: 0141 570 0017

On the main Drymen Road at Bearsden Cross.

A well-established bar and restaurant popular with locals.

- Small restaurant attached to a large wine bar.
- Modern Scottish cooking, with French influences.
- "Wine bar and restaurant offering good Scottish fayre with French influence within a great atmosphere."

Fifty Five BC was, of course, the date that Julius Caesar first arrived in Britain: the restaurant has adopted this date as its name on account of the Roman remains that have been found nearby. Calum Smillie, head chef, has continued to maintain the high standards for which Fifty Five BC has become known. His short à la carte menus are imaginative; his creations make ingenious use of fresh local produce and are beautifully presented and delicious. Robust bar meals (potato skins, burgers, pasta) are served daily. The style of the place is modern, light and airy. Service is casual. Fifty Five BC is particularly popular locally and deserves to be better known.

- Open all year except New Year's Day
- ✕ Lunch £–££
- ✕ Dinner £££
- V Vegetarians welcome
- ⃰ Children welcome
- ⤰ Facilities for disabled visitors
- ⤰ No smoking area – bar food only

Warm chicken salad, fresh salad leaves with onion, mushroom, bacon and raspberry vinegar. Baked suprême of salmon with a fresh baby asparagus sauce and pilaff rice. Caramel apple pie served with fresh cream or home-made ice cream.

💳 Credit cards: Mastercard/Eurocard, American Express, Visa, Diners Club, Switch, Delta, JCB
👤 General Manager: Stewart McVicar

GLEDDOCH HOUSE HOTEL
& COUNTRY ESTATE
Langbank, Renfrewshire PA14 6YE
Tel: 01475 540711
Fax: 01475 540201

M8 towards Greenock. Take B789 Langbank/
Houston exit. Follow signs to left and then right after
1/2 mile – hotel is on left.

**Country house hotel in its own sporting estate
overlooking the Clyde.**

- First-class country house hotel in lovely grounds.
- Modern Scottish cooking.
- "Excellent cuisine in grand style amidst lovely surroundings."

Gleddoch House Hotel stands in a 360 acre estate
and offers a variety of outdoor pursuits including an
18-hole golf course, horse riding, clay pigeon
shooting and off-road driving. Public and private
rooms are all decorated and furnished to a very high
standard. The restaurant is spacious and gracious;
the four course, table d'hôte menu is superbly
cooked and presented by a highly professional chef.
The whole food experience is excellent and
produced with creative skill and attention to detail.
The hotel also has conference and private dining
facilities and has been awarded 2 AA Rosettes. One
of the most prestigious country house hotels in
Scotland – consistently excellent.

Open all year
🏨 Rooms: 38, 36 en suite
🛏 DB&B £92.50–£127.50   B&B £60–£95
SP Special rates available
✕ Food available all day £-££££
✕ Lunch ££
✕ Dinner ££££
Ⅴ Vegetarians welcome
� Children welcome
🐄 Member of the Scotch Beef Club

Assiette of smoked salmon feathered with a
mellow mustard dressing accompanied by capers,
half lemon and brown bread. Prime Scotch beef
tournedos crowned with woodland mushroom
duxelle, glazed with herb hollandaise and
cordoned with a Madeira-flavoured Arran mustard
sauce. Light banana cheesecake with chocolate
fudge sauce and orange fillets.

STB ★★★★ Hotel
💳 Credit cards: Mastercard/Eurocard, American
    Express, Visa, Diners Club, Switch
🅽 General Manager: Leslie W Conn

UPLAWMOOR HOTEL
Neilston Road, Uplawmoor, Glasgow G78 4AF
Tel: 01505 850565   Fax: 01505 850689
E-mail: enquiries@uplawmoor.co.uk
Web: www.uplawmoor.co.uk

Just off the A736 Glasgow to Irvine Road. Approx
4 miles from Barrhead.

Converted 18th century coaching inn.

- Cleverly modernised hotel.
- Good Scottish cooking.
- "Warm, friendly and characterful, offering excellent food."

Set in the centre of the pretty village of Uplawmoor
sits the equally attractive Uplawmoor Hotel. It has
been converted over the years but still retains a
relaxed cottage atmosphere in the restaurant and
bar . It is owned by Stuart and Emma Peacock who
are enthusiastic hosts committed to providing their
guests with excellent fresh meals in a relaxed and
comfortable environment. They have an extremely
good lounge bar where at lunchtime and evenings
quality bar meals are served at reasonable prices
using as much locally-sourced food as possible. The
restaurant and adjoining cocktail bar are only open
in the evening. The à la carte menu offers a wide
choice of freshly prepared meals including many old
favourites, whilst the fortnightly changing table
d'hôte offers a more sophisticated choice for the
discerning diner. Runner-up (Category 2) in The
Taste of Scotland Scotch Lamb Challenge
Competition 1999.

Open all year except Boxing Day + New Year's
Day
🏨 Rooms: 14 en suite
🛏 DB&B £45–£65   B&B £30–£45
SP Special rates available
✕ Food available all day Sun Sat £
✕ Lunch £
✕ Dinner ££
Ⅴ Vegetarians welcome
� Children welcome
🚭 No smoking in restaurant

King scallop, bacon and black pudding salad with
a balsamic vinegar dressing. Prime Aberdeen
Angus fillet served on a haggis croûton flamed in a
whisky sauce. Bread and butter pudding.

STB ★★★ Hotel
💳 Credit cards: Mastercard/Eurocard, Visa,
    Switch, Delta
🅽 Proprietor: Stuart Peacock

THE HOLLY TREE HOTEL
SEAFOOD & GAME RESTAURANT
Kentallen
Near Glencoe
Argyll PA38 4BY
Tel: 01631 740 292 Fax: 01631 740 345

From Glasgow take the A82 to Glencoe, continue towards Ballachulish Bridge, then take the A828 Oban road to Kentallen. Hotel is 2 miles down this road on right hand side beside loch.

Beautifully converted former Edwardian railway station, set in a spectacular setting on the shores of Loch Linnhe.

- Converted Edwardian railway station.
- Skilled handling of seafood.
- "Excellent seafood with captivating views of the loch."

An interesting blend of old and new occurs in this romantic hotel. Lovingly restored in the classical 'Charles Rennie Mackintosh' style (a must for all enthusiasts of the artist), the Holly Tree is a unique place. All rooms overlook Loch Linnhe to the mountains of the Morvern Peninsula and beyond, as does the comfortable restaurant which also overlooks the floodlit gardens. A varied choice of superb fresh seafood is skillfully prepared; the atmosphere is friendly; the hospitality excellent, all combine to make this a most relaxing place to enjoy the astounding scenery and location.

Open all year
- 🏠 Rooms: 10 en suite
- 🛏 DB&B £50–£78   B&B £30–£57.50
- 🆂🅿 Special rates available
- ✗ Food available all day
- ✗ Lunch from £
- ✗ Dinner from £££
- Ⓥ Vegetarians welcome
- ⳣ Children welcome
- ♿ Facilities for disabled visitors
- 🚭 No smoking in restaurant

Grilled oysters topped with Isle of Mull cheese. Venison set on ginger parsnip purée with redcurrant and Moniack wine sauce. Glayva and oatmeal iced parfait.

STB ★★★ Hotel
- 💳 Credit cards: Mastercard/Eurocard, Visa, Switch, Delta
- 🅽 Manager: Annette McFatridge

THE PRINCE'S HOUSE
Glenfinnan, by Fort William
PH37 4LT
Tel: 01397 722 246 Fax: 01397 722 307
E-mail: princeshouse@glenfinnan.co.uk
Web: www.glenfinnan.co.uk

On the A830 'Road to the Isles'. 17 miles from Fort William, 1/2 mile on right past Glenfinnan monument.

Small roadside coaching inn.

- Former coaching inn.
- Innovative modern Scottish cooking.
- "Guests have excellent choice - from home baked scones to à la carte dinner."

Dating back some 350 years, this former inn was providing hospitality even before Bonnie Prince Charlie raised his standard nearby in 1745. It has now been completely modernised as a quality hotel and restaurant and has an established reputation for both its food and service amongst locals and returning guests alike. Chef Carole offers a changing daily table d'hote menu in 'Flora's' restaurant, using the natural larder of the surrounding mountains and lochs, while Robert's carefully chosen wine list complements the cuisine perfectly. A bar meal menu is also available in Pretender's Bar.

Open 5 Mar to 28 Nov
- 🏠 Rooms: 9 en suite
- 🛏 DB&B £49–£75   B&B £42–£59
- 🆂🅿 Special rates available
- ✗ Lunch £
- ✗ Dinner £££
- Ⓥ Vegetarians welcome
- ⳣ Children over 5 years welcome
- 🚭 No smoking in restaurant

Individual fresh loch trout mousse wrapped in smoked salmon with a lemon and dill dressing. Sliced breast of wild pheasant and pigeon pan-fried with cider on an apple potato rösti.

STB ★★★ Hotel
- 💳 Credit cards: Mastercard/Eurocard, American Express, Visa, Switch, Delta
- 🅽 Partners: Robert & Carole Hawkes/ Suzanne Buxton

MINMORE HOUSE
Glenlivet
Banffshire
AB37 9DB
Tel: 01807 590378 Fax: 01807 590472
Web: www.SmoothHound.co.uk/hotels/minmore.html

Take the A95 from Grantown-on-Spey. Right after 15 miles take B9008 – follow signs to The Glenlivet Distillery.

A country house hotel in the heart of whisky country.

- Converted Scottish country house fine views over the River Livet.
- Innovative Scottish cooking.
- "At Minmore House you can indulge in the fine food, relax or explore the Highlands from this wonderful setting."

Minmore is the original home of the founder of The Glenlivet Distillery and lies in its own grounds close by the River Livet. Brett and Christine Holmes are young and enthusiastic hosts who set high standards of hospitality and cooking. The ambience is delightful and a very friendly atmosphere exists here. The chef, Chris O'Halloran, is equally keen and talented using the best of Scottish ingredients in an innovative way. An excellent place to relax or use as your base for exploration.

Open mid Apr to end Oct
🛏 Rooms: 10 en suite
🛏 DB&B £75   B&B £50
SP Special rates available
🍴 Packed Lunch on request
✕ Lunch ££
✕ Dinner £££
Ⓥ Vegetarians welcome
⚘ Children welcome
🚭 No smoking in restaurant

Fettucine of lemon, chilli and garlic, marinated Grampian chicken with white wine and basil. Baked fillet of Lossiemouth cod with stewed tomato, spaghetti courgette and pesto butter sauce. Rich chocolate tart with Glenlivet whisky cream.

STB ★★★ Hotel
💳 Credit cards: Mastercard/Eurocard, Visa, Switch, Delta
🅽 Owners: Brett & Christine Holmes

BALBIRNIE HOUSE HOTEL
Balbirnie Park, Markinch Village
by Glenrothes, Fife KY7 6NE
Tel: 01592 610066 Fax: 01592 610529
E-mail: balbirnie@btinternet.com
Web: www.balbirnie.co.uk

¹/₂ hour equidistant from Edinburgh and St Andrews. Just off A92 on B9130. Follow directions to Markinch Village then Balbirnie Park.

Gracious and elegant country house hotel set in delightful parkland.

- Georgian country house, restored to original splendour.
- Original and accomplished.
- "An exceptionally comfortable country house hotel where nothing is too much trouble."

Balbirnie House is a quite unique multi-award winning hotel which combines understated luxury with superb service and outstanding value. Privately owned and managed, the hotel is a Grade A Listed building of great architectural and historic importance. "There is an air of quiet, friendly efficiency pervading the whole establishment – outstanding." Many feature breaks are available throughout the year – booking in advance is advisable. Balbirnie has 2 AA Rosettes. Winner of the Macallan Taste of Scotland Hotel of the Year Award 1996. Runner-up (Category 1) in The Taste of Scotland Scotch Lamb Challenge Competition 1997 and 1999. *See advert page 23.*

Open all year
🛏 Rooms: 30 en suite
🛏 DB&B £82.50–£142   B&B £85–£112.50
SP Special rates available
✕ Lunch £
✕ Dinner £££
Ⓥ Vegetarians welcome
⚘ Children welcome
♿ Facilities for disabled visitors
🐄 Member of the Scotch Beef Club

Pan-fried breast of pigeon on a fricassee of Scottish girolles, thyme gravy and truffle oil. Grilled fillet of sea bass on a crab, leek and potato pancake with a rich sorrel sauce. Scottish raspberries and heather honey gratin with Drambuie ice cream.

STB ★★★★ Hotel
💳 Credit cards: Mastercard/Eurocard, American Express, Visa, Diners Club
🅽 Proprietors: The Russell Family

DALMUNZIE HOUSE HOTEL
Spittal of Glenshee
Blairgowrie
Perthshire PH10 7QG
Tel: 01250 885 224 Fax: 01250 885 225
E-mail: dalmunzie@aol.com

Approx 22 miles from Blairgowrie on A93.

The hotel in the hills.

* Country house hotel.
* Traditional Scottish cooking.
* "A relaxed, informal country house with delightful 9-hole golf course right on the doorstep."

Dalmunzie House Hotel is a turreted baronial country house standing in its own 6,500 acre mountain estate. It has its own 9-hole golf course (every Sunday there is a 'Golf Marathon', where non-golfers are partnered with good golfers); fishing, stalking, grouse shooting and pony-trekking are available, and the ski slopes of Glenshee are not far away. The Winton family who own the hotel have lived in the glen for decades and are genuine and experienced hosts. The house has a wonderfully friendly atmosphere, with log fires and comfy chairs and is hospitable and informal – the tone set by Simon and Alexandra Winton. The menu is table d'hôte (four/five choices) with a couple of à la carte supplements. The cooking is homestyle but imaginative; everything is fresh and cooked to order. Dalmunzie House Hotel has 1 AA Rosette.

Open 28 Dec to 28 Nov
🏠 Rooms: 17, 16 en suite
🛏 DB&B £60–£70 (3 to 6 days) B&B £42–£53
SP Special rates available
✗ Lunch £
✗ Dinner ££-£££
Ⓥ Vegetarians welcome
☆ Children welcome
♿ Limited facilities for disabled visitors

Lobster, leek and yoghurt tart on rocket salad with yellow capsicum and balsamic dressings. Loin of lamb sliced on parsnip cous cous with tomato and vegetable stew and green salsa. Lasagne of Blairgowrie bramble parfait and crisp dark chocolate.

STB ★★★ Hotel
💳 Credit cards: Mastercard/Eurocard, Visa, Switch
🏠 Owners: Simon & Alexandra Winton

ARDCONNEL HOUSE
Woodlands Terrace
Grantown-on-Spey
PH26 3JU
Tel/Fax: 01479 872 104
E-mail: ardconnel.grantown@virgin.net
Web: http://freespace.virgin.net/ardconnel.grantown/index.html

On A95, south west entry to town.

An elegant Victorian country house furnished with antiques.

* Victorian country house hotel.
* French cooking using Scottish produce.
* "French flair, combined with the best Scottish produce, creates a memorable meal for the discerning guest."

Ardconnel House, standing in its own mature gardens, is owned and run by Barbara and Michel Bouchard. The house is elegantly furnished and decorated in keeping with the Victorian style. The luxurious bedrooms are beautifully furnished in period furniture. Michel is French and brings flair and skill to very good local produce, whilst Barbara tends to the front of the house and extends a warm welcome to their ever-returning guests. Menus have a strong French influence yet stress the locality at the same time. There is a carefully selected, reasonably priced wine list. Ardconnel offers excellent value for money and makes an interesting base in this popular part of the country.

Open Easter to 31 Oct
🏠 Rooms: 6 en suite
🛏 DB&B £43–£52 B&B £25–£34
SP Special rates available
✗ Residents only
✗ Dinner – by arrangement ££
☆ Children over 8 years welcome
🚭 No smoking throughout

Pheasant and wood pigeon terrine wrapped in bacon and served with Ardconnel rowan jelly. Seared salmon on a tartare potato cake with warmed poached egg and lemon butter sauce. Panettone and banana sticky toffee pudding.

STB ★★★★★ Guest House
💳 Credit cards: Mastercard/Eurocard, Visa
🏠 Proprietors: Michel & Barbara Bouchard

THE ARDLARIG

Woodlands Terrace
Grantown-on-Spey
Moray PH26 3JU
Tel: 01479 873245
E-mail: ardlarig@globalnet.co.uk
Web: www.scotsweb.com/the_ardlarig

On A95 south west entry to town.

Impressive Victorian town house with good food in beautiful surroundings.

- Victorian town house.
- Fine Scottish cooking.
- "Neil offers hearty, imaginative meals in a peaceful location - adding to a very comfortable and relaxing stay."

The Ardlarig is a fine country house, set in a large garden, built at the turn-of-the-century. It retains the grandeur and splendour of that time, offering warm traditional Scottish hospitality, well-appointed rooms and fine food. Neil Cairns is an accomplished owner/chef. Excellent food, freshly prepared and presented, emerges from the kitchen making for a very pleasant Scottish experience. At dinner, table d'hôte menus are available. Typical of the area – a large selection of Speyside and island malts are offered. Neil will often join guests for a glass of wine or a 'wee dram'. Please note that Neil also shares his home with two Persian cats.

Open all year except Christmas Day,
Boxing Day + New Year's Eve
- 🏢 Rooms: 7, 4 en suite
- 🛏 DB&B £38–£48   B&B £20–£28.50
- SP Special rates available
- 🍴 Picnic hampers/packed lunch only ££
- ✗ Dinner – booking essential for non-residents ££
- V Vegetarians welcome
- 🕇 Children welcome
- ⌇ No smoking throughout
- 🐂 Member of the Scotch Beef Club

West Coast langoustine with a garlic, lime, chilli and coriander butter on a herb salad. Roast loin of Scotch lamb on wilted spinach with a garlic, lemon and mint jus. Raspberry and Glayva brûlée served with shortbread wafers.

STB ★★★★ Guest House
- 💳 Credit cards: Mastercard/Eurocard, Visa, Switch, Delta, Solo, JCB
- 🕴 Owner/Chef: Neil Cairns

CULDEARN HOUSE HOTEL

Woodlands Terrace, Grantown-on-Spey
Moray PH26 3JU
Tel: 01479 872106
Fax: 01479 873641
E-mail: culdearn@globalnet.co.uk
Web: www.scotsweb.com/culdearn

Entering Grantown on A95 from south west, turn left at 30 mph sign. Culdearn faces you.

A luxuriously appointed country house on the outskirts of Grantown.

- Elegant granite villa.
- Innovative, imaginative cooking.
- "Be completely spoiled by the excellent hospitality offered at Culdearn."

This charming deluxe establishment has achieved many accolades for the style in which it is run. Alasdair and Isobel Little are enthusiastic hosts, and look after their guests excellently. Their house is furnished to a very high quality and is well-appointed throughout. Service is professional and attention to detail meticulous. Personal touches are evident. Isobel is a talented chef and prepares local produce in classic Scots ways. Over 70 malt whiskies on offer and an interesting wine list. Culdearn has 1 AA Rosette.

Open 1 Mar to 30 Oct
- 🏢 Rooms: 9 en suite
- 🛏 DB&B £45–£65
- SP Special rates available
- ✗ Residents only
- ❢ Restricted licence
- 🍴 Picnic lunches to order
- ✗ Dinner – residents only
- ⌇ No smoking in dining room
- 🐂 Member of the Scotch Beef Club

Smoked Scottish salmon and watercress roulade , with a red pepper coulis. Saddle of wild mountain venison served on a parsnip potato cake with port and juniper jus, accompanied by a selection of fresh vegetables. Brandy snap basket with seasonal berries and lemon curd ice cream.

STB ★★★★ Hotel
Green Tourism 🌿🌿🌿 GOLD Award
- 💳 Credit cards: Mastercard/Eurocard, American Express, Visa, Diners Club, Switch, Delta, JCB
- 🕴 Proprietors: Isobel & Alasdair Little

MUCKRACH LODGE HOTEL & RESTAURANT

Dulnain Bridge
Morayshire PH26 3LY
Tel: 01479 851257 Fax: 01479 851325
E-mail: muckrach.lodge@sol.co.uk

3 miles from Grantown-on-Spey on A938 Dulnain Bridge – Carrbridge Road, 400 yards from Dulnain Bridge.

Traditionally built Victorian country house.

- Former shooting lodge.
- Modern Scottish cooking with continental influence.
- "Experience the fine food at Muckrach and sample the delights of the Highlands."

Muckrach Lodge was formerly a Victorian shooting lodge. The house stands in ten acres of landscaped grounds overlooking the River Dulnain and has been tastefully refurbished in keeping with the style of the period, whilst allowing for modern requirements. The cooking is 'the' priority here, with the emphasis on interesting and flavoursome combinations, well-balanced and of excellent quality. The chef is young and enthusiastic about his subject. There are two restaurants here – the bistro bar and the Conservatory, both of which are well-furnished and tastefully appointed. Proprietors James and Dawn Macfarlane are very much 'hands on', ensuring that their guests enjoy their stay at Muckrach. Muckrach Lodge has 1 AA Rosette.

Open all year
🏠 Rooms: 13, 12 en suite
🛏 DB&B £72–£82   B&B £49.50–£59.50
SP Special rates available
✗ Lunch £
✗ Dinner £££
Ⓥ Vegetarians welcome
🕏 Children welcome
🛆 Facilities for disabled visitors
🚭 No smoking in restaurants
🐂 Member of the Scotch Beef Club

Sauteed duck livers on crushed garlic potatoes with Parmesan wafers and a balsamic jus. Venison fillet on a rosemary rösti with a jus of ginger, juniper and orange. Belgian chocolate terrine with amaretto ice cream.

STB ★★★★ Hotel
💳 Credit cards: Mastercard/Eurocard, American Express, Visa, Diners Club, Switch, JCB
👤 Proprietors: James & Dawn Macfarlane

THE PINES

Woodside Avenue, Grantown-on-Spey
Morayshire PH26 3JR
Tel/Fax: 01479 872092
E-mail: enquiry@pinesgrantown.freeserve.co.uk
Web: www.pinesgrantown.freeserve.co.uk

On entering the town take A939 road to Tomintoul. 1st right.

A spacious Victorian house in woodland setting.

- Attractive Victorian house.
- Modern Scottish cooking.
- "A relaxing atmosphere offering good food, only minutes from town centre."

The Pines has undergone extensive structural and refurbishing work since it was taken over by Gwen and Michael Stewart. The owners' philosophy is to make their guests' stay comfortable and memorable, and they succeed. Everything is done meticulously. Michael is front of house and Gwen does the cooking. Good use is made of locally-sourced Scottish produce, complemented by herbs from the hotel's garden. The whole experience at The Pines is one of quality Scottish hospitality.

Open 1 Mar to 31 Oct – or by special arrangement
🏠 Rooms: 8 (7 en suite, 1 with adjacent private facilities)
🛏 DB&B £40–£48   B&B £22–£30
SP Special rates available
✗ Residents only
✗ Dinner ££
Ⓥ Vegetarians welcome
🕏 Children over 12 years welcome
🚬 Smoking occasionally permitted in one lounge
🚭 No smoking throughout

Butternut squash soup with melted cheese. Casserole of Buccleuch beef bourguignonne. Border tart with whisky and honey ice cream.

STB ★★★★ Hotel
💳 Credit cards: Mastercard/Eurocard, Visa, Delta
👤 Owners: Gwen & Michael Stewart

GREYWALLS
WINNER OF THE MACALLAN TASTE OF SCOTLAND AWARD 1999 – COUNTRY LUNCH
Muirfield, Gullane
East Lothian EH31 2EG
Tel: 01620 842144 Fax: 01620 842241
Web: www.greywalls.co.uk

An the eastern end of Gullane village (on the A198), signposted left as a historic building.

Historic hotel of great charm and quiet elegance.

- An Edwardian architectural masterpiece.
- Refined country house cuisine.
- "A magical experience in elegant surroundings, complemented with skilful cooking using the best of Scottish ingredients."

This charming, grand, but understated house was designed at the turn-of-the-century by Sir Edwin Lutyens and his collaborator Gertrude Jekyll. It was one of the architect's favourite buildings and is deservedly listed as being of national importance. It became a hotel in 1948, and is still family-owned. The hotel's lovely walled garden complements the serenity of the house itself, which still has the feel of a family home: relaxed, refined, elegant ... a perfect backdrop for the discreetly attentive service one meets within this distinguished hotel. Chef Simon Burns' menus are table d'hôte and to an excellent standard. His cooking is quite inspirational in the combination of ingredients and presentation. Staff are charming, attentive and unobtrusive. The wine list is exceptional. Greywalls has 2 AA Rosettes.

Open mid Apr to mid Oct
- 🛏 Rooms: 23 en suite
- 🛏 B&B £87.50–£95
- ✕ Lunch ££
- ✕ Dinner ££££
- Ⓥ Vegetarians welcome – prior notice required
- 🧒 Children welcome
- ♿ Facilities for disabled visitors
- 🚭 No smoking in dining room

Seared foie gras on an orange salad with Sauternes sauce. Saddle of Highland roe deer with braised red cabbage and honey roast parsnips. Fresh raspberry crème brûlée with home-made raspberry ice cream.

STB ★★★★ Hotel
- 💳 Credit cards: Mastercard/Eurocard, American Express, Visa, Diners Club, Switch
- Ⓜ Manager: Sue Prime

MAITLANDFIELD HOUSE HOTEL
Sidegate, Haddington, East Lothian EH41 4BZ
Tel: 01620 826513
Fax: 01620 826713

Haddington on A1, take route to town centre. At east end of High Street take Sidegate (signposted Gifford and Lauder B6368) – about 300 yards – opposite St Mary's church.

This country house offers a high degree of comfort and two restaurants.

- Country house.
- Modern Scottish with European and South East Asian influences.
- "New, enthusiastic host committed to providing warm hospitality and good food."

Maitlandfield House Hotel is now under the ownership of Nico De Freitas. It is set in landscaped gardens within minutes of the centre of Haddington and from Lennoxlove Country Estate. The hotel provides high standards of accommodation and facilities. The 16 Kings Restaurant has a tent-like, canopied-ceiling and offers candlelit dinner on polished wooden tables. The table d'hôte menus here use fresh local produce. The conservatory brasserie/carvery offers a more informal and relaxed atmosphere.

Open all year
- 🛏 Rooms: 22 with private facilities
- 🛏 DB&B £39–£75　　B&B £30–£60
- SP Special rates available
- ✕ Food available all day ££
- ✕ Lunch from £
- ✕ Dinner from ££
- Ⓥ Vegetarians welcome
- 🧒 Children welcome
- ♿ Facilities for disabled visitors

Pan-fried scallops in Moniack mead and cream, garnished with wild berries. Marinated Buccleuch beef served on a skewer over a cushion of risotto rice, garnished with seasonal salad. Layer of sponge with mixed fruits, laced with Drambuie liqueur and heather honey, topped with ice cream and meringue-glazed (served hot).

STB ★★★ Hotel
- 💳 Credit cards: Mastercard/Eurocard, American Express, Visa, Switch, Delta
- Ⓜ General Manager/Director: Nico De Freitas

MANSFIELD HOUSE HOTEL
Weensland Road, Hawick
Roxburghshire TD9 8LB
Tel: 01450 373988
Fax: 01450 372007
E-mail: ian@mansfield-house.com

On the A698 Hawick to Kelso road. On the outskirts of the town.

Mansion house overlooking Hawick with beautiful landscaped gardens.

- Family-run small country house hotel.
- Traditional Scottish and contemporary cooking.
- "Charming restaurant lovingly restored to its former Victorian glory."

A Victorian mansion overlooking the River Teviot and the town itself and standing in ten acres of well-kept terraced lawns and mature shrubs and trees. The building retains many of its original features – panelled doors, open fireplaces, ornate plasterwork – and a modern extension provides a large open bar and terrace. The hotel is owned and run by the MacKinnon family and under their supervision Chef David Tate presents well-priced à la carte and 'business lunch' menus in the formal dining room, and bar meals are also available. As well as the usual grills, the à la carte menu features some unusual combinations and meats (hare, kid and duck livers). The hotel's traditional service and atmosphere represents a sound basis of old-fashioned hospitality. *See advert page 260.*

Open all year except 26, 27 Dec, 1 + 2 Jan
- ⌂ Rooms: 12 en suite
- ⇔ DB&B £45–£75   B&B £30–£55
- SP Special rates available
- ✕ Lunch £-££
- ✕ Dinner ££-£££
- Ⓥ Vegetarians welcome
- ✦ Children welcome
- ♿ Facilities for disabled visitors
- ✗ No smoking area in restaurant

Char-grilled crotin goats cheese with griddled pears, served on crisp leaves and walnut balsamic dressing. Grilled collops of cod and sliced grilled aubergines, layered with light cream cheese sauce. Pavlova roulade, meringue rolled with whipped cream and Mansfield lemon curd.

STB ★★★ Hotel
- 💳 Credit cards: Mastercard/Eurocard, American Express, Visa, Diners Club
- ⋈ Owners: Ian & Sheila MacKinnon

KIRKTON HOUSE
Darleith Road, Cardross
Argyll & Bute G82 5EZ
Tel: 01389 841 951
Fax: 01389 841 868
E-mail: info@kirktonhouse.co.uk
Web: www.kirktonhouse.co.uk

Cardross is mid way between Helensburgh and Dumbarton on the north bank of the Clyde. At west end of Cardross village turn north off A814 up Darleith Road. Kirkton House drive ¹/₂ mile on right.

Pleasant family-run accommodation in tranquil location by the River Clyde.

- Old farm guest house.
- Accomplished home cooking.
- "Licensed old farmstead hotel with excellent home cooking and a warm, friendly welcome."

Kirkton House is a converted, late 18th century farmhouse built around a courtyard – described by its owners, Stewart and Gillian Macdonald, as a residential farmstead hotel. Stewart and Gillian are warm and hospitable hosts who set out to make your stay as pleasant as possible. Meals are normally chatty events with guests exchanging views and comments, like a house party but at separate tables. The public rooms have their original stone walls and rustic fireplaces – the fire in the lounge is lit on chilly evenings. Kirkton House has all the facilities of a small hotel, serves a homely dinner and a wonderful breakfast.

Open all year except Dec + Jan
- ⌂ Rooms: 6 en suite
- ⇔ DB&B £41–£55.10   B&B £29.75–£40
- SP Special rates available
- ✕ Non-residents by appointment only
- ❢ Restricted licence
- ✕ Snacks served throughout day – residents only
- ✕ Dinner 4 course menu ££
- Ⓥ Vegetarians welcome
- ✦ Children welcome
- ♿ Facilities for disabled visitors – downstairs rooms only
- ✗ No smoking in dining room

Avocado and king prawn salad. Roast smoked Scottish lamb. Banana 'foster': banana flambé with ice cream.

STB ★★★★ Guest House
- 💳 Credit cards: Mastercard/Eurocard, American Express, Visa, Diners Club, Delta, JCB
- ⋈ Proprietors: Stewart & Gillian Macdonald

NAVIDALE HOUSE HOTEL
Helmsdale
Sutherland KW8 6JS
Tel: 01431 821258
Fax: 01431 821531

³/₄ mile north of Helmsdale on main A9 road overlooking the sea.

A country house hotel in its own gardens and grounds overlooking the Moray Firth.

- Comfortable and friendly small hotel in dramatic Sutherland.
- Excellent home cooking with flair.
- "A tranquil setting, good for all age groups and an ideal place to unwind."

Built as a shooting lodge for the Dukes of Sutherland in the 1830s, Navidale retains that atmosphere. Public rooms are elegant, spacious and well-appointed. Set in seven acres of woodland and garden that lead down to the sea Navidale affords dramatic views over the Moray Firth and the Ord of Caithness, alongside modern comforts. The hotel caters in particular for fishermen and outdoor enthusiasts. The owners and their professional team, aim to ensure that your stay at Navidale is a memorable one. Also two luxury self-catering units available.

Open Feb to 1 Nov
🏨 Rooms: 15 en suite
🛏 DB&B £58–£70   B&B £35–£47
SP Special rates available
🍴 Packed lunch available
✕ Lunch £
✕ Dinner £££
Ⓥ Vegetarians welcome
🉐 Children welcome
♿ Limited facilities for disabled visitors
🚭 No smoking in restaurant

Savoury haggis tartlets served on a rich Drambuie cream sauce. Tenderly braised hind shank of Scottish lamb served with fresh raspberry, pink peppercorn and red wine sauce nestled on crisp stir-fry vegetables. Cranachan with summer berries, fine toasted oatmeal and Scotch whisky with home-made shortbread.

STB ★★★ Hotel
💳 Credit cards: Mastercard/Eurocard, Visa, Switch
👤 Director: Guy Bailey

HOWGATE RESTAURANT
Howgate
Midlothian EH26 8PY
Tel/Fax: 01968 670000

Situated on B6094 about 1 mile north of Leadburn.

Stylish and unique modern restaurant in rural setting.

- Converted stone stables.
- Modern Scottish cooking.
- "A refreshingly modern restaurant offering the latest trends in Scottish cuisine."

Nestling beside a wooded burn in pretty open countryside, the Howgate Restaurant buildings were originally 18th century stables and more recently the home of Howgate Cheese. It is beautifully decorated in polished woods with white walls and pleasing detail. The cooking here is excellent using good local produce which is prepared in an innovative modern style but served in countryside portions. There is a courtesy mini-bus available to parties of 6/10 by prior arrangement.

Open all year except Christmas Day + New Year's Day
✕ Lunch ££
✕ Dinner £££
Ⓥ Vegetarians welcome
🉐 Children welcome
♿ Facilities for disabled visitors

Pan-seared West Coast scallops with chive mash potatoes and caramelised onions. Roast haunch of Borders venison on juniper-flavoured red cabbage, veiled with a rich woodland mushroom jus. White chocolate and Drambuie crème brûlée with home-made shortbread.

💳 Credit cards: Mastercard/Eurocard, American Express, Visa, Diners Club, Switch, Delta
👤 General Manager: Peter Ridgway
Head Chef: Steven Worth

BOWFIELD HOTEL & COUNTRY CLUB
Howwood
Renfrewshire PA9 1DB
Tel: 01505 705225 Fax: 01505 705230

From the M8 at Glasgow Airport take A737 (Irvine) for approx 6 miles. Exit left (Howwood) onto B787 then either take second right onto a single track shortcut or drive into Howwood and take right onto B776 for 1 mile to Bowfield at top of hill (large white gateposts).

Former 18th century mill converted to modern hotel and leisure club.

- 18th century converted mill house.
- Modern Scottish cooking.
- "A lively, informal and relaxing setting where families are welcomed."

Bowfield Hotel & Country Club was established in 1976 by the Campbell family as a sporting club for the country people of Renfrewshire. Today it enjoys many international visitors and is a popular retreat for weekend leisure breaks. The combination of this well-converted building with modern facilities – swimming pool, spa and gymnasium – and a relaxing dining experience offers all that today's leisure guest is looking for. Imaginative menus using good quality produce cooked with skill and flair. *See advert page 26.*

Open all year
🛏 Rooms: 23 en suite
🍴 B&B £37.50–£65
SP Special rates available
✗ Food available all day – limited menu £
✗ Lunch £
✗ Dinner ££
Ⓥ Vegetarians welcome
✶ Children welcome
✗ No smoking in restaurant

Smoked salmon and caper roulade with lemon and dill dressing. Poached suprême of chicken on a haggis croûte topped with a whisky cream. Raspberry and Drambuie ice cream cake with pouring cream.

STB ★★★ Hotel
💳 Credit cards: Mastercard/Eurocard, American Express, Visa, Diners Club, Switch, Delta
👤 General Manager: Aileen Adams

THE OLD MANSE OF MARNOCH
Bridge of Marnoch, by Huntly
Aberdeenshire AB54 7RS
Tel/Fax: 01466 780873

On B9117, less than 1 mile off A97 midway between Huntly and Banff.

A delightful country house hotel on the river Deveron in unspoilt Aberdeenshire.

- Secluded and peaceful, a small hotel of rare distinction.
- Outstanding creative cuisine.
- "The ambience and quality permeates this outstanding establishment."

Renowned for its solitude and peace, this fine Georgian house was built in the 1780s as the manse for the ministers of Marnoch Old Church. Its owners Patrick and Keren Carter have preserved the Georgian elegance in a tasteful and sympathetic conversion to an intimate country house hotel. Using fresh local produce and, in season, herbs and vegetables from their own four acre garden, Keren deserves her growing reputation for imaginative, fine cooking. Her four course dinner changes every day. Her breakfasts are unrivalled. For a small establishment, the wine list is a triumph, both familiar and adventurous and always reasonably priced. Fluent German spoken. The hotel has 2 AA Rosettes.

Open all year except 2 weeks Nov, Christmas + New Year
🛏 Rooms: 6 en suite
🍴 DB&B £73–£78   B&B £44–£49
🍴 Reservations essential for non-residents
✗ Dinner 4 course menu £££
Ⓥ Vegetarians welcome – prior notice required
✶ Children over 12 years welcome
✗ No smoking in dining room

Pheasant and Famous Grouse whisky pâté served with thyme oatcakes and salad leaves. Escalope of Deveron salmon with a tarragon butter sauce. Bitter orange mousse infused with lavender.

STB ★★★★ Hotel
Green Tourism 🍃🍃 SILVER Award
💳 Credit cards: Mastercard/Eurocard, Visa, Delta, Switch, JCB, Solo
👤 Proprietors: Patrick & Keren Carter

TRAQUAIR ARMS HOTEL
Traquair Road, Innerleithen
Peebles-shire EH44 6PD
Tel: 01896 830 229 Fax: 01896 830 260
E-mail: traquair.arms@scottishborders.com
Web: www.trad-inns.co.uk/traquair

On A72 midway between Peebles and Galashiels.
Midway along Innerleithen High Street take B709
Yarrow. Hotel 150 yards on left.

A Victorian village inn unspoilt by time.

- An attractive Victorian village inn.
- Good home cooking.
- "Hub of the village. Vibrant well-run, family hotel."

A pleasant family-owned hotel close to the centre of this small Borders town. It is a sturdy stone building in a quiet street with a well-kept garden. The town, made famous by Sir Walter Scott, is popular with visitors, especially those looking for the cashmeres and tweeds for which these parts are renowned. Hugh and Marian Anderson run their hotel in a relaxed and friendly manner with genuine concern for the comfort of their guests. You can eat, depending on the weather, in the charming secluded garden or beside the blazing fire in the dining room. The bar prides itself in its real ales and there is a range of full meals available all day. *See advert page 265.*

Open all year except Christmas Day,
Boxing Day, 1 + 2 Jan
🛏 Rooms: 10 en suite
🍴 DB&B £39–£55 B&B £26–£42
SP Special rates available
✘ Food available all day £
✘ Lunch ££
✘ Dinner £££
Ⓥ Vegetarians welcome
⏺ Children welcome
♿ Facilities for disabled visitors – dining only
🚭 No smoking in dining room

Fresh vegetables sauteed in butter, mixed with soft cream cheese, wrapped in filo pastry then baked in the oven and served with a salad garnish. Slices of pan-fried duckling set on lyonnaise potatoes with sauteed mushrooms, seared capsicums and surrounded with a redcurrant jus. Bread and butter pudding.

STB ★★★ Hotel
💳 Credit cards: Mastercard/Eurocard, American Express, Visa, Diners Club, Switch, Delta
🅺 Owners: Hugh & Marian Anderson

THE STAGGER INN
Glenfalloch, Inverarnan
Ardlui, Dunbartonshire G83 7ZZ
Tel: 01301 704274 Fax: 01567 820269

On the roadside at Inverarnan, 7 miles south of Crianlarich on the A82 to Glasgow.

An informal restaurant serving good food.

- Attractive converted byre.
- Skilled and imaginative Scottish cooking.
- "Excellent choice of interesting dishes – you won't know what to choose."

The Stagger Inn takes its name from a local fishing pool – as opposed to the other possible interpretation! The owners also run a shop on the premises which sells venison and other items from the estate. The inn has been imaginatively converted, with its white stonewashed walls and plenty of use of colour in the fixtures and fittings. Venison is a speciality here as are hearty portions which are particularly welcomed by the many walkers who visit. All customers are assured of a quality meal cooked and presented in a professional and skilled way by head chef Rob Watkinson. Runner-up (Category 1) in The Taste of Scotland Scotch Lamb Challenge Competition 1999. Finalist in The Taste of Scotland Scottish Field Black Pudding Competition 1999.

Open 1 Apr to 30 Sept + weekends only in Oct
Closed lunch Mon to Fri
✘ Lunch Sat + Sun only ££
✘ Dinner ££
Ⓥ Vegetarians welcome
⏺ Children welcome
♿ Facilities for disabled visitors
🚬 Smoking is permitted in the restaurant after last orders (9 pm)

Black pudding with clapshot cake with a mustard sauce. Rabbit loin with Dunsyre Blue cheese and bacon. Steamed date and orange pudding with a butterscotch sauce.

💳 Credit cards: Mastercard, Visa, Switch
🅺 Proprietors: Alan & Nicki Cory-Wright

GORDON'S RESTAURANT
WINNER OF THE MACALLAN TASTE OF SCOTLAND AWARD 1999 – RURAL RESTAURANT
Main Street, Inverkeilor
by Arbroath, Angus DD11 5RN
Tel/Fax: 01241 830364

A92 Arbroath to Montrose, turn off at sign for Inverkeilor.

Small, intimate restaurant with rooms.

• Victorian terrace house.
• Modern Scottish with French influence.
• "Superb, an absolute gem."

A recent new interior of stained-glass windows, an open fire, beamed ceiling and sandstone walls set the scene in this welcoming family-run restaurant with rooms. Being so close to Arbroath and Lunan Bay, Gordon's Restaurant uses the best local fish, meats and fruits, which are used to produce imaginative, artistically presented modern Scottish cooking. The husband, wife and son team (Gordon, Maria and Garry) are always striving for perfection, making everything from their own breads, petit fours to savoury tasters. An à la carte menu changes regularly according to seasonal availability. Gordon's has 2 AA Rosettes. Winner (Category 2) and Overall Winner in The Taste of Scotland Scotch Lamb Challenge Competition 1999. Shortlisted and Commended for The Macallan Taste of Scotland Awards 1999 (*Restaurant with Rooms category*).

Open all year except last 2 weeks Jan
🏠 Rooms: 2 en suite
🛏 DB&B £54–£58   B&B £25–£30
Closed Mon – residents only
✕ Lunch except Mon – residents only ££
✕ Dinner except Mon – residents only £££
Ⓥ Vegetarians welcome
🕯 Children welcome
♿ Facilities for disabled visitors
✂ No smoking area in restaurant
🐂 Member of the Scotch Beef Club

White crab and ginger pave with guacamole chive blinis, coriander and orange vinaigrettes. Fillet of Angus beef glazed with Dunsyre Blue cheese soufflé, claret jus. Banana malt and toffee torte with candy crunch accompanied with a trio of banana.

STB ★★★ Restaurant with Rooms
💳 Credit cards: Mastercard/Eurocard, Visa
👤 Owners: Gordon & Maria Watson

BUNCHREW HOUSE HOTEL
Bunchrew, Inverness-shire IV3 8TA
Tel: 01463 234917
Fax: 01463 710260
E-mail: welcome@bunchrew-inverness.co.uk
Web: www.bunchrew-inverness.co.uk

On A862 Inverness to Beauly. 10 minutes from the centre of Inverness.

17th century country mansion set on the beautiful shores of Beauly Firth.

• 17th century mansion.
• Excellent Scottish cooking with an imaginative modern flair.
• "A unique dining experience in such delightful surroundings with wonderful views over the Beauly Firth."

Bunchrew House Hotel is a short way out of Inverness nestling on the shores of the Beauly Firth, in 20 acres of woodland. The magnificent dining room overlooks the sea where guests can enjoy imaginative and skilful cooking whilst admiring the superb sea view. The style of cooking is a fusion of traditional and modern styles using only the very best Scottish produce. The style of the hotel and the high standard in the furnishing and fittings is in keeping with the attention to detail found in the cooking – all of which makes Bunchrew a very special place indeed.

Open all year
🏠 Rooms: 11 en suite
🛏 DB&B £70–£115   B&B £50–£85
SP Special rates available
✕ Food available all day £
✕ Lunch ££
✕ Dinner £££
Ⓥ Vegetarians welcome
🕯 Children welcome
✂ No smoking in restaurant
🐕 No dogs in public rooms
🐂 Member of the Scotch Beef Club

Grilled fillet of red mullet with braised scallops and seafood fondue. Duo of Highland pheasant, roast breast and confit of leg resting on a pool of port and Madeira sauce. Pear Charlotte topped with a baby saffron pear in a caramel cage surrounded by a sauce Da Vinci.

STB ★★★★ Hotel
💳 Credit cards: Mastercard/Eurocard, American Express, Visa, Switch, Delta, JCB
👤 Owner: Graham Cross

CAFE 1
75 Castle Street
Inverness
IV2 3EA
Tel: 01463 226200
Fax: 01463 716363

Centrally located on Castle Street near castle.

City restaurant.

- Intimate yet modern, informal restaurant.
- Modern Scottish cooking.
- "Warm and friendly city centre restaurant."

Cafe 1 has a new owner and a complete change of staff. It now has a bistro-ambience which is enhanced by its friendly staff. It is a popular venue and used by locals. The chef uses high quality local produce, balancing the combination of textures and flavours.

Open all year except Christmas Day,
Boxing Day + New Year's Day
Closed Sun Nov to Jun
✗ Lunch £
✗ Dinner ££-£££
Ⓥ Vegetarians welcome
☆ Children welcome
Smoking discouraged before 2.30 pm (Lunch) + 9.30 pm (Dinner)

Seared scallops, crispy vegetables and black bean jus. Roasted chump of lamb, tain of aubergine, roasted potatoes and jus niçoise. Caramelised apple tart, cinnamon ice cream.

- Credit cards: Mastercard/Eurocard, American Express, Visa, Switch, Delta
- Owner: Norman MacDonald

CULLODEN HOUSE HOTEL
Inverness, Inverness-shire IV2 7BZ
Tel: 01463 790461/0800 980 4561
Fax: 01463 792181/0800 373 7987
E-mail: info@cullodenhouse.co.uk
Web: www.cullodenhouse.co.uk

3 miles from the centre of Inverness, off the A96 Inverness to Aberdeen road.

Historic and deluxe country house hotel.

- Georgian Palladian mansion.
- Country house cooking.
- "A peaceful and elegant historical house with excellent food."

Culloden House Hotel is an upmarket country house hotel in lovely grounds. The atmosphere is formal but comfortable, and there is a majestic splendour and romance about the place. The standard of cooking is high, prepared by a chef obviously committed to high quality and who understands his subject well and cooks with enthusiasm. The hotel is steeped in history, having been the headquarters for Bonnie Prince Charlie's Jacobite Army in 1746. It is therefore an excellent place from which to explore the surrounding area whilst enjoying luxurious surroundings and excellent hospitality. Culloden House Hotel has 2 AA Rosettes. *See advert page 28.*

Open all year
🛏 Rooms: 28 en suite
🛌 DB&B £170–£320   B&B £135–£270
SP Special rates available off season
✗ Food available all day ££££
✗ Lunch ££
✗ Dinner ££££
Ⓥ Vegetarians welcome
☆ Children welcome
No smoking in dining room
🐂 Member of the Scotch Beef Club

Tartan of Scottish salmon served with a creamed horseradish dressing. Rich beef consommé flavoured with tomato and saffron. Breast of Guinea fowl with wild mushroom mousse, red onion potato rösti and butternut squash set on a thmye jus. White chocolate tart with a raspberry compote and vanilla ice cream.

STB ★★★★ Hotel
- Credit cards: Mastercard/Eurocard, American Express, Visa, Diners Club, Switch, Delta, JCB
- General Manager/Director: Major R H Gillis

CULLODEN MOOR VISITOR CENTRE RESTAURANT

(NTS)
Culloden Moor
Inverness IV2 5EU
Tel: 01463 790607 (Ext 25)
Fax: 01463 794294

B9006, 5 miles east of Inverness on National Cycle Routes 1 and 7.

Excellent self-service restaurant at the Culloden Battlefield.

- Visitor attraction with restaurant.
- Traditional Scottish.
- "A relaxed and friendly place serving Scottish fayre."

Culloden Moor visitor centre is a spacious building located by the famous historic battlefield and is well worth a visit. The centre offers a great insight into the history and events in the area and there is the opportunity to walk the battlefield yourself and try and imagine what life must have been like all those years ago when Bonnie Prince Charlie's army fought the troops of the Government in 1746. The restaurant is well-thought out and offers good, honest Scottish food to suit all appetites and tastes with a strong emphasis on quality local produce.

   Open 1 Feb to 31 Dec except 24, 25 + 26 Dec
✗ Food available all day £
✗ Lunch £
Ⓥ Vegetarians welcome
ᚸ Children welcome
ሬ Facilities for disabled visitors
⊬ No smoking throughout

Leek and tattie soup served with oatcakes or cheese and herb scone. Smoked salmon and cream cheese quiche with tossed green salad. Bramble and oat crumble with lemon curd ice cream.

⊞ Credit cards: Mastercard, Visa, Switch, Delta
Ⅺ Restaurant Manager: Mrs Daska MacKintosh

DUNAIN PARK HOTEL

(On The A82) Inverness IV3 8JN
Tel: 01463 230512 Fax: 01463 224532
E-mail: dunainparkhotel@btinternet.com
Web: www.dunainparkhotel.co.uk

On A82, on left hand side, 1 mile from the Inverness town boundary.

A country house hotel offering outstanding cuisine, cooked by a Master Chef.

- A handsome 18th century 'Georgian Italianate' hunting lodge.
- First rate Scottish cooking, with assured French influences.
- "A lovely country house hotel with fine food yet so close to Inverness."

Dunain Park is a fine Georgian country house, standing in six acres of gardens and woodlands. The large kitchen garden supplies herbs, vegetables and soft fruit. Ann and Edward Nicoll have won a high reputation for their establishment and several awards. Public and private rooms are immaculately furnished – and there is an indoor swimming pool and sauna – but it is for its food that Dunain Park is particularly renowned. Ann Nicoll goes to great lengths to source top quality local produce – the only beef she will use is from Highland cattle or Aberdeen Angus – and her style of cooking brings out the flavour of fresh produce, and enhances it with wonderfully assured sauces.

   Open all year
🛏 Rooms: 13 en suite
🛏 DB&B £104–£124   B&B £79–£99
ꜱᴘ Special rates available in the low season
✗ Dinner £££
Ⓥ Vegetarians welcome
ᚸ Well-behaved children welcome
ሬ Facilities for disabled visitors – residents only
⊬ No smoking in dining room
🐂 Member of the Scotch Beef Club

Ballantine of Scottish salmon grain mustard and parsley served with pickled mussels, crisp leaves and a pesto olive oil. Heather honey roasted breast of duck served with a rösti potato, roast parsnips and a sweet berry jus. Blueberry financier topped with lemon sorbet and finished with a blueberry compote.

STB ★★★★ Hotel
Green Tourism Ⓟ **BRONZE** Award
⊞ Credit cards: Mastercard/Eurocard, American Express, Visa, Switch, Delta
Ⅺ Owners: Ann & Edward Nicoll

GLENDRUIDH HOUSE HOTEL

by Castle Heather
Old Edinburgh Road South
Inverness IV2 6AR
Tel: 01463 226499 Fax: 01463 710745
E-mail: tos@cozzee-nessie-bed.co.uk
Web: www.cozzee-nessie-bed.co.uk/intro.html

2 miles from Inverness centre. ½ mile south off Sir Walter Scott Drive. At the 2nd roundabout turn left and take the first right at the 'Hotel 300 yds' sign.

A quiet oasis with extensive grounds, comfortably furnished bedrooms, and good quality cooking.

- A most unusual building, dating mainly from the 1850s.
- Traditional Scottish cooking.
- "Traditional food and a warm welcome awaits you in this family home."

This is an unusual and attractive small country house set in three acres of woodland and lawns overlooking the Moray Firth: seclusion and privacy within minutes of Inverness – smoking is prohibited even in the grounds. The Druid's Glen Bar provides an excellent range of whiskies and the relaxing sitting room has the unusual feature of being completely circular, its windows and doors shaped to the contour of the room. The elegant dining room (residents only) has an Italian marble fireplace and overlooks the tidy gardens. Christine Smith's well-balanced table d'hôte menus change daily and offer classic dishes employing local game and fish.

Open all year except Christmas Day
🏠 Rooms: 5 en suite (+ 3 en suite rooms in Garden Villa)
🛏 DB&B £44–£79   B&B £19–£49.50
SP Special rates available
✗ Lunch – residents only ££
✗ Dinner – residents only ££-£££
Ⅴ Vegetarians welcome
🧒 Children welcome
♿ Limited facilities for disabled visitors
🚭 No smoking throughout

Cream of Strathdon soup, made from Aberdeenshire's creamy blue cheese. Guinea fowl suprême (raised at Craofurdland Estate) served with a rich Madeira sauce. Compote of apple with cinnamon ice cream.

STB ★★★★ Hotel
💳 Credit cards: Mastercard/Eurocard, American Express, Visa, Diners Club, Switch, JCB
👤 Proprietors: Michael & Christine Smith

THE RIVERHOUSE RESTAURANT

1 Greig Street
Inverness IV3 5PT
Tel: 01463 222033 Fax: 01463 220890

Situated on the corner of Greig Street and Huntly Street, on the west side of the River Ness close to Balnain House.

An attractive, small restaurant situated on the banks of the River Ness, close to the centre of Inverness.

- Ground floor of a converted Victorian building.
- A blend of traditional and contemporary Scottish cooking.
- "Delicious food in delightful location."

Ideally situated in a converted Victorian building, on the banks of the River Ness, the Riverhouse Restaurant is small, intimate and stylishly decorated. Chef/Patron, Marcus Blackwell, prepares meals in the open plan kitchen, in full view of the guests, which leaves no doubts as to the skill and level of work in the production of each dish. Eating at the Riverhouse is a leisurely experience and although there is an interesting and appetising range of fish dishes, meat and game dishes are certainly worthy of a mention. Food products from throughout the Highlands and Islands can be found in Inverness, and Marcus, along with his wife Colleen, take full advantage of this, enabling them to source the quality of produce they require for the restaurant. Booking essential.

Open 1 Feb to 30 Dec except Christmas Day + Boxing Day
Closed Sun Mon – 1 Oct to 1 June
✗ Dinner £££
Ⅴ Vegetarians welcome
🧒 Children welcome
♿ Facilities for disabled visitors
🚭 No smoking throughout

Riverhouse seafood platter with langoustine, smoked salmon, taramasalata, smoked mackerel, marinated herrings, oyster and velvet crab. Pigeon, hare, pan-seared rabbit and venison served on a bed of cabbage and red onion served with a juniper sauce. Elderflower crème brûlée.

💳 Credit cards: Mastercard/Eurocard, American Express, Visa, Switch, Delta
👤 Owner: M Blackwell

FALLS OF SHIN VISITOR CENTRE
Invershin
Sutherland IV27 4EE
Tel: 01549 402231
Fax: 01863 766500

Next to Shin Falls Waterfall on B837 Lairg to Bonar-Bridge.

A visitor centre by the Shin Falls offering a range of woodland walks, a salmon leap and adventure playground.

• Attractive pine lodge in woodland setting.
• Home cooking and baking.
• "Very good food indeed both in the restaurant and in the shop where Highland cheeses, smoked foods, preserves and whiskies can be found."

The Falls of Shin Visitor Centre is dramatically positioned alongside the waterfalls from which it takes its name. It is well worth a visit, for the breathtaking experience of watching the wild Atlantic salmon leap to survival, the forestry walks and, of course, for the visitor centre which comprises a shop and restaurant. The self service, licensed restaurant is large and airy, with a commendable commitment to the quality produce of the Highlands, from simple but superb home-made beefburgers to salmon dishes. Dishes vary daily and there is a fine range of home baking and good coffee. Peter Campbell and his efficient, friendly team have earned the Investor in People Award and this is reflected in the high level of care afforded to visitors.

Open 19 Feb to 24 Dec
✕ Food available all day £
✕ Lunch £
✕ Dinner July + Aug only £
Ⓥ Vegetarians welcome
♰ Children welcome
♿ Facilities for disabled visitors
⚱ Smoking area in dining room

Pickled herring, salad and oatcakes. Salmon steaks, mashed potatoes with fresh salad. Banoffee pie and locally made ice cream.

🆔 Credit cards: Mastercard/Eurocard, Visa, Switch, Delta
Ⓜ Owner: Peter Campbell

PITTODRIE HOUSE HOTEL
Chapel of Garioch
by Inverurie, Aberdeenshire AB51 5HS
Tel: 01467 681444
Fax: 01467 681648
E-mail: info@pittodrie.macdonald-hotels.co.uk
Web: www.macdonald.hotels.co.uk

Off A96 just north of Inverurie 21 miles north of Aberdeen, 17 miles north of airport.

A country house hotel offering indoor and outdoor recreational facilities.

• Scottish baronial mansion, incorporating many architectural details of its long history.
• Well-cooked Scottish cuisine.
• "Country house hotel sitting at the foot of Bennachie offering the best of fresh local produce."

Pittodrie House originally belonged to a branch of the family of the Earls of Mar, the estate being granted to them by Robert the Bruce for their loyalty at the Battle of Bannockburn. The house was built in 1480, and added to in the baronial style in 1850. The period atmosphere has been carefully maintained throughout the hotel. In the dining room the robust table d'hôte menus are well-balanced and offer just the kind of dishes one would expect in a grand country house, accompanied by herbs and vegetables from the hotel's own garden and a delicious selection of desserts.

Open all year
🏨 Rooms: 27 en suite
🛏 DB&B £62.50–£72.50   B&B £70–£80
🆂🅿 Special rates available
✕ Lunch £-££
✕ Dinner £££
Ⓥ Vegetarians welcome
♰ Children welcome
⚱ No smoking in dining room

Ramekin of poached smoked haddoch topped with a Gruyere and garlic crust. Roast monkfish wrapped in smoked bacon set on crisp vegetables, complemented by a fresh mussel sauce. Vanilla crème brûlée flavoured with stem ginger, accompanied by home-made shortbread fingers.

STB ★★★ Hotel
🆔 Credit cards: Mastercard/Eurocard, American Express, Visa, Diners Club, Switch, Delta
Ⓜ General Manager: Nigel Guthrie

THAINSTONE HOUSE HOTEL & COUNTRY CLUB
Inverurie, Aberdeenshire AB51 5NT
Tel: 01467 621643
Fax: 01467 625084

On A96 north of Aberdeen, 8 miles from airport turn left at first roundabout after Kintore.

A country house hotel and country club near Aberdeen, offering first class cooking and hospitality.

- Converted country mansion.
- Modern Scottish cuisine.
- "A delightful and stylish palladian mansion, offering a high quality experience in all aspects."

This charming house has been modernised to become a comfortable hotel and country club. The executive chef Martin Ward offers both à la carte and table d'hôte menus in 'Simpsons' Restaurant. There is an ambitious and bold feeling about many of the dishes; the presentation is influenced by nouvelle cuisine, but portion sizes and the quality of the raw materials are influenced only by the rich farming country within which Thainstone stands. You can also eat in Cammie's Bar, where the food and atmosphere is more informal. The hotel has 2 AA Rosettes. *See advert page 264.*

    Open all year
🏨   Rooms: 48 en suite
🛏   DB&B £66–£90   B&B £45–£80
SP   Special rates available
✕   Food available all day ££-£££
✕   Lunch £££
✕   Dinner ££££
Ⓥ   Vegetarians welcome
☂   Children welcome
♿   Facilities for disabled visitors
✘   No smoking in restaurant

Chicken, smoked bacon, wild mushroom terrine with a warm balsamic dressing. Seared fillet medallions of beef finished with a wild mushroom, button onion and tarragon tomato jus. Glazed lemon tart with citrus fruit sorbet and passion fruit sauce.

STB ★★★ Hotel
💳   Credit cards: Mastercard/Eurocard, American Express, Visa, Diners Club, Switch, Delta
Ⓜ   General Manager: Sylvia Simpson

MONTGREENAN MANSION HOUSE HOTEL
Montgreenan Estate
Irvine, by Kilwinning
Ayrshire KA13 7QZ
Tel: 01294 557733
Fax: 01294 850397
E-mail: montgreenan.mansion@virgin.net

Just off the A736, 4 miles north of Irvine. 30 minutes from Glasgow, 20 minutes from Ayr.

A luxury country house hotel in its own grounds.

- An impeccably restored and maintained Georgian mansion.
- Modern Scottish.
- "Enjoy your stay in this elegant, comfortable hotel."

Built in 1817 by a wealthy tobacco baron, and set in 50 acres of secluded parklands and beautiful gardens, Montgreenan still retains the impressive architecture and decorative features of the period. The hotel has recently changed hands and is now under the ownership of the Leckie Family, who also own the prestigious Crieff Hydro Hotel. Accommodation has been refurbished to a very high standard. Public rooms are elegant and comfortable. Commitment to Scottish produce is evident. The staff at Montgreenan are friendly, efficient and attentive. The hotel has 1 AA Rosette.

    Open all year
🏨   Rooms: 21 en suite
🛏   DB&B £65–£109.50 B&B £80–£175
SP   Special rates available
✕   Food available all day ££
✕   Lunch ££
✕   Dinner £££
Ⓥ   Vegetarians welcome
☂   Children welcome
✘   No smoking in restaurant

Roast quail on a casserole of venison sausage and woodland mushrooms in rich game sauce. Rack of lamb with carrot chervil cous cous served with red wine sauce. Lemon mousse.

STB ★★★★ Hotel
💳   Credit cards: Mastercard/Eurocard, American Express, Visa, Diners Club
Ⓜ   Proprietors: James & Nicole Leckie

APPLE LODGE

Lochranza
Isle of Arran KA27 8HJ
Tel/Fax: 01770 830229

From Brodick, head north and follow the road to Lochranza (around 14 miles). As you enter the village pass the distillery and Apple Lodge is situated 300 yards on the left opposite golf course.

Attractive country house in charming island village.

- Edwardian house with adjoining cottage.
- High quality home cooking.
- "A delightful and comfortable house with the best of home cooking."

Originally the village manse, Apple Lodge is tranquilly located on the northern part of Arran in the delightful village of Lochranza, where the ferry from Kintyre docks. Set in its own appealing gardens, both the lodge – and the south-facing suite addition – Apple Cottage – are furnished beautifully to a very high standard. One can relax in the comfortable surroundings watching wild deer graze a few yards from the garden, whilst an eagle soars overhead. Meanwhile, Jeannie Boyd will be creating a deliciously mouth-watering dinner for all to enjoy.

Open all year except Christmas week
- 🏠 Rooms: 4 en suite
- 🛏 DB&B £46–£51   B&B £30–£35
- SP Special rates available
- ✗ Residents only
- UL Unlicensed – guests welcome to take own wine
- 🍴 Packed lunches £
- ✗ Dinner ££
- V Vegetarians welcome
- ⚐ Children over 12 years welcome
- ✗ No smoking in dining room + bedrooms

Cream of asparagus soup with crusty garlic bread. Char-grilled sea bass on baby spinach leaves with roasted red pepper, tomato and basil salsa accompanied by leek and potato cakes and baby seasonal vegetables. Boozy bread and butter pudding with mango.

STB ★★★★ Guest House
- 💳 No credit cards
- 👤 Proprietor/Chef: Jeannie Boyd

ARGENTINE HOUSE HOTEL

Shore Road, Whiting Bay
Isle of Arran KA27 8PZ
Tel: 01770 700662
Fax: 01770 700693
E-mail: info@argentinearran.co.uk
Web: www.argentinearran.co.uk

8 miles south of ferry terminal. First hotel on seafront at village entrance.

Family-run guest house with comfortable bedrooms.

- Victorian seaside villa.
- Scottish produce with a continental touch.
- "Unusual international influences complement local produce."

Assya and Bruno Baumgärtner, originally from Switzerland, have made Arran their home and have refurbished this lovely villa to suit both the local heritage and extend their own culture. Rooms have been carefully furnished to provide a comfortable and relaxing stay for their guests, who are made more than welcome. Menus change daily, depending on produce available and guests' taste. Vegetarians are well-cared for and every taste is met. Food combinations are interesting, innovative and well-executed. Shortlisted and Commended for The Macallan Taste of Scotland Awards 1999.

Open Feb to mid Jan
- 🏠 Rooms: 5 en suite
- 🛏 DB&B £52–£66   B&B £34–£48
- SP Special rates available
- ✗ Non-residents – by arrangement
- ✗ Dinner ££-£££
- V Vegetarians welcome
- ✗ No smoking in dining room

Ravioli with black pudding and apple filling, served with sage butter and flowers. Arran lamb with garlic and sun-dried tomato cream, thyme potatoes and bean parcels. Cranachan parfait with raspberries.

STB ★★★ Guest House
- 💳 Credit cards: Mastercard/Eurocard, Visa
- 👤 Owners: Assya & Bruno Baumgärtner

AUCHRANNIE COUNTRY HOUSE HOTEL
Brodick
Isle of Arran KA27 8BZ
Tel: 01770 302234 Fax: 01770 302812
E-mail: info@auchrannie.co.uk
Web: www.auchrannie.co.uk

One mile north of Brodick Ferry Terminal and 400 yards from Brodick Golf Club.

Country house hotel and country club in Brodick.

- 19th century mansion, with substantial additions.
- Modern Scottish cooking.
- "A comfortable hotel with facilities for all the family."

Auchrannie House is a pink sandstone Victorian country house, formerly the home of the Dowager Duchess of Hamilton. The hotel is furnished in a reproduction period style with modern comforts. A number of luxury lodges have been built in the grounds, (each accommodating up to six people), also a state-of-the-art leisure complex with 20m pool. Brambles Bistro is a popular venue for families for snacks and meals, and the Garden Restaurant (which extends the original dining room with a conservatory) offers more formal dining. The sizeable table d'hôte menu offers a good range of local Scottish meat and fish dishes complemented by fresh vegetables and a daily vegetarian speciality. The Garden Restaurant has 2 AA Rosettes.

Open all year
🏨 Rooms: 28 en suite
🛏 DB&B £46.50–£74.50   B&B £30–£54.50
SP Special rates available
✕ Food available all day £
✕ Lunch £
✕ Dinner £££
Ⓥ Vegetarians welcome
🧍 Children welcome
♿ Facilities for disabled visitors
🚭 No smoking in Garden Restaurant
🚭 Smoking area in Brambles Bistro

Ravioli of Lamlash scallops. Loin of Kilmory lamb, with bread mousse, glazed shallots, turned vegetables glazed with Madeira essence. Iced Drambuie and Heather Honey parfait.

STB ★★★★ Hotel STB ★★★★★ Lodges
💳 Credit cards: Mastercard/Eurocard, American Express, Visa, Switch
🅼 Managing Director: Iain Johnston

BRODICK CASTLE RESTAURANT
The National Trust for Scotland
Brodick, Isle of Arran
KA27 8HY
Tel: 01770 302202
Fax: 01770 302312
E-mail: mrkenthorburn@thenationaltrustforscotland.org.uk
Web: www.the nationaltrustforscotland.org.uk

2 miles north out of Brodick on the Lochranza Road. Follow signs for the castle.

A restaurant using regional recipes and fresh Arran produce.

- Converted old servants hall on ground floor of castle.
- Home cooking and baking.
- "Wonderful home baking and lunch dishes served in the castle."

Visitors wind their way 150 metres from the reception centre and well-stocked shop to the castle which is situated on a plateau overlooking Brodick Bay and surrounded by glorious woodland gardens and terraced lawns. In the castle itself is the restaurant which, during the season, is open all day providing very reasonable priced tasty home cooked meals and light snacks, the ingredients of which are all locally sourced on the island. The mouthwatering display and array of home baking is hard to resist. On a sunny day visitors may also sit outside to eat on the terrace and enjoy magnificent views.

Open 1 Apr to 31 Oct
🍷 Licensed
✕ Food available all day £
✕ Lunch £
Ⓥ Vegetarians welcome
🧍 Children welcome
♿ Facilities for disabled visitors
🚭 No smoking throughout

Country-style soups with home baked bread. Hot smoked Arran salmon pâté with oat fingers. Castle venison pies. Savoury tart of spinach and goats cheese. Traditional puddings both hot and cold.

STB Commended Visitor Attraction
💳 Credit cards: Mastercard/Eurocard, Visa
🅼 Property Manager: Mr Ken Thorburn

CREELERS SEAFOOD RESTAURANT

The Home Farm, Brodick
Isle of Arran KA27 8DD
Tel: 01770 302810
Fax: 01770 302797

From Brodick Pier, go north following coast road towards Brodick Castle and Corrie for 1½ miles. Restaurant on right.

Seafood bistro within Arran Visitors Centre.

- Sophisticated seafood bistro.
- Fish and modern Scottish cooking.
- "Fresh seafood supplied by Creelers own smokery."

Creelers Seafood Restaurant is based in the old bothy of the Brodick Castle Home Farm. Tim and Fran James have established it as an excellent seafood restaurant, where the decor is simple and colourful and the atmosphere has something continental about it. Tim, once a trawlerman on the West Coast, still provides much of the shellfish through his own boat. The rest of the produce is either purchased on the quayside of Kintyre or carefully sourced on the island or the mainland. There is also their own smokery adjacent, with the resulting produce appearing on the menu or for sale. Daily changing menus appear on blackboards, and are extremely good value. Service is friendly and efficient. Chef Stewart Gilchrist is professional and enthusiastic, and the style of his cooking is minimalistic, with flashes of colour and fascinating textures.

Open mid Mar to 31 Oct
Closed Mon except Bank Holidays + during Aug
✗ Lunch except Mon £-££
✗ Dinner except Mon ££
Ⓥ Vegetarians welcome
⚲ Children welcome
⚹ Facilities for disabled visitors

Tart tatin of endive and Parma ham with queen scallops. Scallop and monkfish satay with wilted greens and fondant potato. Chocolate Salzburg with nougat glacé.

⊞ Credit cards: Mastercard/Eurocard, Visa
Ⓜ Proprietors: Tim & Fran James

GLEN CLOY FARM GUEST HOUSE

Glencloy Road, Brodick
Isle of Arran KA27 8DA
Tel: 01770 302351
E-mail: mvpglencloy@compuserve.com
Web: SmoothHound.co.uk/hotels/glencloy.html

On heading out of Brodick, towards Brodick Castle, turn left up the road with the post box on the wall. Follow signs for Glen Cloy – road becomes farm track.

A family-run farm guest house on Arran.

- Old sandstone farmhouse situated in quiet Glen just outside Brodick.
- Traditional and modern cooking.
- "Good cooking in this small guest house."

This is a charming old sandstone building in a little glen on the road to Brodick Castle. The bedrooms have a very homely air about them and two have private facilities. Mark and Vicki Padfield run the house and also do the cooking. They bake their own bread, and the vegetables and herbs come from the garden. The food is traditional fare, locally sourced and carefully prepared and is served in the attractive, homely dining room overlooking the countryside. Coffee is served in the drawing room where one is surrounded by interesting local books, Vicki Padfield's embroideries, family photos, etc. – a most relaxing and enjoyable experience.

Open 1 Mar to 7 Nov
Restaurant closed Sun evening
▥ Rooms: 5, 2 en suite
⊨ DB&B £39.50–£43.50 B&B £22–£27
ⓈⓅ Special rates available
ⓊⓁ Unlicensed – guests welcome to take own wine
✗ Dinner residents only ££
Ⓥ Vegetarians welcome
⚲ Children welcome
⌿ No smoking in dining room

Home-made cauliflower and red pepper soup. Roast leg of Arran lamb with home-made redcurrant jelly. Glen Cloy raspberry trifle.

STB ★★★ Guest House
⊞ Credit cards: Mastercard/Eurocard, Visa, Delta
Ⓜ Proprietors: Mark & Vicki Padfield

HAROLD'S RESTAURANT

Lochranza
Isle of Arran KA27 8HJ
Tel: 01770 830264 Fax: 01770 830364
E-mail: arran.distillers@btinternet.com
Web: www.arranwhisky.com

From Brodick follow signs to Lochranza. Harold's Restaurant is located on the upper floor of the distillery visitor centre.

Modern purpose-built visitor centre and distillery.

- Innovatively designed restaurant alongside distillery with shop and excellent tour.
- Fresh and innovative to suit all tastes.
- "A menu which will surprise and delight."

Arran's delightful distillery set amidst the beautiful scenery on the edge of Lochranza gives one yet another excellent reason for visiting this lovely village with its picturesque postcard views of castle, yachts and golf course. The centre is exceptionally well thought out and imaginatively designed within. Harold's offers a fine quality of dining but with an informality – particularly during the day – to appeal to all tastes and ages. Evening dinner is a candlelit affair with a more formal approach. General Manager Padraig Ahern, having spent some time in the Caribbean, has brought elements of this land to his cooking on Arran with great success, creating some unique yet very appealing dishes alongside the more traditional to tempt all.

Open all year except 10 Jan to 8 Feb
Closed Wed evening
✗ Food available all day except Wed evening £
✗ Lunch £
✗ Dinner except Wed ££
Ⓥ Vegetarians welcome
☆ Children welcome
♿ Facilities for disabled visitors
✗ Smoking area in restaurant

Timbale of lobster and crab suspended in a lobster jelly. Isle of Bute fillet steak with parsnip crisps and grilled spring onions, served with Arran single malt scented jus. Cold lemon soufflé in a brandy snap basket with a citrus sauce.

STB Highly Commended Visitor Attraction
▣ Credit cards: Mastercard/Eurocard, Visa, Switch, Delta, JCB
⋈ General Manager: Padraig Ahern

KILMICHAEL COUNTRY HOUSE HOTEL

Glen Cloy, by Brodick
Isle of Arran KA27 8BY
Tel: 01770 302219 Fax: 01770 302068

From Brodick Pier take road north 1½ miles, then turn inland at golf course following signs about ¾ mile.

Charming country house hotel set in a beautiful glen.

- Historic house with great period character.
- Superb modern cooking.
- "A romantic treat where perfection is the standard, and is consistently achieved."

Kilmichael is believed to be the oldest house on Arran – the present building is late 17th century, but there was an early Christian cell on the site. Described as a 'mansion' in the records, it is in fact an elegant and compact lodge, exquisitely furnished (oriental antiques are a feature) by its present owners, who engagingly describe its attractions in order of importance as "... comfort, tranquillity, books and home-made ice cream." The menus presented in the dining room are very interesting and demonstrate French and Italian influences. A table d'hôte menu of three or five courses is available at dinner. Every dish has something unique and authentic about it, with piquant flavours and delicately spiced sauces. Winner of The Macallan Taste of Scotland Country House Hotel of the Year Award 1998.

Open all year except Christmas week
🛏 Rooms: 9 en suite
🛏 DB&B £70–£95 B&B £45–£70
ⓈⓅ Special rates available
✗ Dinner £££
⋈ Dinner for non-residents – booking essential
Ⓥ Vegetarians welcome
♿ Facilities for disabled visitors
✗ No smoking in dining room + bedrooms

Savoury chocolate ravioli filled with hare and rosemary, served with redcurrant sauce. Fillet of skate with a pimento and coriander salsa and a Chardonnay and saffron butter dressing. Steamed figgy pudding with port and honey, served with proper custard.

▣ Credit cards: Mastercard/Eurocard, Visa, Switch
⋈ Partners: Geoffrey Botterill & Anthony Butterworth

STEPPING STONE RESTAURANT
Balivanich, Benbecula
Western Isles HS7 5DA
Tel: 01870 60 3377
Fax: 01870 60 3121

Drive south from Lochmaddy – heading for Benbecula, take sign for Balivanich – after 2½ miles turn into restaurant, just of the main road.

Modern architecturally designed restaurant offering wholesome Scottish fayre.

- Modern, bright, unique island restaurant.
- Wholesome Scottish.
- "No visit to Benbecula would be complete without seeking out the Stepping Stone Restaurant."

This is a charming cultural magnet for the island of Benbecula, considered as the *stepping stone* in the Western Isles, hence the name. The Stepping Stone is an inspirational restaurant, opened by the MacLean brothers from Uist. It is beautifully decorated in bold colours and samples of eclectic art abound. The windows have half shutters on them with small individual panels of stained glass. Furniture is heavy pine, handcrafted on the island by local craftsmen. The staff are uniformed and provide service to a very high standard. Food is available all day from 10 am–9 pm including a mixture of sandwiches, rolls and baking (all from their own bakery) to more substantial meals. In the evening there is also a table d'hôte menu offering three, four or five course options including a Scottish cheeseboard. Take away food is also available.

Open all year – 7 days a week
✕ Food available all day £££
✕ Lunch ££
✕ Dinner £££
Ⓥ Vegetarians welcome
☩ Children welcome
♿ Facilities for disabled visitors
🚭 No smoking throughout

Pan-fried local cockles in oatmeal. Roast Uist venison with rowanberry jelly. Home-grown strawberries with whisky cream.

💳 Credit cards: Mastercard/Eurocard, Visa, Switch, Delta
Ⓜ Manager: Ewen MacLean

NEW FARM BED & BREAKFAST RESTAURANT
New Farm, Mount Stuart
Isle of Bute PA20 9NA
Tel: 01700 831646
E-mail: newfarm@isleofbute.freeserve.co.uk
Web: www.isle-of-bute.com/newfarm

Turn left on leaving Wemyss Bay to Isle of Bute ferry terminal. Drive 6 miles. Signposted on right 1½ miles past entrance to Mount Stuart House and Gardens.

Whitewashed converted cottage farmhouse on working dairy and sheep farm.

- 200 year old whitewashed farmhouse.
- Enthusiastic, adventurous and talented cooking.
- "A joy of home cooking and fresh, farm produce."

New Farm is set on a 1,000 acre farm on the beautiful Island of Bute. It is the home of Carole and Michael Howard. It features freehand wallpainting by Jessica Herriot which extends to delicate teapots and crockery, but the warmest welcome is from Carole Howard. To stay here and sample Carole's creative cooking and wonderful baking is a joy. Journey through the steadings where the dairy herd supply the milk for cheese; hens for eggs; sheep for lamb; and pigs for home-cured hams. On arrival you are offered home-baked afternoon tea. Guests are invited to pick their own vegetables for dinner. Breakfast is a feast! As Carole says "If we are unable to grow it, make it or rear it we will certainly source it locally from our island, the Isle of Bute." Guests can choose to eat on their own but most people prefer to join the other guests and have an interesting and convivial evening after being welcomed in Gaelic to the table.

Open all year
🛏 Rooms: 7, 5 en suite
🍴 DB&B £39.50–£47   B&B £25–£32.50
🆖 Unlicensed – guests welcome to take own wine
✕ Lunch – reservation essential £
✕ Dinner – reservation essential ££
Ⓥ Vegetarians welcome
♿ Facilities for disabled visitors

Home-made broths served with home-baked bread. Honey glazed New Farm lamb casseroled on a bed of apricots and fresh tarragon. Bournville baked bananas served in a 'puddle' of cream.

STB ★★★★ B&B
💳 No credit cards
Ⓜ Proprietor: Carole Howard

ALLAN COTTAGE GUEST HOUSE

Tarbert
Isle of Harris HS3 3DJ
Tel/Fax: 01859 502146
Web: www.witb.co.uk/links/allancottage.htm

From ferry turn left, then hard first right on to the main village street.

An attractive family-run guest house in Harris' main village.

- A deceptively spacious cottage.
- Carefully prepared food using the best of local produce.
- "Good, substantial home cooking at its best."

This attractive old building has been interestingly converted maintaining many of the original features. It has been extended to form a house of unusual charm; quiet and homely. Rooms are all well-furnished in cottage style and the bedrooms have private facilities. Bill and Evelyn Reed are wonderfully enthusiastic and look after guests with true island hospitality. The dinner menu is discussed with guests in the morning, so that individual preferences can be taken into account. The cooking is interesting and imaginative and of a very high standard; Bill makes use of fresh local produce whenever it can be obtained. A charming establishment.

Open 1 Apr to 30 Sep
- ▥ Rooms: 3 (2 en suite, 1 private facilities)
- ⊯ DB&B £55–£60 B&B £30–£35
- ⑤ᴾ Special rates available
- ✗ Residents only
- ⑪ᴸ Unlicensed
- ✗ Dinner 4 course menu £££
- ⑨ Vegetarians welcome – by prior arrangement
- ⋆ Children over 10 years welcome
- ⇞ No smoking in dining room + bedrooms

Fresh wild Lewis salmon mousse served with green salad with balsamic vinegar dressing and home-made rolls. Suprême of chicken stuffed with local haggis, flambéd in whisky with cream sauce. Apple and raspberry crumble with hazelnut topping.

STB ★★★★ Guest House
- ⊞ No credit cards
- ⋈ Proprietors: Bill & Evelyn Reed

ARDVOURLIE CASTLE

Isle of Harris HS3 3AB
Tel: 01859 50 2307 Fax: 01859 50 2348

¼ mile off A859. 24 miles from Stornoway, 10 miles from Tarbert.

A lovingly restored house run by Derek and Pamela Martin, with four elegant and comfortable bedrooms.

- Recently restored 19th century hunting lodge on the island of Harris.
- Accomplished Scottish cooking.
- "Ardvourlie has such a unique charm and excellent food you will wish to return again and again – and many do just that."

Ardvourlie Castle stands on the shores of Loch Seaforth under the imposing crags of Clisham. The castle is set in a glorious location which offsets its elegant architecture. Derek and Pamela Martin are gracious hosts who provide all home comforts - what more could one ask for! They have restored the place magnificently, with sensitivity and outstandingly good taste. The castle is furnished in keeping with its period. The dining room offers views over the garden to the wilderness beyond and it uses designs and furniture from the Victorian and Art Nouveau periods. Here you will encounter the Martins' fine cooking, which comprises dishes to suit all tastes using as much local produce as is available on this remote island. Much of the raw materials that are unavailable locally are very carefully sourced on the mainland. Shortlisted and Commended for The Macallan Taste of Scotland Awards 1999.

Open 1 Apr to 31 Oct
- ▥ Rooms: 3 with private facilities (occasionally 4)
- ⊯ DB&B £80–£110   B&B £55–£85
- ✗ Residents only
- ❢ Restricted licence
- ✗ Dinner 4 course menu £££
- ⑨ Vegetarians welcome – advance notice essential
- ⋆ Children old enough to dine with their parents welcome
- ⇞ No smoking in dining room

Grilled, sugared segments of fresh grapefruit. Half roast duckling basted with honey, served with spiced preserved plums, creamed potatoes baked with a crispy topping, and peas. Tipsy Laird.

STB ★★★★★ Guest House
- ⊞ No credit cards
- ⋈ Owner: D G Martin

LEACHIN HOUSE

Tarbert
Isle of Harris
HS3 3AH
Tel/Fax: 01859 502157
E-mail: leachin.house@virgin.net

1 mile from Tarbert on A859 to Stornoway, sign-posted at gate.

Charming Victorian house of local interest.

- Substantial lochside Victorian house.
- Modern Scottish cooking.
- "It is difficult to emphasise what is best about Leachin – the food, the ambience or the lovely old house with its superb outlook. All of these combine to make eating here a most enjoyable experience."

Linda and Diarmuid Evelyn Wood have turned Leachin House (which means house among the rocks) into a most attractive and welcoming guest house, without losing any of the charms and gracious proportions of this lovely Victorian building. Dining at Leachin is a most enjoyable experience. The views across the loch are breath-taking and the dining room itself is fascinating with its French hand-painted wallpaper (over 100 years old). The skill and care with which Linda cooks and presents the food is worth a journey to Harris just to eat there! The wonderful produce of the islands, particularly lamb and seafood, feature regularly on the fixed menu and each course illustrates a well-judged mix of both simple and complex food preparation. French spoken.

Open all year except Christmas + New Year
- 🏠 Rooms: 3 (1 en suite, 1 with private facilities)
- 🛏 DB&B £70   B&B £43
- SP Special rates available
- ✗ Residents only
- UL Unlicensed
- ✗ Dinner £££
- 木 Children over 10 years welcome
- ⚊ No smoking in dining room or bedrooms

Smoked wild venison with asparagus salad. Fillet of halibut in a lobster and prawn sauce. Ecclefechan tart with whisky and heather honey ice cream.

STB ★★★★ Guest House
- 🆔 Credit cards: Mastercard/Eurocard, Visa, Delta
- 🅜 Owners: Linda & Diarmuid Evelyn Wood

SCARISTA HOUSE

Isle of Harris HS3 3HX
Tel: 01859 550 238   Fax: 01859 550 277
E-mail: ian@scaristahouse.demon.co.uk
Web: www.scaristahouse.demon.co.uk

On A859, 15 miles south-west of Tarbert (Western Isles).

Distinctive country guest house in a peaceful island location by the sea.

- Converted Georgian manse with magnificent views.
- Creative cooking using the finest ingredients.
- "Delightful fare in marvellous location, with warm hospitality."

Scarista House overlooks a three mile long shell sand beach on the dramatic Atlantic coast of Harris. All bedrooms have excellent views over the walled gardens out to sea, most in a single-storey annexe. This makes for an ever-changing panorama of scenery and atmosphere. There is an extensive library and a tranquil drawing room, both of which have open fires. There is no television or radio. The hotel's dining room has featured in many guides worldwide and is known particularly for its superb fish and shellfish, fresh vegetables and herbs from the garden together with fresh eggs from the hotel's hens and the best of home-made bread. The set menu changes daily – guests are consulted about dietary requirements in advance – and there is a very decent wine list chosen to complement the dishes on offer.

Open May to Sep
- 🏠 Rooms: 5 en suite
- 🛏 DB&B £88–£106   B&B £58–£73
- ✗ Residents licence
- ✗ Dinner £££
- V Vegetarians welcome
- 木 Children over eight years welcome
- ⚊ No smoking in main house, dining room + sitting rooms

Mussel and leek soup with cream and saffron. Ragoût of turbot, lobster and scallops, duchess potatoes with lovage, and herb garden salad. Praline ice with raspberries and vanilla biscuits.

STB ★★★★ Guest House
- 🆔 Credit cards: Mastercard/Eurocard, Visa
- 🅜 Proprietors: Ian & Jane Callaghan

THE CROFT KITCHEN

Port Charlotte
Isle of Islay
Argyll PA49 7UN
Tel: 01496 850230
E-mail: douglas@croft kitchen.demon.co.uk

On the main road into Port Charlotte opposite the Museum of Islay Life.

Informal restaurant and tea-room for all the family.

• Informal self-styled village restaurant.
• Modern Scottish plus home baking.
• "Sample the best of Islay produce and good home baking."

The Croft Kitchen is situated on the shore of Loch Indaal, next to a safe sandy beach, with views of the Paps of Jura. The daytime menu offers home baking, home-made soups, snacks and a good range of daily specials chosen from a blackboard at very reasonable prices. You will also find seafood freshly caught and simply yet skilfully prepared. There is a separate menu for dinner in the evening, which makes much of local produce. A friendly, informal place where the whole family is made welcome.

Open mid Mar to mid Oct
Note: Closed 2nd Thu in Aug (Islay Show Day)
🍷 Licensed
✕ Food available all day £
✕ Lunch £
✕ Dinner ££
Ⓥ Vegetarians welcome
🜨 Children welcome
🚭 No smoking in restaurant

Fresh steamed mussels with garlic mayonnaise. Haunch of Islay venison with home-made rowan jelly. Raspberry and Bowmore malt whisky cranachan.

⊞ Credit cards: Mastercard/Eurocard, Visa
🅽 Joint Proprietors: Joy & Douglas Law

GLENMACHRIE

Port Ellen, Isle of Islay
Argyll PA42 7AW
Tel/Fax: 01496 30 2560
E-mail: glenmachrie@isle-of-islay.com
Web: www.isle-of-islay.com/group.guest/glenmachrie

Midway on A846 between Port Ellen and Bowmore.

Relaxing and comfortable farmhouse with excellent guest care.

• Carefully modernised farmhouse set in a lovely garden.
• The best of home cooking.
• "A gastronomic delight aimed to satisfy the largest appetites."

Relax in the atmosphere of this family-run working farmhouse. No effort is spared by proprietor, Rachel Whyte, to meet the slightest whim of the guests. Information is abundant on how to make the most of a holiday on this beautiful island. Rachel and her family are most attentive hosts. In addition to the splendid home cooking the accommodation is luxurious with supplies of everything the traveller may have left at home – from a toothbrush to a comb. Menus include Islay beef and lamb and the home baking is to die for!

Open all year
🛏 Rooms: 5 en suite (2 twin, 3 double)
🛏 DB&B from £48   B&B from £28
✕ Residents only
Ⓤ Unlicensed – guests welcome to take own wine
✕ Dinner ££
🜨 Children over five years welcome
♿ Facilities for disabled visitors (ground floor bedroom)
🚭 No smoking throughout

Smoked trout served with horseradish cream beside mixed salad leaves. Islay beef carbonade with nettle and hedgerow dumplings. Warm treacle tart with vanilla sauce.

STB ★★★★ Guest House
Green Tourism 🍃🍃🍃 GOLD Award
⊞ No credit cards
🅽 Proprietor: Rachel Whyte

KILMENY COUNTRY GUEST HOUSE
Ballygrant, Isle of Islay
Argyll PA45 7QW
Tel/Fax: 01496 840 668
Web: www.isle-of-islay.com/group/guest/kilmeny

½ mile south of Ballygrant village – look for sign at road end, ¾ mile up private road.

Charming stone-built farmhouse with panoramic views.

- Delightful country home set in beautiful countryside.
- Unpretentious top quality cuisine.
- "Fine island views and sensational food."

Kilmeny farm and country guest house enjoys an elevated position on their 300 acre beef farm which is within easy reach of Port Askaig. Margaret and Blair Rozga have been running their carefully restored country house for over 20 years and enjoy a loyal following of guests from all over the world. This is a haven of peace and, quiet and tranquillity despite being on a fully operational farm. The bedrooms and public rooms are very elegantly decorated, with many fine antiques and luxurious furnishings. Margaret is a highly accomplished cook and uses only the finest produce all of which is locally sourced, to its best advantage creating mouthwatering dishes. Her menus are well-planned and imaginative requiring a great deal of skill and careful organisation – all of which she accomplishes single-handedly to great effect.

Open all year except Christmas + New Year
🏠 Rooms: 3 en suite
🛏 DB&B £58   B&B £35
SP Special rates available
✗ Residents only
UL Unlicensed – guests welcome to take own wine
✗ Dinner except Sun ££
V Vegetarians welcome
🕆 Children welcome
🚭 No smoking throughout

Tobermory smoked trout and avocado terrine. Cream of onion soup with Islay cheese. Roast loin of Islay lamb with a bramble and rosemary sauce, served with pureed parsnips. Apple and almond tart with crème fraîche and cinnamon ice cream.

STB ★★★★★ Guest House
💳 No credit cards
👤 Proprietor: Margaret Rozga

HANDA
18 Keose Glebe (Ceos), Lochs
Isle of Lewis HS2 9JX
Tel: 01851 830 334

1½ miles off A859, 12 miles south of Stornoway, 25 miles north of Tarbert, Harris: last house in village of Ceos among the lochs of eastern Lewis.

A hilltop house on the Hebridean island of Lewis; a small family-run bed and breakfast which provides comfortable accommodation and good food.

- This is a lovely home, furnished in pine with all modern facilities.
- Accomplished home cooking.
- "Breathtaking views from every window and the warmth of Christine's hospitality and home cooking make for a wonderful stay."

This is the last house in the Hebridean haven of Keose village. It is idyllically appointed on top of a hill overlooking a private loch and ideally positioned for exploring the island and nearby Harris. Stepping from the house itself you can follow a range of pursuits from bird-watching to hill-walking and (if you are fortunate) otter sighting. The loch provides brown trout fishing for guests. The owner, Christine Morrison, winner of The Macallan Personality of the Year Award 1995, runs the guest house with genuine island hospitality. Alongside traditional recipes, she does all of her own baking and uses the best of local seafood and fresh produce from her garden.

Open 4 May to 5 Oct
🏠 Rooms: 3, 1 en suite
🛏 DB&B £35–£40   B&B £18–£23
✗ Residents only
UL Unlicensed – guests welcome to take own wine
✗ Dinner ££
🚭 No smoking throughout

Avocado, melon and tomato in mint dressing served with garlic bread. Loch Erisort scallops flambéd, served with baby courgettes, tossed in wholegrain mustard. Meringues in 'deadly' chocolate.

STB ★★★★ B&B
💳 No credit cards
👤 Owners: Murdo & Christine Morrison

THE PARK GUEST HOUSE
& RESTAURANT
30 James Street, Stornoway
Isle of Lewis, Western Isles HS1 2QN
Tel: 01851 702485
Fax: 01851 703482

500 yards from ferry terminal. At junction of
Matheson Road, James Street and A866 to
airport and Eye peninsula.

A traditional family-run guest house in the centre of town.

- A stone-built Victorian guest house.
- Modern Scottish cooking with a continental influence.
- "A visit to this restaurant is a must when in Stornoway, Roddy Afrin uses Hebridean produce with flair and imagination."

A substantial stone-built B Listed building dating from the 1880s, standing in the centre of Stornoway. This house has a homely atmosphere and Roddy and Catherine Afrin are friendly hosts. Catherine was trained in interior design at the Glasgow School of Art, and the house has benefited from her skill and good taste. Note the original Glasgow-style fireplace in the dining room. Roddy was formerly head chef on an oil rig in the North Sea. His robust à la carte menus use fresh fish from Stornoway and the West Coast fishing boats, and local lamb and venison. Each dish is cooked to order.

Open all year except 24 Dec to 5 Jan
Note: Restaurant closed Sun Mon
🏠 Rooms: 8, 3 en suite
🛏 DB&B £38.50–£54   B&B £24–£29
🍴 Packed lunches available £
✕ Dinner – residents only ££-£££
✕ Dinner (Restaurant) Tue to Sat £££
Ⅴ Vegetarians welcome
大 Children welcome
♿ Facilities for non-residential disabled visitors

Millefeuille of Stornoway black pudding and sweet potato, balsamic dressing. Fillet of halibut with herb crust, served on risotto bed. Apple ice cream on a choux pastry ring, butterscotch sauce.

STB ★★★ Guest House
💳 Credit cards: Mastercard/Eurocard, Visa, Delta
👤 Proprietor: Catherine Afrin
Chef/Proprietor: Roddy Afrin

ARDFENAIG HOUSE
by Bunessan, Isle of Mull
Argyll PA67 6DX
Tel/Fax: 01681 700210
E-mail: davidson@ardfenaig.demon.co.uk

2 miles west of Bunessan on A849, turn right on
private road to Ardfenaig House, ½ mile.

A lovely old country house hotel surrounded by woodland, sea and moorland on the Isle of Mull.

- Originally an estate factor's house, then shooting lodge, in a glorious position on the shores of Loch Caol on the Ross of Mull.
- Assured country house cooking.
- "Stylish elegant dining with comfortable, peaceful rooms and a great breakfast!"

Ardfenaig House stands in the southwest corner of Mull midway between Bunessan and Fionnphort, where hospitable and welcoming hosts look after you charmingly. It has five en suite bedrooms and the Coach House, by a small burn 50 yards away, provides additional self-catering accommodation for four to six people. In front of the house is a small jetty. The drawing room has magnificent views over Loch Caol with a conservatory dining room which can easily accommodate all residents and non-residents if necessary. The excellent food is freshly prepared in the kitchen from fresh local produce and is beautifully presented. Menus are short but imaginative and the wine list is rather special.

Open 1 Apr to 31 Oct
🏠 Rooms: 5 en suite
🛏 DB&B £76–£90
🍷 Restricted licence
✕ Dinner 4 course menu £££
Ⅴ Vegetarians welcome
🚭 No smoking in dining room + bedrooms

Smoked wild venison with cranberry sauce. Fillet of Scottish salmon with lemon butter sauce. Iced Grand Marnier nougat with an apricot coulis.

STB ★★★★ Hotel
💳 Credit cards: Mastercard/Eurocard, Visa
👤 Owners: Malcolm & Jane Davidson

ASSAPOL HOUSE HOTEL
Bunessan, Isle of Mull
Argyll PA67 6DW
Tel: 01681 700 258 Fax: 01681 700 445
E-mail: alex@assapolhouse.demon.co.uk
Web: www.assapolhouse.demon.co.uk

From Craignure – A849 towards Fionnphort. When approaching Bunessan, pass village school on the right, take first road on left signed Assapol House Hotel.

A delightful, spacious old house in a sheltered corner of Mull.

- Small country house hotel.
- Stylish country cooking.
- "A real Scottish cheese experience at Assapol accompanied by an excellent wine list."

The feature that immediately impresses the visitor to Assapol is the care and attention to detail that your hosts, the Robertson family, manifest in every department: fresh flowers in the bedrooms, beds turned down, sewing kits supplied, etc. Assapol House Hotel, itself a former manse, is over 200 years old and overlooks the loch of the same name, with the Burg Peninsula, the Treshnish Isles and Staffa beyond. Wildlife, secluded beaches and historical sites abound in this delightful corner of Mull. The dinner menu offers a choice of starters and puddings and a set main course. The food is locally sourced and features local delicacies; it is sensitively cooked and imaginatively presented; and is extremely good value. Assapol House Hotel has 1 AA Rosette.

Open Apr to Oct
🏨 Rooms: 5, 4 en suite
🛏 DB&B £56–£70
SP Special rates available
✗ Residents only
🍷 Restricted hotel licence
✗ Dinner ££
Ⓥ Vegetarians welcome – by prior arrangement
👶 Children over 10 years welcome
🚭 No smoking throughout

Smoked trout and salmon terrine with dill mayonnaise. Saddle of venison with rösti potatoes, roast vegetables and a juniper jus. Blackcurrant, apple and Calvados crumble tart.

STB ★★★★ Hotel
💳 Credit cards: Mastercard/Eurocard, Visa, Switch, Delta
👤 Partners: Onny, Thomas & Alex Robertson

CALGARY FARMHOUSE HOTEL
Calgary, nr Dervaig
Isle of Mull, Argyll PA75 6QW
Tel/Fax: 01688 400256
E-mail: calgaryfarmhouse@virgin.net
Web: calgary.co.uk

About 4½ miles from Dervaig on B8073, just up the hill from Calgary beach.

Converted farmhouse hotel with restaurant and separate tea-room and gallery.

- Converted farm steadings.
- Modern Scottish cooking.
- "Friendly and homely atmosphere with great family accommodation and wholesome fare."

Calgary Farmhouse is just up the hill from the beautiful white sands of Calgary Beach. The farm buildings and courtyard have been sensitively converted by Julia and Matthew Reade into nine bedrooms and two public rooms. Exposed stonework, wooden furniture and wood-burning stoves all contribute to a warm and cosy environment. The Dovecote Restaurant offers an à la carte menu which changes four times a week according to the seasonal produce available. The accent is on skilful home cooking in an informal atmosphere while the family's fishing connections ensure a wonderful supply of Mull's bountiful catches. There is also a tea-room, The Carthouse Gallery, charmingly converted and open throughout the day for light lunches and home baking. A changing exhibition of pictures by local artists is displayed here, many of them for sale.

Open Apr to Oct incl
🏨 Rooms: 9 en suite
🛏 DB&B £47.50–£51   B&B £31.50–£35
✗ Lunch £
✗ Dinner ££
Ⓥ Vegetarians welcome
👶 Children welcome
🚭 Smoking discouraged whilst others are eating

Tartlet of Mull smoked mussels with a horseradish cream. Roast Guinea fowl with Puy lentils and a rich Madeira sauce. Dark chocolate and caramel délice.

STB ★★★ Hotel
💳 Credit cards: Mastercard/Eurocard, Visa, Switch
👤 Proprietors: Matthew & Julia Reade

DRUIMARD COUNTRY HOUSE
Dervaig, Isle of Mull
Argyllshire PA75 6QW
Tel: 01688 400345/400291 Fax: 01688 400345
Web: www.smoothhound.co.uk/hotels/
druimard.html.

Situated adjacent to Mull Little Theatre, well
signposted from Dervaig village.

**Restored Victorian manse overlooking River and
Glen Bellart.**

- Victorian manse on outskirts of attractive village.
- Impressive and competent Scottish cuisine.
- "Wendy's vitality and enthusiasm are reflected in
  her charming country home and outstanding
  dinners."

Druimard is just on the outskirts of the pretty
village of Dervaig, eight miles from Tobermory. The
old house has been beautifully restored by Haydn
and Wendy Hubbard, who run their hotel with the
standards of comfort one would expect from a
country house: service is professional, the en suite
bedrooms are very comfortable, the restaurant has
a strong reputation, and has been recognised by the
award of 2 AA Rosettes. The table d'hôte menu has
moved with the current eating trends towards a
large choice of fish which is locally caught and
meat which is traditionally reared. The cooking is
assured, fresh and imaginative with unusual sauces
and everything is prepared to order.

Open end Mar to end Oct
- ♨ Rooms: 7 en suite
- ⊨ DB&B £60–£74
- SP Special rates available
- ♥ Restaurant licence only
- ✗ Lunch – residents only £
- ✗ Dinner – non-residents welcome £££
- Ⓥ Vegetarians welcome
- ⚘ Children welcome
- ✗ No smoking in restaurant

**Gâteau of charred aubergine, sea trout and goats
cheese with balsamic syrup and herb oil. Pan-
seared sea bass with fennel purée, fennel confit,
spiced lentils and a bouillabaisse sauce.
Chocolate crème fraîche torte with raspberry and
vanilla sauce.**

STB ★★★★ Hotel
- ⊟ Credit cards: Mastercard/Eurocard, Visa
- ⋈ Partners: Mr & Mrs H R Hubbard

DRUIMNACROISH HOTEL
Dervaig, Isle of Mull
Argyll PA75 6QW
Tel/ Fax: 01688 400274
E-mail: taste@druimnacroish.co.uk
Web: www.druimnacroish.co.uk

Leaving ferry turn right to Tobermory. 1 mile after
Salen take the left turning to Dervaig.
Druimnacroish is 9 miles along road on left.

**Converted 17th century settlement and water mill in
a delightfully tranquil setting.**

- Converted 17th century buildings.
- Good quality Scottish cuisine.
- "A welcoming, friendly hotel with young
  enthusiastic hosts with skilled and assured
  cooking."

Druimnacroish is a secluded water mill situated on
a hillside one and a half miles from the village of
Dervaig. It has recently re-opened after
refurbishment by its current owners who have
worked to restore interesting features into a
comfortable country house hotel. The hosts are
welcoming and Neil's cooking is skilled and assured
and definitely something to look forward to after a
day exploring Mull. Games and 'wellies' are
provided for guests who wish to stroll in the
delightful gardens which lead down to the Glen.

Open all year
- ♨ Rooms: 6 en suite
- ⊨ DB&B £58–£70   B&B £42–£49
- SP Special rates available
- ✗ Lunch (in winter by arrangement) £
- ✗ Dinner ££
- Ⓥ Vegetarians welcome
- ✗ No smoking in dining room
- ⋔ Dogs by arrangement

**Hot mousse of Tobermory smoked trout. Wild
mushroom gougere. Drambuie and orange parfait.**

STB ★★★ Hotel
- ⊟ Credit cards: Mastercard/Eurocard, American
  Express, Visa, Delta
- ⋈ Owners: Neil Hutton & Margriet van de Pol

HIGHLAND COTTAGE

Breadalbane Street, Tobermory
Isle of Mull, Argyll PA75 6PD
Tel: 01688 302030
Fax: 01688 302727

On approaching Tobermory at the roundabout, carry on straight across narrow stone bridge and immediately turn right (signposted Tobermory-Breadalbane Street). Follow road round until it opens out. Highland Cottage is the cream-painted building on the right, opposite the Fire Station.

Cottage with wonderful views over Tobermory.

- Small main street converted cottage.
- Skilled use of modern culinary trends.
- "A real home-from-home with wonderful food – beware portions are not for the faint-hearted!"

Highland Cottage is a delightful hotel with bedrooms named after Scottish islands. Each room is individually characterised, with antique beds being a major feature. Josephine Currie, chef/owner, is a talented cook and her presentation is very professional. Her husband Dave is an attentive host and likes his guests to feel totally relaxed. His desire is that guests treat the hotel as a home-from-home where they can 'kick off their shoes' and enjoy themselves. The spacious dining room with traditional furniture is extremely popular with locals. The quality of produce here is excellent. Highland Cottage has 1 AA Rosette.

Open all year
🏦 Rooms: 6 en suite
🛏 DB&B £49.90–£62.50 B&B £29.50–£53
SP Special rates available
✕ Food available all day (residents only) £££
✕ Snack/Light Lunch (residents only)
✕ Dinner £££
Ⓥ Vegetarians welcome
ⴕ Children welcome
♿ Facilities for disabled visitors
Ⰶ No smoking in dining room
ⵏ Dogs welcome

Tobermory smoked salmon and trout roulade with mixed leaves and dill dressing. Pan-fried collops of venison with a redcurrant and lemon sauce served with skirlie mash. Brown sugar meringues with crushed raspberries and crème anglaise.

STB ★★★★ Hotel
💳 Credit cards: Mastercard/Eurocard, Visa, Switch, Delta
🍴 Chef/Owner: Josephine Currie

KILLIECHRONAN HOUSE

Aros, Isle of Mull
Argyll PA72 6JU
Tel: 01680 300403
Fax: 01680 300463

Leaving ferry turn right to Tobermory A849. At Salen turn left to B8035. After 2 miles turn right to Ulva ferry B8073. Killiechronan House on right after 300 metres.

Former lodge set in over 5,000 acres of beautiful island countryside.

- Small Victorian country house hotel.
- Accomplished gourmet cooking.
- "Elegant and impeccable dining style here, accompanied by a fine choice of menu."

Killiechronan is the lodge house of its own 5,000 acre estate. Charming bedrooms offer comfort and style in a peaceful setting, while the dining room and two distinctively furnished lounges are a quiet haven to relax and enjoy. The house has a happy and relaxed atmosphere, reflected by the staff under the professional eye of Donna McCann. The food here is excellent, deserving its 1 AA Rosette. Customers' every needs are well-catered for with menus made available early afternoon so that any dietary requirements can be met. Ideal for a relaxed holiday in a wonderful setting. *See advert page 256.*

Open 4 Mar to 31 Oct
🏦 Rooms: 6 en suite
🛏 DB&B £59–£85
SP Special rates available
Ⴘ Residents licence
✕ Lunch Sun only ££
✕ Dinner £££
Ⓥ Vegetarians welcome
Ⰶ No smoking in dining room + bedrooms

Ceviche of scallops. Loin of Mull venison with Caboc and cranberries. Honey and praline parfait with blueberries and Ledaig whisky.

STB ★★★★ Hotel
💳 Credit cards: Mastercard/Eurocard, American Express, Visa, Switch, Delta
🍴 Manageress: Donna McCann

THE OLD BYRE HERITAGE CENTRE
Dervaig
Isle of Mull PA75 6QR
Tel: 01688 400229

1½ miles from Dervaig. Take Calgary road for
¾ mile, turn left along Torloisk road for ¼ mile,
then left down private road following signs.

Tea-room within an interesting heritage complex.

- Converted barn.
- Home cooking and baking.
- "A lovely little laid-back spot where you can
  enjoy some real clootie dumpling and the history
  of Mull."

A remotely situated, picturesque old cattle byre in
Glen Bellart (near Dervaig) has been restored and
converted into a heritage centre which explores the
traditions and natural history of the Isle of Mull,
from the first settlers to the present day. There are
audio-visual displays and exhibits as well as a gift
shop with souvenirs and crafts for sale. The
licensed tea-room offers a range of light meals,
home baking and daily specials, using fresh Mull
produce. Vegetarians are well catered for, and
meals can be organised for groups by prior
arrangement. At the Old Byre orders are placed at
the counter, but the food is served at the table for
the customer.

Open 5 Apr to 30 Oct
✖   Light meals served throughout day £
❢   Licensed
Ⓥ   Vegetarians welcome
🕈   Children welcome

**Home-made crofter's soup. Tobermory trout with
salad and warm roll. Clootie dumpling served
warm with cream.**

STB Commended Visitor Attraction
Ⓔ   No credit cards
🖩   Joint Owners: Ursula & Michael Bradley

THE WESTERN ISLES HOTEL
Tobermory
Isle of Mull PA75 6PR
Tel: 01688 302012   Fax: 01688 302297
E-mail: wihotel@aol.com

Leaving Tobermory seafront on the Dervaig Road
take a sharp right and turn halfway up the hillside.

**Splendid example of Victorian architecture in
historic fishing community.**

- Majestic building overlooking harbour.
- Scottish cooking with continental flair.
- "A grand hotel with interesting objet d'art,
  offering guests total freedom and relaxation in a
  magnificent setting."

The Western Isles Hotel occupies one of the finest
positions in the Western Isles set above the village
of Tobermory. There is a choice of two places in
which to eat here – the dining room and the sunny
conservatory which is very well set out with
panoramic views and is popular with guests and
visitors to the island who drop in for lunch or even
coffee. The bar lunch menu is extensive with a very
wide choice, from soup of the day and filled
sandwiches to a full three or four course meal of hot
and cold dishes and salads. The dinner menu offers
four courses on a table d'hôte menu of good,
traditional Scottish cooking accompanied by a
reasonably priced wine list. *See advert page 265.*

Open all year except 14 to 28 Dec
🛏   Rooms: 25 en suite
🛏   DB&B £60–£110   B&B £38–£87
ⓈⓅ   Special rates available
✖   Lunch £
✖   Dinner £££
Ⓥ   Vegetarians welcome
🕈   Children welcome
🚭   No smoking in dining room

**Tobermory smoked whisky salmon on various
leaves with lemon and dill vinaigrette. Pan-fried
venison slices with local wild mushroom and
Honey Cream sauce. Crème brûlée served with fine
shortbread biscuits.**

STB ★★★★ Hotel
Ⓔ   Credit cards: Mastercard/Eurocard, American
     Express, Visa, Switch
🖩   Proprietors: Sue & Michael Fink

LANGASS LODGE
Locheport, Isle of North Uist
The Western Isles HS6 5HA
Tel: 01876 580285 Fax: 01876 580385
E-mail: langass@aol.com
Web: Western Isles Tourist Board Web Site

Take the B867 south from Lochmaddy for 10 miles. The hotel is clearly signposted from the main road.

Former estate shooting lodge.

- A small and comfortable country house hotel.
- Modern Scottish.
- "Seriously good seafood dishes at affordable prices."

Langass Lodge has been converted from a traditional estate shooting lodge to a small country house hotel and makes a delightful retreat for visitors. The fishing in the area is renowned, naturalists can enjoy the wildlife, and a short walk from the lodge will take one to a neolithic site complete with standing stones and burial chamber. Chef John Buchanan's daily changing menu features mainly fish dishes and the understated 'selection of seafood' is a memorable experience. The Year 2000 will see the addition of a conservatory overlooking the loch.

    Open all year except Christmas Day
🏠 Rooms: 6 en suite
🛏 DB&B £54–£70 B&B £36–£60
✗ Food available all day ££
✗ Lunch ££
✗ Dinner £££
Ⓥ Vegetarians welcome
🛧 Children welcome
👍 Facilities for disabled visitors
🐾 Dogs welcome

Char-grilled monkfish with coconut and ginger dressing. Poached fillet of turbot hollandaise. Deep-fried strawberries in filo pastry.

STB ★★★ Hotel
💳 Credit cards: Mastercard/Eurocard, Visa
👤 Manager: Niall Leveson-Gower

CLEATON HOUSE HOTEL
Cleaton, Westray
Orkney KW17 2DB
Tel: 01857 677508 Fax: 01857 677442
E-mail: cleaton@orkney.com
Web: www.orknet.co.uk/cleaton

Signposted 5 miles from Rapness (Westray) Ferry terminal on road to Pierowall Village.

A friendly, family-run hotel on the Island of Westray.

- Victorian manse of distinctive 'ink bottle' design.
- Modern Scottish cuisine using high quality Orcadian produce.
- "Cleaton is a must for all visitors to Westray."

A regular roll-on, roll-off ferry service connects Westray to Kirkwall, and Cleaton's owner, Malcolm Stout, is happy to meet you at the pier. Such personal concern for guests is manifested in every aspect of this delightful small hotel – no wonder guests return again and again. Chef Lorna Reid combines her many years working in 'top class' kitchens, with outstanding local ingredients, to produce quality cuisine, and the meal is further enhanced with a choice from Malcolm's carefully selected wine list. When in season, herbs, vegetables and salad leaves all come from the hotel's large walled vegetable garden. The food here is a testament to all Orkney's excellent produce.

    Open all year except New Year's Day
🏠 Rooms: 6 en suite
🛏 DB&B £47–£56 B&B £32–£36
[SP] Special rates available
✗ Lunch £
✗ Dinner ££
Ⓥ Vegetarians welcome
🛧 Children welcome
👍 Facilities for disabled visitors
🚭 No smoking in dining room

Orkney farm cheese soufflé, leaf salad and creamy orange dressing. Loin of 'Aikerness Holm' lamb (100% seaweed eating) presented on parsnip crumble, red wine sauce, flavoured with mint and redcurrant. Brandy snap biscuit filled with home-made parfaits and fresh fruit.

STB ★★★★ Hotel
💳 Credit cards: Mastercard/Eurocard, Visa, Delta
👤 Proprietor: Malcolm Stout

CREEL RESTAURANT & ROOMS

Front Road, St Margaret's Hope, Orkney KW17 2SL
Tel: 01856 831 311
E-mail: alan@thecreel.freeserve.co.uk
Web: www.orknet-services

Take A961 south across the Churchill Barriers into St Margaret's Hope. 14 miles from Kirkwall.

Alan and Joyce's commitment goes from strength to strength.

- Historic seafront house stark, freshly painted and gabled, overlooking St Margaret's Hope.
- Innovative modern cooking with strong influences of traditional Orcadian recipes.
- "Alan's continued recognition is justly deserved and speaks for itself."

The clean white walls of the Creel shine out on the quayside; a small, family-run restaurant with an international reputation. This year considerable and extensive alterations and refurbishments have been carried out. Chef/owner Alan Craigie, winner of The Macallan Personality of the Year Award 1997, presents a short menu which changes daily according to the availability of local produce and features Orcadian specialities. He cooks with great skill, respecting textures and flavours, creating original and unusual sauces, and spectacular desserts. The Creel has become a place of pilgrimage for gourmets, but its cheerful understated ambience has not changed, nor its incredibly reasonable prices. The Creel has 2 AA Rosettes.

Open weekends Oct to Mar except Jan: daily Apr to Sep – advisable to book, especially in low season
Closed Christmas Day + Boxing Day, Jan + 2 weeks Oct
🏨 Rooms: 3 en suite
🛏 B&B £30–£35
✕ Dinner £££
Ⓥ Vegetarians welcome
🕯 Children 5 years and over welcome
⤝ No smoking in restaurant
🐂 Member of the Scotch Beef Club

Crab and wolf-fish soup: a rich crab soup with chunks of wolf-fish. Orcadian fish stew: halibut, scallops and salmon served on a root vegetable, tomato and basil stew. Rhubarb and lemon tart with apple crumble ice cream.

STB ★★★ Restaurant with Rooms
Ⓔ Credit cards: Mastercard/Eurocard, Visa
Ⅺ Owners: Joyce & Alan Craigie

FOVERAN HOTEL AND RESTAURANT

St Ola, Kirkwall
Orkney KW15 1SF
Tel: 01856 872389
Fax: 01856 876430

From Kirkwall take the A964 Orphir Road, 2½ miles from Kirkwall on left, off the main road.

Modern hotel with excellent hospitality.

- Small modern hotel.
- Modern Scottish with Orcadian influence.
- "A delightful small hotel with outstanding views across the Scapa Flow."

Lorraine Moodie and her team already established themselves firmly at Foveran having taken over from previous long standing owners late in 1998. The enthusiasm of the owner and staff is evident to customers who can enjoy a real Orcadian experience in comfortable surroundings. The cooking here is skilled and makes the very best use of some of Orkney's exceptional quality produce all freshly prepared to order. The Foveran will surely go from strength to strength under this enthusiastic new owner.

Open mid Feb to Dec
🏨 Rooms: 8 en suite
🛏 B&B £35–£45
ⓈⓅ Special rates available
✕ Food available all day on request only £
✕ Lunch on request
✕ Dinner £££
Ⓥ Vegetarians welcome
🕯 Children welcome
♿ Facilities for disabled visitors – ground floor restaurant
⤝ Smoking in lounge only
🐕 Dogs by arrangement

Peedie pots of Orkney cheese: red/white Swanney cheese soufflé. Orkney sirloin steak stuffed with haggis and served with Highland Park sauce. Foveran Fog: the chef's own blend of meringue, summer fruits, cream and laced with crème de cassis.

STB ★★★ Hotel
Ⓔ Credit cards: Mastercard/Eurocard, Visa, Switch, Delta
Ⅺ Owner: Lorraine Moodie

WOODWICK HOUSE
Evie
Orkney
KW17 2PQ
Tel: 01856 751 330
Fax: 01856 751 383

From the A965 turn off to Evie. After 15 minutes, drive c. 7 miles turn right at sign to Woodwick House. Turn first left, pass by farm on left and continue to the burn and trees ahead. Go over small bridge.

Wonderful food in welcome surroundings.

- Country house hotel.
- Orcadian produce imaginatively prepared.
- "A warm welcome and good food awaits you here."

Woodwick House is situated on the west mainland of Orkney, just 20 minutes from both main towns of Kirkwall and Stromness. Built in 1912 it is an attractive country house with delightful views, sitting in 12 acres of woodland with a burn which runs down to the bay. The style of the house is tasteful and effective with the commitment to Orkney hospitality evident throughout. The cooking is very good with interesting, well-balanced menus extremely well-presented. There is an obvious commitment to the use of local produce. This is an excellent place from which to explore the island and those looking for that little bit more should ask for the programme on cultural events.

Open all year
- 🏠 Rooms: 7, 4 en suite
- 🛏 DB&B £40–£67   B&B £25–£40
- SP Special rates available
- ✕ Lunch £
- ✕ Dinner ££-£££
- Ⅴ Vegetarians welcome
- ☇ Children welcome
- ♿ Facilities for disabled visitors
- ✍ No smoking in dining room

Fresh Orkney oysters served with lemon and home-baked herb soda bread. Seared local king scallops with thinly sliced fresh ginger, leeks and creamy white wine sauce. Woodwick raspberries mixed with crumbly hazelnut meringue and a thick whisky cream.

STB ★★★ Hotel
- ⊞ Credit cards: Mastercard/Eurocard, Visa, Delta
- ⋈ Co-Proprietor: Ann Herdman

ALMARA
Upper Urafirth, Hillswick
Shetland ZE2 9RH
Tel/Fax: 01806 503261
E-mail: almara@zetnet.co.uk
Web: www.users.zetnet.co.uk/almara/

Follow the A970 north to Hillswick. 1½ miles before Hillswick follow signs to Upper Urafirth and Almara.

Family-run guest house with wonderful food.

- Modern bungalow.
- Traditional home cooking.
- "Take time to be looked after and fed on Shetland's finest produce."

Marcia's hospitality is a true reflection of her commitment to make every single guest's experience of Shetland a memorable one. Nothing is too much trouble. The whole house is surrounded by working crofts, and is most comfortable with a large lounge to relax in. The guest house is unlicensed, however guests are most welcome to take their own wine. Cooking here is accomplished yet kept simple, making the best of what is available locally. This is a little treasure.

Open all year
- 🏠 Rooms: 3, 2 en suite
- 🛏 DB&B £30–£33 B&B £17–£20
- SP Special rates available
- UL Unlicensed – guests welcome to take own wine
- ✕ Residents only
- ✕ Dinner ££
- Ⅴ Vegetarians welcome
- ☇ Children welcome
- ✍ No smoking in bedrooms + sitting room

Dressed Eshaness crab with Rebecca sauce. Scallop Arianne: scallop and monktail sauteed in sherry, topped with a delicious Parmesan sauce. Rachel's bombe.

STB ★★★★ B&B
Green Tourism 🌿🌿🌿 GOLD Award
- ⊞ No credit cards
- ⋈ Proprietor: Marcia Williamson

BURRASTOW HOUSE

Walls, Shetland ZE2 9PD
Tel: 01595 809307 Fax: 01595 809213
E-mail: burr.hs.hotel@zetnet.co.uk
Web: www.users.zetnet.co.uk/burrastow-house-hotel

Take A971 west to Walls and Sandness and drive until you reach Walls. Drive straight through, go over cattle grid and turn left at top of hill. Signposted Burrastow – follow road to end (2 miles).

A country house hotel where ancient meets modern.

- Country house hotel.
- Fine cuisine with exceptional flavours.
- "Relax in luxurious surroundings beside peat fires."

Burrastow is totally committed to the comfort of its guests. An extension houses some more modern rooms. The main part of the house is old and interesting with furniture and style to suit the surroundings. There is also a mosaic staircase which leads to a meeting facility complete with demonstration kitchen. Bo Simmons is a wonderful cook and has just published her first cookery book which promotes the use of local produce. This house will appeal to all ages and tastes.

Open all year except Jan, Feb, Oct half-term, Christmas Day + New Year's Day
Closed Sun night + Mon to non residents
🛏 Rooms: 5 en suite
🍴 DB&B £80–£85 B&B £58
SP Special rates available off season
🍷 Table licence only
✕ Light lunch no booking, booking required 12 hours' in advance for 3 course lunch £-££
✕ Dinner (except Mon to non residents) £££
Ⓥ Vegetarians welcome
🧒 Children welcome
♿ Facilities for disabled visitors
🚭 No smoking in dining room + bedrooms
🐕 Dogs on request only

Courgette, lemon and rocket carpaccio in a lemon and olive oil dressing served with curls of Parmesan. Poached fillet of turbot with a saffron and chive butter sauce. Dark chocolate mousse millefeuilles with blackcurrant sauce.

STB ★★★★ Hotel
Green Tourism [ⓅⓅⓅ] GOLD Award
💳 Credit cards: Mastercard/Eurocard, American Express, Visa, Switch, Delta
🍳 Chef Proprietor: Bo Simmons

BUSTA HOUSE HOTEL

Busta, Brae
Shetland ZE2 9QN
Tel: 01806 522 506
Fax: 01806 522 588
E-mail: busta@mes.co.uk
Web: www.mes.co.uk/busta

On the Muckle Roe road, 1 mile off A970 Hillswick road.

Historic Shetland house with wonderful views.

- 16th century laird's house.
- Scottish produce with modern influences.
- "Historic house with a long history."

The history of Busta House is full of superstition, ghosts and family feuds. Fear not, as the hospitality and enthusiasm of Peter and Judith Jones make you welcome to their tastefully restored home. One of the few Listed buildings in Shetland, it has many interesting features, amongst which are its walled gardens and private pier. Whether it is a special event or a simple bar lunch you will not be disappointed at Busta. The chef prepares high quality meals from the delicious local produce. Enjoy an aperitif in the Long Room before dinner, gently absorbing the atmosphere of the historic Busta House.

Open all year except 22 Dec to 2 Jan
🛏 Rooms: 20 en suite
🍴 DB&B £65.75–£79.50 B&B £41.25–£70
SP Special rates available
✕ Lunch £-££
✕ Dinner ££-£££
Ⓥ Vegetarians welcome
🧒 Children welcome
🚭 No smoking in dining room

Fresh local crab garnished with the claws, and served with a lemon and coriander dressing. Marinated venison with a red onion marmalade. Chocolate dessert cups with light shortbread biscuits and Scottish berries.

STB ★★★ Hotel
Green Tourism [ⓅⓅ] SILVER Award
💳 Credit cards: Mastercard/Eurocard, American Express, Visa, Diners Club, Switch, Delta
🍳 Owners: Peter & Judith Jones
     Manageress: Jeanette Watt

MONTY'S BISTRO
Mounthooly Street
Lerwick, Shetland Isles
ZE1 OBJ
Tel: 01595 696555
Fax: 01595 696955

Centre of Lerwick, behind Tourist Information Centre. Up Mounthooly Street, 20 yards on the left.

Intimate restaurant in building over 100 years old.

- Bistro restaurant.
- Modern Scottish cooking.
- "Excellent bistro for all ages and occasions - with wonderful coffee."

Monty's is an intimate restaurant, with a wonderful atmosphere, situated in a building over 100 years old. The original stone walls and floor set the mood for a cosy, relaxed and informal eating experience. The menu and blackboard specialities are well-balanced and full of Shetland's finest ingredients. Raymond, who is a perfect host and now oversees the front of house, has been a chef for over 20 years and has travelled and worked the world over. Guests at Monty's benefit from his in-depth knowledge of cooking and his accomplished, innovative style. A great place to take the family for lunch or dinner.

Open all year except Christmas Day, Boxing Day, 1 Jan + last Wed in Feb
Closed Sun
✕ Lunch except Sun £
✕ Dinner except Sun ££
Ⓥ Vegetarians welcome
ⵏ Children welcome
✗ No smoking throughout

Crab tart on green salad, preserved lemon dressing. Grilled Shetland beef rib eye steak, marinated in olive oil, red wine and aromatics with stove tatties, buttered carrots and its own marination. Local strawberry brûlée gratinated with hazelnut praline.

⊞ Credit cards: Mastercard/Eurocard, Visa, Switch, Delta, JCB
ⵕ Proprietor: Raymond Smith

ATHOLL HOUSE HOTEL
& CHIMES RESTAURANT
Dunvegan, Isle of Skye IV55 8WA
Tel: 01470 521 219 Fax: 01470 521 481
E-mail: reservations@athollhotel.demon.co.uk
Web: www.athollhotel.demon.co.uk

In the centre of the village of Dunvegan. From the bridge – follow A850 to Sligachan, turn left to Dunvegan – 22 miles.

A small hotel in 'heart of the village'.

- Late 19th century manse now a comfortable small hotel.
- Modern Scottish cooking with care.
- "Small and cosy with good food and service."

Situated at the head of Loch Dunvegan, the Atholl House Hotel looks out on to the twin flat-topped mountains – the Macleod's Tables. Built in 1910 the Atholl House Hotel is a former manse which retains many of the original features. The bedrooms are well-maintained with quality furnishings – two of which have four posters. The atmosphere is friendly and the cooking accomplished using much of the excellent local Skye produce. Atholl House Hotel has 1 AA Red Rosette. *See advert page 23.*

Open all year except Jan + Feb
🛏 Rooms: 9 (8 en suite, 1 with private facilities)
🛏 DB&B £40–£56   B&B £24–£40
SP Special rates available
🍸 Full hotel licence
✕ Food available all day £££
🍱 Packed lunch available
✕ Lunch £
✕ Dinner £££
Ⓥ Vegetarians welcome
ⵏ Children welcome
♿ Facilities for disabled visitors
✗ No smoking in restaurant

Loch Caroy mussels with a fresh herb and saffron risotto. Loch Bracadale darne of salmon with dill marinaded cucumber spaghetti garnished with local prawns and drizzled with a coriander butter. Crisp tuile basket filled with a chocolate and Drambuie parfait, set on a pool of raspberry and strawberry coulis finished with orange segments.

STB ★★★ Hotel
⊞ Credit cards: Mastercard/Eurocard, American Express, Visa, Switch
ⵕ Owner: Joan M Macleod MHCIMA

BOSVILLE HOTEL

Bosville Terrace, Portree
Isle of Skye IV51 9DG
Tel: 01478 612846 Fax: 01478 613434
E-mail: bosville@macleodhotels.co.uk
Web: www.macleodhotels.co.uk/bosville/

Town centre, on terrace above Portree harbour.

Hotel in the centre of Portree village offering quality food and accommodation.

- Town centre hotel.
- Stylish Scottish cuisine.
- "Good food and hospitality makes the Bosville an ideal base for touring Skye."

At the Bosville, the Chandlery Restaurant excels itself by being committed to its role in producing meals, reflecting the local produce, with some exceptional presentation. It is also achieving high standards in the culinary field. The popular restaurant fronts the street; diners come and go and locals drop in for a chat, or to deliver goods and fresh produce. The hotel stands on a brae and commands fine views across the harbour, with the Cuillin Mountains beyond. Table d'hôte lunch and dinner menus are presented, using local produce wherever possible and featuring a number of Scottish specialities. The Chandlery has 1 AA Rosette. *See advert page 25.*

Open all year
- Rooms: 15 en suite
- DB&B £44–£85   B&B £35–£60
- SP Special rates available
- ✗ Food available all day £
- ✗ Lunch £
- ✗ Dinner ££
- V Vegetarians welcome
- ☆ Children welcome
- ⅙ Facilities for disabled visitors
- ⅄ No smoking throughout

Smoked salmon filled with crab meat and aïoli, served on a crisp salad and drizzled with lemon dressing. Medallions of Aberdeen Angus, highland venison and king scallops grilled on redcurrant jelly and rosemary and wild oyster mushroom cream. Orange flavoured shortbread layered with Drambuie cream and garnished with wild seasonal berries, set on a pool of strawberry coulis.

STB ★★★★ Hotel
- Credit cards: Mastercard/Eurocard, American Express, Visa, Switch, Delta
- Hotel Manager: Kevin Stewart

CUILLIN HILLS HOTEL

Portree
Isle of Skye IV51 9QU
Tel: 01478 612003 Fax: 01478 613092
E-mail: office@cuillinhills.demon.co.uk
Web: www.cuillinhills.demon.co.uk

Turn right ¼ north of Portree on A855 and follow hotel signs.

Former hunting lodge with spectacular views.

- Spacious country house hotel.
- French/Scottish traditional.
- "Modern comfort and fine dining, yet it still retains its historic charm."

Built c. 1870 as a hunting lodge for Lord Macdonald of the Isles, the Cuillin Hills Hotel enjoys some of the finest and most spectacular views. The hotel stands in 15 acres of mature, private ground, overlooking Portree Bay. Bedrooms are comfortable and well-appointed. The new restaurant was not yet complete at time of inspection. It is split-level and will be in keeping with the rest of house e.g. bay windowed. Public rooms have been decorated with quality furnishings which complement the charm and character of Cuillin Hills. The daily changing menu offers four courses, featuring fresh, local produce presented in an imaginative way. Service is helpful and friendly in this busy hotel.

Open all year.
- Rooms: 30 en suite
- DB&B £35–£82 B&B £35–£56
- SP Special rates available
- ✗ Lunch £
- ✗ Dinner £££
- V Vegetarians welcome
- ☆ Children welcome
- ⅙ Facilities for disabled visitors
- ⅄ No smoking in restaurant
- ⴕ Dogs welcome

Talisker whisky-cured salmon tartare with a lime dressing. Mignon of Scottish fillet steak with a duxelle of mushroom and oyster en croûte with a Madeira sauce. Caramel mousse brûlée with sugar curls and ice cream in a tuille cone.

STB ★★★★ Hotel
- Credit cards: Mastercard/Eurocard, American Express, Visa, Switch, Delta
- General Manager: Mr Murray McPhee

DUISDALE COUNTRY HOUSE HOTEL
Sleat
Isle of Skye IV43 8QW
Tel: 01471 833 202 Fax: 01471 833404
E-mail: marie@duisdalehotel.demon.co.uk
Web: www.duisdale.com

7 miles on the Armadale Road from Broadford on A851.

A traditional hunting lodge overlooking Knoydart.

- Country house hotel.
- Traditional Scottish cooking.
- "Traditional country house elegance with good food and company."

Duisdale Country House hotel is a most appealing house, set in delightful gardens with stunning views overlooking Knoydart. The hotel itself offers comfortable accommodation which has been upgraded since it was taken over by Marie Campbell, who trained in Paris at the Ritz-Escoffier. Marie and chef Stuart Robertson have created menus which offer superb local produce, imaginatively cooked and presented. *See advert page 29.*

Open Mar to Oct
🏫 Rooms: 17 en suite
🛏 DB&B £83–£92 B&B £56–£65
SP Special rates available
✕ Dinner £££
Ⅴ Vegetarians welcome
† Children welcome
½ No smoking in dining room

Local shellfish served with a garden herb sauce (scallops, langoustine and lobster). Saddle of venison, marinated in Drambuie and rosemary served with vegetables from Duisdale's kitchen garden. Chestnut and malt whisky tart with Talisker cream.

STB ★★★ Hotel
⊞ Credit cards: Mastercard/Eurocard, American Express, Visa, Switch, Delta
Ⓜ Proprietor: Mrs Marie Campbell

DUNORIN HOUSE HOTEL
Herebost
Dunvegan
Isle of Skye IV55 8GZ
Tel/Fax: 01470 521488
E-mail: dunorinhouse@msn.com

From Skye Bridge A87 to Sligachan, then A863 to Dunvegan. 2 miles south of Dunvegan turn left at Roag/Orbost junction, 200m on right.

A small and modern, family-run hotel in a beautiful corner of Skye.

- Purpose-built with modern comforts in mind.
- Scottish cooking with island recipes/hotel cooking.
- "A relaxed home in beautiful country."

Dunorin House is the brainchild of Gaelic-speaking native islanders Joan and Alasdair MacLean. Built in 1989, it offers comfortable accommodation in ten en suite rooms. The hotel enjoys panoramic views across Loch Roag to the Cuillin Hills. All bedrooms and public rooms are on ground level with wide corridors and so are especially suitable for the disabled. With many local recipes, the hotel's daily changing table d'hôte menu seeks to make the most of fresh local produce such as scallops, venison, salmon, beef and lamb. The wine list is reasonably priced and varied.

Open 1 Apr to 15 Nov except 2 weeks Oct
🏫 Rooms: 10 en suite
🛏 DB&B £48–£60 B&B £30–£42
SP Special rates available
✕ Non-residents – bookings only
♟ Restricted hotel licence
✕ Dinner £££
Ⅴ Vegetarians welcome
† Children welcome
♿ Facilities for disabled visitors
½ No smoking in dining room

Scallops in garlic butter. Fillet of West Coast lemon sole pan-fried in seasoned butter and lemon juice. Cloutie dumpling.

STB ★★★★ Hotel
⊞ Credit cards: Mastercard/Eurocard, Visa
Ⓜ Partners: Alasdair & Joan MacLean

FLODIGARRY COUNTRY HOUSE HOTEL & THE WATER HORSE RESTAURANT
Staffin, Isle of Skye
Inverness-shire IV51 9HZ
Tel: 01470 552203 Fax: 01470 552301
Web: www.milford.co.uk/go/flodigarry.html

A855 north from Portree to Staffin, 4 miles from Staffin to Flodigarry.

Country hotel at the north end of Skye.

• Historic house with unsurpassed views.
• Scottish cuisine.
• "Relaxed but grand country house with wonderful views."

This historic country house hotel nestles beneath the towering pinnacles of the Quiraing and has panoramic sea views over Flodigarry Island, and across Staffin Bay to the mainland. Its 19th century castellate additions lend it the air of folklore, especially being so close to the mysterious 'Fairy Glen'. Adjacent is Flora Macdonald's cottage (with seven luxury en suite rooms, five with sea views). In the Water Horse Restaurant, residents and non-residents can enjoy a daily changing table d'hôte menu, featuring traditional dishes, or choose from an à la carte menu. Bar meals are served in the conservatory and on the terrace. Winner of The Macallan Taste of Scotland Country House Hotel of the Year Award 1995. *See advert page 28.*

    Open all year
🏨 Rooms: 19 en suite
🛏️ DB&B £73–£99   B&B £48–£75
SP Special rates available
✕ Lunch Sun (Restaurant) ££
✕ Dinner 4 course menu £££
Ⓥ Vegetarians welcome
🜸 Children welcome
♿ Facilities for disabled visitors
🚭 No smoking in restaurant, conservatory or bedrooms

Local lobster and langoustine. Medallions of prime Scottish beef set on a bed of haggis with a pink peppercorn and mushroom sauce. Janet's steamed Talisker and raisin sponge.

STB ★★★★ Hotel
💳 Credit cards: Mastercard/Eurocard, Visa, Switch, Delta
👤 Proprietors: Andrew & Pamela Butler

GLENVIEW INN & RESTAURANT
Culnacnoc, Staffin
Isle of Skye
Inverness-shire IV51 9JH
Tel: 01470 562 248
Fax: 01470 562 211

12 miles from Portree on the Staffin road – signposted off the A855.

A comfortable west highland inn near Staffin.

• Restaurant with rooms.
• Good quality cooking of fresh local seafood.
• "A friendly atmosphere with creative use of Scottish produce."

Tucked into a sheltered corner up in the north end of the island, this little hostelry is big in all the home comforts. The fresh sea catch of the day is quickly brought to the table, while in the afternoon, home baking is a temptation to linger over. Whatever the time of day – the Glenview will rise to the occasion. Paul's cooking uses local produce and eclectic techniques to produce well-priced and varied meals selected from an à la carte menu and blackboard featuring daily specials – from fresh local seafood and game to vegetarian and ethnic dishes.

    Open mid Mar to early Nov
🏨 Rooms: 5 (4 en suite, 1 private facilities)
🛏️ DB&B £37.50–£47.50   B&B £25–£35
SP Special rates available
✕ Lunch ££
✕ Dinner £££
Ⓥ Vegetarians welcome
🜸 Children welcome
🚭 Smoking restricted to certain areas

Grilled brochette of creeled Staffin Bay prawns with whole fresh garlic roasted in olive oil. Shank of Scottish lamb braised with Heather Ale. White chocolate and hazelnut pudding.

STB ★★ Hotel
💳 Credit cards: Mastercard/Eurocard, Switch
👤 Owners: Paul & Cathie Booth

HOTEL EILEAN IARMAIN

Isle Ornsay, Sleat, Isle of Skye
Inverness-shire IV43 8QR
Tel: 01471 833 332
Fax: 01471 833 275

From Mallaig/Armadale ferry turn right on to A851 for 8 miles, then right at sign Isle Ornsay, hotel is down at waters edge. From Skye Bridge take road to Broadford and turn off at junction signed A851 to Armadale.

Gaelic charm at 'The Inn on the Sea'.

• Small whitewashed island hotel.
• Modern Scottish cooking.
• "Elegant and charming hotel in a beautiful corner of Skye."

Hotel Eilean Iarmain (Isle Ornsay Hotel) stands on the small rocky bay of Isle Ornsay in the south of Skye, with expansive views over the Sound of Sleat to the hills of Knoydart. The hotel was built in 1888 and retains the charm and old-world character of a gentler age. It is owned by Sir Iain and Lady Noble – who have done so much for Gaelic culture and language: a good number of the staff are Gaelic speakers. The award-winning restaurant serves a four course table d'hôte menu (in Gaelic, but translated) which features local shellfish (landed only yards from the hotel), game, venison (from the estate) and vegetables. The restaurant and lounge have recently been extended, decor by Lady Noble. The restaurant has 1 AA Rosette. *See advert page 257.*

Open all year
🏨 Rooms: 16 (12 en suite + 4 suites)
🛏 DB&B £86–£116 B&B £55–£85
ᔭ Special rates available
✗ Lunch – booking essential ££
✗ Dinner – advance reservation advisable £££
Ⅴ Vegetarians welcome
ᘐ Children welcome
ᔙ No smoking in restaurant

Eilean Iarmain Estate venison pâté set on green leaves and accompanied by rowanberry jelly. Poached paupiettes of lemon sole stuffed with wild West Coast salmon, served with a Mediterranean dressing. Rich dark chocolate and ginger Marquise with a prune and cognac compote.

STB ★★★ Hotel
🆔 Credit cards: Mastercard/Eurocard, American Express, Visa, Switch
ᔫ Proprietors: Sir Iain & Lady Noble

KINLOCH LODGE

Sleat, Isle Ornsay, Isle of Skye IV43 8QY
Tel: 01471 833214 Fax: 01471 833277
E-mail: kinloch@dial.pipex.com.
Web: www.kinloch-lodge.co.uk

8 miles south of Broadford on A851. 10 miles north of Armadale on A851. 1 mile off A851.

The home of the High Chief of Clan Donald and Lady Macdonald.

• Country house hotel in Sleat.
• Outstanding traditional cooking with innovative influences.
• "A real treat – delicious food in a lovely setting."

Kinloch Lodge was built in 1680, as a farmhouse, and was expanded into a sporting lodge in the 19th century. As the home of Lord Macdonald of Macdonald, it is full of portraits of ancestors, old furniture and family treasures. It is very much a family home, with two comfortable drawing rooms, log fires and a variety of bedrooms. Lady Claire Macdonald is one of the best known cooks in Scotland: an award-winning journalist. Assisted by a small team she presents a five course table d'hôte menu each night which uses only fresh seasonal produce. The breakfasts are a very special treat. The new house, with its wonderful demonstration kitchen, is less than 50m from Kinloch Lodge and guests take meals in the Lodge. Kinloch Lodge has 2 AA Red Rosettes. Winner of The Macallan Taste of Scotland Best Breakfast Award 1998. *See advert page 259.*

Open all year except Christmas
🏨 Rooms: 15, 13 en suite
🛏 DB&B £70–£130 B&B £45–£95
ᔭ Special rates available
✗ Dinner 5 course menu ££££
Ⅴ Vegetarians welcome – prior notice required
ᘐ Children welcome by arrangement
ᔙ No smoking in dining room
🐄 Member of the Scotch Beef Club

Scallop soufflé with sauce Bercy and locally grown herb salad. Roast rack of black face lamb with crushed black pepper and pinhead oatmeal crust and sauce paloise (mint and hollandaise). Vanilla meringue roulade with lemon and elderflower curd and strawberries marinated in elderflower.

STB ★★★★ Hotel
🆔 Credit cards: Mastercard/Eurocard, American Express, Visa
ᔫ Proprietors: Lord & Lady Macdonald

ROSEDALE HOTEL
Beaumont Crescent, Portree
Isle of Skye IV51 9DB
Tel: 01478 613131
Fax: 01478 612531

Down in the actual harbour, 100 yards from village square.

A small hotel in Skye's principal village with views directly over the harbour.

- Harbourside fishermen's cottages comfortably converted to accommodate this friendly hotel.
- Modern Scottish.
- "Fine dining and fine views."

The Rosedale Hotel, now under the new ownership of Paul and Allison Rouse, was originally a row of William IV cottages adjacent to the harbour in the heart of old Portree. The hotel has now spread its wings in all directions and has added a new coffee shop and a wine bar which overlook the harbour. There are many unique and interesting features – not least of which is finding your way to the first floor restaurant! – from where there are splendid views out over the bay. Chef presents a daily changing table d'hôte dinner menu which offers a good choice of imaginative dishes, based upon fresh local produce whenever it is available. The Rosedale Hotel has 1 AA Rosette. *See advert page 262.*

Open all year
- 🏚 Rooms: 23 en suite
- 🛏 DB&B £57–£68   B&B £36-43
- 🆂🅿 Special rates available
- ✗ Lunch £
- ✗ Dinner £££
- Ⓥ Vegetarians welcome
- 大 Children welcome
- ⊁ No smoking in restaurant
- 🐕 Dogs welcome

Open ravioli with locally-caught scallops and monkfish in a shellfish broth. Blackcurrant and orange-glazed loin of Highland lamb served with citrus fruits and blackcurrant jus. Gaelic coffee chocolate cake served with a Talisker whisky cream.

STB ★★★★ Hotel
- 💳 Credit cards: Mastercard/Eurocard, Visa, Switch, Delta
- 🅽 Owners: Paul & Allison Rouse

ROSKHILL HOUSE
by Dunvegan
Isle of Skye IV55 8ZD
Tel: 01470 521317   Fax: 01470 521761
E-mail: stay@roskhill.demon.co.uk
Web: www.roskhill.demon.co.uk

2 miles south of Dunvegan on A863, turn off road at River Rosgill.

Country guest house on the outskirts of Dunvegan.

- Croft house dating back to 1890.
- Traditional Scottish cooking.
- "Situated in this lovely part of Skye offering a homely atmosphere and good food."

Roskhill House is a traditional croft house which was built in 1890. The dining room was originally the village store and post office until 1960. Owner Gillian Griffith succeeds in offering a very high level of comfort; warm and sincere Scottish hospitality, coupled with excellent home cooking. Menus are well-thought out and use excellent locally-sourced produce which is then cooked in a sympathetic style.

Open all year (Christmas + New Year half board only)
- 🏚 Rooms: 5 (4 en suite, 1 private facilities)
- 🛏 DB&B £41.50–£49.50   B&B £27–£35
- 🆂🅿 Special rates available
- ✗ Non residents – prior booking essential
- 🍷 Restricted hotel licence
- ✗ Dinner ££
- Ⓥ Vegetarian and special diets catered for
- 大 Children over 10 years welcome
- ⊁ No smoking throughout

Gently braised chunks of Scottish topside of beef enclosed in an extra short crust pie with a hint of horseradish and seasonal vegetables. Steamed raspberry sponge pudding with fresh berries and real custard.

STB ★★★★ Guest House
- 💳 Credit cards: Mastercard/Eurocard, American Express, Visa, Switch, Delta, JCB, Solo
- 🅽 Proprietor: Gillian Griffith

SKEABOST HOUSE HOTEL

Skeabost Bridge, Isle of Skye IV51 9NP
Tel: 01470 532 202 Fax: 01470 532 454
E-mail: skeabost@sol.co.uk.
Web: www.sol.co.uk/s/skeabost

4 miles north of Portree on Dunvegan road.

An imposing family-run hotel on the shores of Loch Snizort.

- A 19th century hunting lodge set in lovely grounds.
- Skilled contemporary cooking.
- "A peaceful haven with fine food."

Built in 1870 this former hunting lodge has been a family-run establishment by the Stuart and McNab families for 30 years. It is an oasis of cultivated serenity within the wild and rugged terrain of Skye. Positioned in 12 acres of lovely grounds which stretch down to the waterside. A period conservatory overlooks the loch and was added to the main building to extend the hotel's dining facilities. A buffet menu is available during the day and in the more formal surroundings of the elegant wood-panelled dining room. Angus McNab presents daily changing table d'hôte menus which demonstrate considerable flair and skill, particularly with fish and game. *See advert page 263.*

Open Mar to Nov
- ⊞ Rooms: 26, 24 en suite
- 🛏 DB&B £54–£78   B&B £36–£57.50
- ⊞ Special rates available
- ✕ Lunch £
- ✕ Dinner £££
- Ⓥ Vegetarians welcome
- ✶ Children welcome
- ♿ Facilities for disabled visitors
- ⚮ No smoking in dining room
- 🐄 Member of the Scotch Beef Club

Dressed Glendale salad leaves with flaky roast smoked Hebridean salmon, crisp mangetout and topped with chive crème fraîche. Sauté loin of Highland venison with horseshoe black pudding, buttered celeriac purée and a port wine game sauce. Home-made Drambuie crème brûlée with fresh oranges and crisp vanilla tuilles.

STB ★★★ Hotel
- ⊞ Credit cards: Mastercard/Eurocard, Visa, Switch
- ⋈ Proprietors: Stuart & McNab Families

TALISKER HOUSE

Talisker
Isle of Skye
Inverness-shire
IV47 8SF
Tel: 01478 640245 Fax: 01478 640214
E-mail: jon_and_ros.wathen@virgin.net
Web: www.talisker.co.uk

Take the A863 from Sligachan. Turn left towards Carbost on the B8009. At top of Carbost village veer left and follow signs to Talisker.

Historic country house.

- Delightful country house in spectacular location.
- Wholesome, hearty cooking.
- "A perfect haven with a warm welcome."

Talisker House welcomes guests as warmly today as it did Johnson and Boswell during their historic tour of the Hebrides in 1773. This is a hidden treasure of a house run by Australians Jon and Ros Wathen, who specialise in home cooking and personal service. The house is beautifully maintained as is the extensive garden which supplies the kitchen with vegetables and herbs. The cooking is accomplished, menus are interesting and make best use of the excellent home-grown and local produce available on Skye. Jon and Ros' Australian influence is evident on the wine list.

Open Mar to Oct incl
- ⊞ Rooms: 4 en suite
- 🛏 DB&B £63   B&B £40
- ✕ Residents only
- 🥪 Packed lunch – by request
- ✕ Dinner ££
- Ⓥ Vegetarians welcome
- ✶ Children welcome
- ♿ Limited facilities for disabled visitors - please telephone
- ⚮ No smoking throughout

Home-made pasta with melted Dunsyre Blue cheese and leeks. Pan-fried fillet of Isle of Skye monkfish with coriander and coconut milk sauce, served with jasmine rice and Thai-inspired salad. Fresh Glendrynoch strawberries with strawberry sorbet and glass biscuits.

STB ★★★★ Guest House
Credit cards: Mastercard/Eurocard, Visa, JCB
- ⋈ Proprietors: Jon & Ros Wathen

**THREE CHIMNEYS RESTAURANT
AND THE HOUSE OVER-BY
WINNER OF THE MACALLAN
TASTE OF SCOTLAND AWARDS 1999
– OVERALL EXCELLENCE &
RESTAURANT WITH ROOMS**
Colbost, Dunvegan, Isle of Skye IV55 8ZT
Tel: 01470 511258 Fax: 01470 511358
E-mail: eatandstay@threechimneys.co.uk
Web: www.threechimneys.co.uk

4 miles west of Dunvegan on B884 road to Glendale.
Look out for Glendale Visitor Route signs.

Island restaurant with rooms in an idyllic setting.

- Delightful restaurant in converted crofter's cottage.
- Natural skilled Scottish cooking.
- "Award winning restaurant in a class of its own!"

Three Chimneys has six newly added rooms,
sumptuous suites, luxuriously appointed with
spectacular sea views. Dinner offers a selection from
a three-course fixed price menu or the 'seafood
specialities' à la carte menu. The wine list is
extensive and carefully compiled. Fresh Skye
seafood is a speciality but fish, lamb, beef, game and
a vegetarian option are also on offer. Shirley is a
brilliant and artistic cook – not to be missed! Three
Chimneys has 2 AA Rosettes, plus several Scottish
restaurant awards. Joint winner of The Macallan
Taste of Scotland Restaurant of the Year Award 1998.

    Open virtually all year
    Closed Sun lunch
🛏 Rooms: 6 en suite
✕ Lunch except Sun £-££££
✕ Dinner 3 course menu £££-££££
Ⓥ Vegetarians welcome
⚘ Children welcome
♿ Disabled access
🚭 No smoking in restaurant
🐂 Member of the Scotch Beef Club

**Warm salad of seared scallops and roast breast of
mallard with heather honey and grainy mustard
dressing. Red deer collops-in-the-pan, skirlie mash,
juniper Savoy and a rich game gravy with prunes and
bitter chocolate. Chilled rhubarb compote with stem
ginger ice cream and Three Chimneys shortbread.**

STB ★★★★★ Restaurant with Rooms
💳 Credit cards: Mastercard/Eurocard, American
    Express, Visa, Switch
👤 Owners: Eddie & Shirley Spear

ORASAY INN
Lochcarnan
South Uist, Western Isles H58 5PD
Tel: 01870 610298 Fax: 01870 610390
E-mail: orasayinn@btinternet.com

20 miles from Lochboisdale A865, 28 miles from
Lochmaddy.

**Small hotel with a wealth of hospitality and good
food.**

- Small modern hotel.
- Fine Scottish cooking.
- "Wide-ranging menu and big portions, with the
  emphasis on fresh fish."

Orasay Inn is a small house which has been
extended as customer has demanded to form a
small country hotel. Isobel and Alan Graham play
the perfect hosts to North Uist, Benbecula, South
Uist and their tiny village of Lochcarnan. This is an
area of outstanding natural beauty with some of the
island's finest produce served here. The dining
room commands stunning views across the Minch
and also to the mountains of South Uist. There is
also a very comfortable lounge in which to relax and
enjoy the comforts in front of the peat fire.

    Open all year except Christmas Day
🛏 Rooms: 9 en suite
🛏 DB&B £30–£70   B&B £25–£43
ⓢⓟ Special rates available
✕ Food available all day £-££
✕ Lunch £
✕ Dinner ££
Ⓥ Vegetarians welcome
⚘ Children welcome
♿ Facilities for disabled visitors
🚭 No smoking in dining room

**Smoked salmon duo: a mix of Herbridean hot-
smoked and cold-smoked salmon, served with
green salad. Medallions of venison with redcurrant
and port sauce, garnished with chestnuts. Home-
made apple crumble with caramel sauce.**

STB ★★ Inn
💳 Credit cards: Mastercard/Eurocard, Visa,
    Switch, Delta JCB
👤 Proprietors: Alan & Isobel Graham

SIMPLY SCOTTISH
High Street
Jedburgh
Roxburghshire TD8 6AG
Tel: 01835 864696
Fax: 01573 228246

Centre of Jedburgh just off A68.

Modern bistro/restaurant specialising in local quality produce with cook shop and coffee shop.

- Modern bistro-style town restaurant.
- Wholesome Scottish.
- "Friendly and lively bistro-style restaurant offering traditional Scottish cooking with flair."

The Simply Scottish restaurant, coffee shop and craft cook-shop has been converted from the old Co-op department store. It is a popular local meeting place with very high standards. The interior of the bistro/restaurant has a light, modern country feel, with heavy pine furniture and stripped pine flooring. As the name Simply Scottish suggests the emphasis is on using good, freshly-sourced local produce, served simply but with some interesting combinations of flavours and presented with style.

Open all year
✕ Food available all day £-££
✕ Lunch £
✕ Dinner except some week nights in winter (please phone) ££
Ⓥ Vegetarians welcome
☆ Children welcome
⚅ Facilities for disabled visitors
✔ No smoking area

Haggis with whisky and white onion sauce. Grilled Border lamb steak with Arran mustard sauce. Summer fruit pudding.

⊞ Credit cards: Mastercard/Eurocard, Visa
🅰 Proprietors: Linda Fergusson & Charles Masraff

COBBLES INN RESTAURANT
7 Bowmont Street, Kelso, Roxburghshire TD5 7JH
Tel/Fax: 01573 223548
E-mail: david@cobblesinn.preserve.co.uk
Web: www.cobblesinn.preserve.co.uk

Just off the main square in Kelso.

Black and white List B building in historic Borders town.

- 1800s Listed building.
- Imaginative home cooking.
- "A warm, friendly and informal Borders welcome awaits you here."

This black and white Listed building has a traditional pub-style atmosphere with open fire, black beams in ceiling and leaded windows (port cullis-style). It is a small and busy restaurant which is popular with locals and visitors alike. The cooking is very much based on fresh Scottish produce with a wide range of dishes on a standard menu with daily specials on a blackboard.

Open all year except 17 to 24 Jan, Christmas Day + New Year's Day
✕ Lunch £
✕ Dinner ££
Ⓥ Vegetarians welcome
☆ Children welcome
⚅ Facilities for disabled visitors
✔ No smoking area in restaurant

Cobbles salmon parcel: smoked salmon wrapped around smoked trout mousse, served with chive sauce. Pan-fried venison with haggis and whisky cream garnished with straw potatoes. Sticky toffee pudding served with toffee sauce and cream or ice cream.

⊞ Credit cards: Mastercard/Eurocard, Visa, Switch, Delta
🅰 Director: Joan Forrest
Manager: Colin Maxwell

EDNAM HOUSE HOTEL

Bridge Street, Kelso, Roxburghshire TD5 7HT
Tel: 01573 224168 Fax: 01573 226319
E-mail: ednamhouse@excite.co.uk
Web: www.ednamhouse.com

Situated on Bridge Street, halfway between town square and abbey.

A family-run Georgian mansion of historic importance.

- Georgian mansion – banks of Tweed.
- Traditional and modern Scottish cooking.
- "A delightful establishment in a superb location."

Enjoying wonderful views, Ednam House Hotel is considered to be the finest Georgian mansion in Roxburghshire. It is set in three acres of magnificent gardens. Ednam has been the home of the Brooks family since 1928. Public rooms and bedrooms are furnished and styled in keeping with the hotel. Proprietor/chef Ralph Brooks describes his cooking as 'straightforward, but along classical lines' and creates original dishes using unusual ingredients such as Berwickshire ostrich and wood pigeon, preferring to fashion his menus from the fresh ingredients he can obtain locally and seasonally. This is a most comfortable and easy hotel where the customer comes first.

Open all year except Christmas + New Year
🏠 Rooms: 32 en suite
🛏 DB&B £56–£76 B&B £38–£58
SP Special rates available
✗ Food available all day £-££
✗ Lunch £
✗ Dinner ££
V Vegetarians welcome – prior notice required
🕇 Children welcome

Loch Awe mussels steamed with Pernod and garlic. Braised shank of Tweed Valley lamb in its rich gravy. Drambuie mousse served with raspberry coulis.

STB ★★★ Hotel
Green Tourism 🅟 **BRONZE** Award
💳 Credit cards: Mastercard/Eurocard, Visa, Switch
🗚 Proprietors: R A & R W Brook

THE OLD PRIORY & COACH HOUSE

12 Abbey Row
Kelso, Roxburghshire TD5 7JF
Tel: 01573 223030 Fax: 01573 228246

In centre of Kelso a few minutes from Square, 200 yards.

Country town hotel set in own walled garden.

- 18th century town house.
- Fresh modern Scottish cooking.
- "No airs and graces, just simple Scottish cooking."

The Old Priory & Coach House is an 18th century stone-built town house in its own walled garden in the heart of historic Kelso which is full of architectural interest. The Old Priory is opposite the abbey which dates back to the 12th century. The owners, Charles Masraff and Linda Fergusson have completely refurbished the house to create an ambience of comfortable elegance where one can enjoy good cooking in simple style offering good value for money. The addition of a conservatory/dining room is planned for the year 2000.

Open all year
🏠 Rooms: 8 en suite
🛏 DB&B £32.50–£42.50 B&B £20–£30
SP Special rates available
✗ Food available all day ££
✗ Lunch £
✗ Dinner ££
V Vegetarians welcome
🕇 Children welcome
🚭 Smoking permitted in restricted area only

Smoked Argyll ham and melon. Poached fillet of Scottish salmon with herb butter. Heather honey ice cream.

STB ★★★ Guest House
💳 Credit cards: Mastercard/Eurocard, Visa, Switch, Delta
🗚 Proprietors: Linda Fergusson & Charles Masraff

THE ROXBURGHE HOTEL AND GOLF COURSE
Heiton, Kelso
Roxburghshire TD5 8JZ
Tel: 01573 450331 Fax: 01573 450611
E-mail: sunlaws.roxgc@virgin.net
Web: www.roxburghe.bordernet.co.uk

Situated at the village of Heiton, on the A698 Kelso-Hawick road. Signposted at western end of village.

Jacobean-style mansion owned by the Duke and Duchess of Roxburghe.

• Country house hotel and championship golf course.
• Traditional Scottish, with grand hotel touches.
• "A wonderful blend of warm Scottish hospitality, excellent food and setting steeped in history."

The Roxburghe Hotel stands on the banks of the River Teviot in 200 acres of park and woodland. The hotel offers a variety of country pursuits and its own golf course. Although it is an imposing mansion, the Roxburghe retains the common touch, the welcome is genuinely hospitable. Well-constructed menus for lunch and dinner offer both light and complex dishes and a good range of meat, fish and poultry. The Roxburghe Hotel has 2 AA Rosettes. *See advert page 263.*

Open all year
🏠 Rooms: 22 en suite
🛏 DB&B £90–£155   B&B £75–£130
SP Special rates available
✕ Lunch ££
✕ Dinner £££-££££
V Vegetarians welcome
✻ Children welcome
⅍ No smoking in dining room
🐂 Member of the Scotch Beef Club

Globe artichoke heart filled with salmon, crayfish and spring onion crème fraîche. Oven-baked saddle of venison with boulangere potatoes and cracked black pepper. Banana shortcake served with caramelised bananas and toffee sauce.

STB ★★★★ Hotel
💳 Credit cards: Mastercard/Eurocard, American Express, Visa, Diners Club, Switch
👤 General Manager: Stephen Browning

THE BUTTERCHURN
Cocklaw Mains Farm
Kelty, Fife
KY4 0JR
Tel: 01383 830169
Fax: 01383 831614

Just off the M90 motorway at junction 4 on B914. 500 yards west of junction

Informal modern restaurant in renovated farm steading with super new crafts and food shop attached.

• Sympathetically renovated farm buildings.
• Fresh home style cooking.
• "Home style cooking, informal relaxed atmosphere catering for all the family with an excellent play area."

The Butterchurn restaurant not only serves delightful fresh food, but also houses 'The Scottish Food and Craft Centre' with speciality Scottish foods and home baking, and is home to food demonstration events. There is a super children's play area to keep everyone happy and children are also welcome to see the farmyard animals. Light meals, lunch and home baking are available all day right through to traditional Scottish high teas, and dinner. This whitewashed steading is a welcome place for the weary traveller.

Open all year except 25, 26 Dec + 1, 2 Jan
♀ Licensed
✕ Food available all day £
✕ Lunch ££
✕ Dinner ££
V Vegetarians welcome
✻ Children welcome
♿ Facilities for disabled visitors

Smoked venison salad with orange. Breast of Barbary duck with tangy papaya salsa. Home-made lemon meringue pie.

💳 Credit cards: Mastercard/Eurocard, Visa, Switch, Delta
👤 Proprietors: Mr & Mrs K Thomson

ARDSHEAL HOUSE
Kentallen, Argyll PA38 4BX
Tel: 01631 740227 Fax: 01631 740342
E-mail: info@ardsheal.co.uk
Web: www.ardsheal.co.uk

On A828 Oban road, 4 miles south of Ballachulish Bridge, 33 miles north of Oban. About 1 mile up private road, signposted at main road.

An impressive historic country house in beautiful gardens.

- A charming country house.
- Innovative country house cooking.
- "Philippa's light heartedness and enjoyment in her culinary skills is evident in a delightful dinner and breakfast."

Everywhere you turn, as you travel up the mile and a half long drive, there are ancient trees, and between them glimpses of sea and mountains. The house is beautifully appointed, with a magnificent oak-panelled hall, traditional billiards room, dining room and a conservatory in the garden area. Throughout it is furnished with fine antiques, and log fires burn in the sitting rooms on chilly days. Neil and Philippa Sutherland have opened their family home to guests whose comfort and enjoyment is their main concern. Philippa is an accomplished cook and her set, four course menus change daily, Neil is a most attentive host. The atmosphere of the house is relaxed – the quiet of an earlier age. Winner of The Macallan Taste of Scotland Country House Hotel of the Year Award 1996. *See advert page 22.*

Open all year except Dec to Feb – when open by prior arrangement only
🏠 Rooms: 6 en suite
🛏 DB&B from £66   B&B from £42
🍷 Restricted Hotel licence
✕ Dinner £££
Ⓥ Vegetarians welcome
🚭 No smoking in dining room

Highland venison terrine. Wild salmon with deep-fried leeks. Home-grown rhubarb tart.

STB ★★★★ Hotel
💳 Credit cards: Mastercard/Eurocard, American Express, Visa
👤 Owners: Neil & Philippa Sutherland

ARDANAISEIG HOTEL
Kilchrenan, by Taynuilt
Argyll PA35 1HE
Tel: 01866 833333 Fax: 01866 833222
E-mail: ardanaiseig@clara.net
Web: www.ardanaiseig-hotel.com

1 mile east of Taynuilt, turn sharp left. Follow B845 to Kilchrenan. At Kilchrenan Inn turn left – 3 miles on single track road to Ardanaiseig.

Impressive Victorian country house with beautiful gardens and spectacular views.

- Luxury mansion house hotel.
- Very experienced and beautifully presented modern Scottish cooking.
- "Skilful cuisine with friendly, impeccable service in a tranquil setting."

Style and opulence are key words to describe this secluded and grand hotel. The house has been skilfully restored and furnished with beautiful antiques, paintings and eye-catching objets d'art. In the dining room true Scottish hospitality is delivered by chef Gary Goldie who selects only the best local produce and presents it with flair and sophistication. Staff are friendly, although the service is impeccable and professional with little surprises added to an excellent dinner. Relaxation and an air of tranquillity, with sophistication, is the atmosphere which comes across here. Everything about Ardanaiseig is exquisite from the gardens and nature reserve to the tiniest details. They even bottle their own spring water!

Open all year except 2 Jan to 14 Feb
🏠 Rooms: 16 en suite
🛏 DB&B £90–£152.50   B&B £58–£118
✕ Food available all day from £
✕ Lunch from £
✕ Dinner ££££

Tartare of salmon with avocado, caviar and herb water dressing. Canon of Scotch lamb encased in a herb mousse with basil ratatouille, maxime potato, wilted spinach and Chateau-Chalon sauce. Fondant of chocolate with glazed banana and caramel sauce.

STB ★★★★ Hotel
💳 Credit cards: Mastercard/Eurocard, American Express, Visa, Diners Club
👤 General Manager: Robert Francis

TAYCHREGGAN HOTEL
Kilchrenan, Taynuilt
Argyll PA35 1HQ
Tel: 01866 833 211/833 366
Fax: 01866 833 244
E-mail: taychreggan@btinternet.com

Leave A85 at Taynuilt on to B845 through village of
Kilchrenan to the loch side.

**A small, excellently appointed hotel on the shores
of Loch Awe.**

- A highly regarded, award-winning hotel of
  great distinction.
- Elegant modern British cuisine.
- "Enjoy the charm and location of this converted
  Drover's Inn while experiencing modern culinary
  trends in a beautifully appointed dining room."

There has been an hotel here, nestling on the
shores of Loch Awe, for over 300 years.
Taychreggan was a cattle drovers inn. With its
cobbled courtyard and great charm, it retains a
sense of peace and history. But under proprietor
Annie Paul no effort has been spared to restore and
enhance the hotel's unique ambience. Her
emphasis and that of her dedicated staff is to make
visitors, even well-behaved canine ones, feel like
house guests. An experienced brigade of chefs
present imaginative fine cuisine in the hotel's dining
room. More simple bar lunches are no less carefully
prepared. Euan Paul's wine list is a revelation and
well-priced. Taychreggan Hotel has 2 AA Rosettes.
See advert page 264.

Open all year
🛏 Rooms: 19 en suite
🍴 DB&B £80–£125   B&B £52–£97
SP Special rates available
✗ Lunch ££
✗ Dinner 5 course menu £££
Ⓥ Vegetarians welcome
🚭 No smoking in dining room
🐄 Member of the Scotch Beef Club

**Roast Oban Bay scallops served with fresh
tagliatelle and a light port jus. Grilled lamb fillet
with a wild mushroom potato and glazed with
bernaise sauce. Drambuie mille feuille served with
peppermint ice cream.**

STB ★★★★ Hotel
💳 Credit cards: Mastercard/Eurocard, American
   Express, Visa, Switch
👤 Proprietor: Annie Paul

KILFINAN HOTEL
Near Tighnabruaich
Argyll
PA21 2EP
Tel: 01700 821201
Fax: 01700 821205
Web: www.kilfinan.com

6 miles north of Tighnabruaich on B8000, east coast
of Loch Fyne.

Charming inn with gourmet dining.

- 18th century whitewashed inn.
- Modern Scottish.
- "A fine country inn set amidst the stunning Argyll
  hills and lochs."

Kilfinan Hotel is a very charming inn steeped in
character reached by a single-track road down the
Cowal Peninsula. The hotel is set amidst
spectacular Highland scenery on the shores of Loch
Fyne and this location makes it the perfect all-year
retreat. Combine this with the skills of Rolf Mueller,
Master Chef of Great Britain, and the dream is
complete. Rolf's cooking is famed throughout
Scotland for its innovative style and use of prime
produce. Lynne Mueller takes care of the front of
house with an expert eye. The Muellers have their
own distinctive style which has created Kilfinan
over the last seven years. Local produce is a large
and important part of the menus here and while
lunch is informal, dinner is much more upmarket
with diners travelling for many miles to sample the
special cuisine. Rooms are furnished attractively
and there is a sunny terrace to the rear of the
building for that welcome cup of tea on arrival.
Kilfinan Hotel has 3 AA Rosettes.

Open 1 Mar to 31 Jan
🛏 Rooms: 11 en suite
🍴 B&B £39–£49
SP Special rates available
✗ Lunch £
✗ Dinner 4 course menu £££
Ⓥ Vegetarians welcome – prior booking required
🚭 No smoking in dining room
🐄 Member of the Scotch Beef Club

**Fresh Loch Fyne scallops sauteed in hazelnut oil.
Noisettes of Kilfinan venison topped with Arran
mustard. Timbale of pear bavarois.**

STB ★★★ Hotel
💳 Credit cards: Mastercard/Eurocard, American
   Express, Visa, Switch
👤 Manager: Lynne Mueller

THE GATHERING

4B John Finnie Street
Kilmarnock, Ayrshire KA1 1DD
Tel/Fax: 01563 529 022
E-mail: thegathering@fsbdial.co.uk

In centre of Kilmarnock next to the train station on the A77 Glasgow to Kilmarnock Road.

A modern Scottish brasserie restaurant.

* Traditional, red sandstone building.
* Informal modern Scottish.
* "With its roots firmly in Scottish heritage this modern city restaurant offers the best in new creative cooking."

Enter through the wrought iron portcullis and you will find yourself in a lively bustling restaurant where you can watch people come and go. Prop yourself up at the bar and read the daily newspapers provided, or just sit and admire the many symbols of Scottish history which adorn the walls. This decidedly Scottish restaurant has cheerful friendly staff who still find time for a chat as they serve you. Menus offer a variety of dishes and there is a good selection of locally sourced seafoods and meats.

Open all year except Christmas Day
✖ Food available all day £
✖ Lunch £
✖ Dinner £
Ⓥ Vegetarians welcome
☆ Children welcome until 7 pm
♿ Facilities for disabled visitors

Arbroath smokie croquettes served with salad leaves and a sea food dip. Finest Ayrshire lamb cutlets marinated in rosemary and garlic, presented with a redcurrant and mint preserve. Poached pears in red wine and cinnamon served with a lemon curd and a red wine syrup.

💳 Credit cards: Mastercard, Visa, Switch, Delta
Ⓚ Owner: Nicky Connolly

BISTRO AT FERN GROVE

Kilmun, by Dunoon
Argyll PA23 8SB
Tel/Fax: 01369 840 334

6 miles from Dunoon on A880 on the side of the Holy Loch.

Small bistro with some bedrooms.

* Victorian villa.
* Good quality home cooking.
* "Wonderful home cooking in this little bistro offering warm and genuine hospitality."

This 19th century house was at one time the home of the Campbells of Kilmun overlooking Holy Loch. It is situated beside the shore road and is a combination of the family house, the village Post Office, the bistro and some letting rooms. It has carefully maintained gardens to the front with parking for 3-4 cars, off the road. There is a private conservatory to the left of the front door and Post Office, full of miscellaneous personal items. Ian and Estralita Murray, proprietors, are very warm and friendly hosts. A daily changing blackboard menu of chef's specials is supplemented by an à la carte menu of snacks. Accommodation is limited to three rooms, and plays a secondary role to the restaurant. The Bistro has 1 AA Rosette.

Open all year except Nov, weekends only Dec to 1 Apr
Closed Mon
🛏 Rooms: 3 en suite
🛏 DB&B £36–£40   B&B £18–£25
SP Special rates available
✖ Food available all day £
✖ Dinner ££
Ⓥ Vegetarians welcome
☆ Children welcome
♿ Facilities for disabled visitors
🚭 No smoking in restaurant + bedrooms

Cullen skink with home-made bread. Breast of pheasant wrapped in bacon, served with wild mushrooms and cream. Coffee and walnut ice cream, hot fudge sauce.

💳 Credit cards: Mastercard/Eurocard, Visa
Ⓚ Proprietors: Ian & Estralita Murray

MARCH HOUSE

Lagganlia, Feshiebridge, Kincraig
Inverness-shire PH21 1NG
Tel/Fax: 01540 651 388
E-mail: caroline@marchhse01.freeserve.co.uk
Web: www.kincraig.com

From Kincraig follow B970 to Feshiebridge. Cross the bridge and climb until red telephone box on right. Turn right and follow no through road for ½ mile. Turn left down drive.

A modern alpine-style guest house situated in beautiful countryside.

- Secluded alpine-style house.
- Simple home cooking.
- "Friendly, small guest house situated in a dramatically beautiful area of the Highlands."

Standing in a glade of mature pines at the mouth of lovely Glenfeshie, March House enjoys wonderful views of the Cairngorm Mountains. The house is modern and alpine in style – with timber cladding, a large wood-burning stove and old stripped pine furniture. The spacious pine conservatory overlooking the mountains provides an idyllic setting for dinner (non-residents are welcome, but should telephone). It is owned and enthusiastically run by Caroline Hayes, whose cooking and baking matches the clean, fresh atmosphere of March House itself. She uses all fresh local produce and presents a very well-priced table d'hôte menu. Small lunch party bookings also welcome.

Open all year except 26 Nov to 26 Dec
🏠 Rooms: 6, 5 en suite
🛏 DB&B £36–£41   B&B £20–£25
SP Special rates available
✗ Reservations essential for non-residents
UL Unlicensed – guests welcome to take own wine
✗ Lunch – pre-arranged parties ££
✗ Dinner ££
V Vegetarians welcome
⚘ Children welcome
✗ Smoking permitted in the woodshed

Smoked haddock soufflé with hollandaise served with crusty wholemeal soda bread rolls. Fillet of pork with caramelised red onions and served with a herb and white wine sauce. Cinnamon and plum flan with home-made ice cream.

STB ★★★ Guest House
💳 Credit card: Visa
🅺 Proprietor: Caroline Hayes

THE CROSS

Tweed Mill Brae, Ardbroilach Road
Kingussie, Inverness-shire PH21 1TC
Tel: 01540 661166 Fax: 01540 661080
E-mail: fabulousfood@thecross.co.uk

From traffic lights in centre of village, travel uphill along Ardbroilach Road for c. 200 yards, then turn left down private drive (Tweed Mill Brae).

Outstanding award-winning restaurant.

- Restaurant with comfortable en suite rooms.
- Innovative Scottish cooking.
- "One of the most outstanding eating establishments in the Highlands, and arguably one of the country's best."

The Cross was built as a tweed mill in the late 19th century and is situated in a wonderful waterside setting. Here they have retained some interesting features including the exposed original beams in the dining room and the upstairs lounge with its coombed ceilings. Ruth Hadley is a member of the Master Chefs of Great Britain. She treats her ingredients deftly and there is an experimental energy behind some dishes. Where she can, she uses less common produce such as wild mushrooms, mountain hare, pike or fresh turbot, and she grows her own herbs. Tony Hadley's waiting style is renowned; he also makes a nightly selection of wines, from one of the best cellars in Scotland, which will complement the menu. The Cross has 3 AA Rosettes.

Open 1 Mar to 1 Dec + 27 Dec to 5 Jan
Closed Tue
🏠 Rooms: 9 en suite
🛏 DB&B £95–£115
✗ Lunch – private party bookings by arrangement
✗ Dinner except Tue ££££
V Vegetarians welcome – prior notice required
♿ Facilities for non-residential disabled visitors
✗ No smoking in dining room + bedrooms
🐄 Member of the Scotch Beef Club

West Coast scallops with asparagus and Thai-dressed noodles. Saddle of mountain hare lightly pan-fried with a rich game sauce. Crème caramel, compote of plums, caramel ice cream.

💳 Credit cards: Mastercard/Eurocard, Visa, Switch, Delta
🅺 Partners/Proprietors: Tony & Ruth Hadley

THE OSPREY HOTEL
Ruthven Road
Kingussie
Inverness-shire PH21 1EN
Tel/Fax: 01540 661510
E-mail: aileen@ospreyhotel.freeserve.co.uk
Web: www.ospreyhotel.freeserve.co.uk

South end of Kingussie main street.

An attractive small hotel in a quiet Highland town.

- A stone-built town house.
- Traditional Scottish cooking with French influences.
- "Comfortable and friendly small hotel in the centre of Kingussie offering a consistenly high standard of skilled cooking."

Conveniently situated in the centre of Kingussie, overlooking the memorial gardens, the Osprey Hotel is an excellent base from which to explore this part of the Highlands. Attention to detail, good food and a fine cellar are all features of the Osprey which bring so many guests back to the hotel time after time. Aileen Burrow uses only fresh ingredients always cooking to order with great care, skill and imagination. Bread rolls are baked daily on the premises and desserts are understated and memorable. Both Robert and Aileen have an excellent local knowledge and this combined with their skill as friendly hosts ensures that guests thoroughly enjoy their stay at the hotel. The Osprey Hotel has 1 AA Rosette.

Open all year
⊞ Rooms: 8 en suite
🛏 DB&B £42–£56   B&B £24–£36
SP Special rates available
✕ Dinner £££
Ⓥ Vegetarians welcome
☂ Children over 10 years welcome
⚹ Facilities for disabled visitors
✍ No smoking in dining room + most bedrooms

Crab and red pepper cake with a tomato and herb dressing. Medallions of Scottish lamb with a rosemary and onion sauce. Rhubarb and cassis torte served with clotted cream.

STB ★★★ Hotel
⊞ Credit cards: Mastercard/Eurocard, American Express, Visa, Diners Club
⋈ Proprietors: Robert & Aileen Burrow

BUNRANNOCH HOUSE
Kinloch Rannoch
Perthshire PH16 5QB
Tel/Fax: 01882 632407

Turn right after 500 yards on Schiehallion road, just outside Kinloch Rannoch off B846. White 3-storey building on left-hand side.

A family-run country guest house in Highland Perthshire.

- An old hunting lodge in lovely surroundings.
- Creative Scottish cooking.
- "Bunrannoch continues to offer the best of a taste of Scotland."

Set amidst mature trees, Bunrannoch is a Listed building and stands on the site of a medieval settlement, in the shadow of the 'sleeping giant' mountain, close to Loch Rannoch. There is an easy informality within this comfortable family home, making guests feel completely at ease and totally relaxed. The cosy lounge, log fires and uninterrupted Highland views complement the delicious aromas from the kitchen. Jennifer Skeaping is the chef/proprietor and her good cooking and friendly manner assure you of an enjoyable stay. The menus (a choice of two main courses) change daily, fresh food is sourced locally and tastefully prepared.

Open all year except Christmas + New Year
⊞ Rooms: 7, 5 en suite
🛏 DB&B £32–£35   B&B £18–£20
SP Special rates available
✕ Dinner ££
Ⓥ Vegetarians welcome – prior notice required
✍ No smoking throughout

Three cheese tartlets with smoked venison. Tender lamb fillets in Madeira sauce garnished with sauteed kidneys and mushrooms. Lacy oat biscuits topped with heather honey and whisky ice cream and strawberries.

STB ★★ Guest House
⊞ Credit cards: Mastercard/Eurocard, Visa
⋈ Proprietor: Jennifer Skeaping

SKIARY
Loch Hourn, Invergarry
Inverness-shire PH35 4HD
Tel: 01809 511214

From Invergarry (on A82 Fort William–Inverness road) take A87 Invergarry–Kyle road. After 5 miles turn left to Kinlochourn. Proceed for 22 miles to end of single track road (allow 1 hour). Park beyond farm car park, on small parking area marked 'For Skiary only', you will then be met by boat by arrangement.

Remote, small guest house without mains electricity, accessible only by boat or on foot.

- A unique guest house on the shore of a dramatic West Highland sea-loch.
- Assured home cooking.
- "Pure air, pure spring water from Skiary burn – a pure experience of simple living with excellent hospitality and skilled cooking."

This must be the most remote guest house in Scotland but the journey is worth it. Christina's cooking is miraculous, she uses excellent fresh local game, meat and fish whenever possible. Vegetables, herbs and soft fruit come from the garden; and bread, scones and pastry are baked daily. The tiny bedrooms are charming. Views from the house are truly spectacular with an abundance of wildlife to be seen. A fantastic experience, not for the faint-hearted. Dine in the conservatory outside the cottage, overlooking the loch.

    Open Apr to Oct
🏠 Rooms: 3
🛏 £400 per week Full Board
    £70 per night DB&B + packed/light lunch
SP Special rates available
✗ Residents only
UL Unlicensed – guests welcome to take own wine
✗ Food available all day
♿ Downstairs bedroom suitable for mildly disabled visitors
🅿 No parking at establishment but parking at end of the road

Traditional home-made soups. Braised venison with oranges and red wine. Salmon baked with soured cream and tomatoes. Old-fashioned puddings, chocolate Marquise, home-made ice creams and parfaits.

💳 No credit cards
👤 Owners: John & Christina Everett

CARLIN MAGGIE'S
191 High Street
Kinross, Tayside
KY13 8DB
Tel/Fax: 01577 863652

Exit M90 at Junction 6 into town centre. Turn right at mini roundabout on to B966. Restaurant ¼ mile on left.

Innovative Scottish cuisine with international flavour.

- Small town restaurant.
- Good cooking with international accent.
- "Relaxed atmosphere, family-run restaurant with very good use of local produce."

Carlin Maggie's takes its name from a local legendary witch by the same name. The restaurant is owned by Roy and Carol Smith, Roy is chef and Carol front of house. The cooking here is skilled using good locally sourced produce which is prepared with an international and innovative flavour. This is a very welcoming, family restaurant where good food may be enjoyed in convivial and relaxed surroundings.

    Open all year except 1, 2 Jan + 30 Oct to 7 Nov
    Closed Mon
✗ Lunch except Mon £
✗ Dinner except Mon £££
V Vegetarians welcome
♢ Children welcome
♿ Facilities for disabled visitors

Smoked mussels and scallops in a herb cous cous timbale drizzled with coriander pesto. Roast saddle of venison with celeriac rösti and roasted beetroot and red wine, juniper jus. Iced raspberry parfait on a Glayva vanilla cream and pistachio tuille.

💳 Credit cards: Mastercard/Eurocard Visa, Switch, Delta, Solo, Visa Electron
👤 Proprietors: Roy and Carol Smith

THE GROUSE & CLARET RESTAURANT
Heatheryford Country Centre
Kinross
KY13 0NQ
Tel: 01577 864212
Fax: 01577 864920

Exit at Junction 6 M90 then 1st left on A977 (opposite service station).

Restaurant with rooms, Art Gallery and Fly Fishing.

- Converted sandstone farm buildings.
- Modern Scottish cooking with some oriental flavours.
- "Converted farm restaurant with rooms and art gallery in peaceful rural setting."

This popular family-run restaurant is owned by Meriel Cairns and managed by her sister Vicki Futong, whose husband David is the chef. The restaurant offers modern Scottish cooking, beautifully presented and includes traditional and speciality dishes such as seasonal game and fresh shellfish, using local produce with a daily vegetarian choice. Tastes of the orient are available in a monthly banquet. The detached accommodation is comfortable and of a good standard with some bedrooms overlooking the trout lochans. The Heatheryford Gallery has regular exhibitions of contemporary art and lends itself to corporate events, special parties and weddings.

Open all year except 2 weeks end Jan, Boxing Day + New Year's Day
Note: Closed Sun night + all day Mon
- Rooms: 3 en suite
- DB&B £55–£65   B&B £32.50–£39
- Table licence
- Lunch except Mon ££
- Dinner except Sun Mon ££-£££
- Vegetarians welcome
- Children welcome
- Facilities for disabled visitors
- No smoking in restaurant

Scottish smoked salmon, filled with smoked trout mousse on a bed of salad leaves and garden herbs with a lime and coriander dressing. Grilled breast of Gressingham duck served with oriental noodles, stir-fry vegetables and a black bean sauce. Strawberry shortcake with vanilla cream.

STB ★★★ Restaurant with Rooms
- Credit cards: Mastercard, Visa
- Proprietor: Meriel Cairns
  General Manager: Vicki Futong

DUNNIKIER HOUSE HOTEL
Dunnikier Park, Kirkcaldy
Fife KY1 3LP
Tel: 01592 268393
Fax: 01592 642340

Situated to the north of Kirkcaldy town in the grounds of Dunnikier Park. From the A92, 2 miles from Kirkcaldy west exit. 1 mile from Kirkcaldy east exit.

Country house hotel adjacent to Dunnikier Golf Club.

- 18th century hotel in parkland setting.
- Elegant Scottish cuisine.
- "A popular country house with a warm welcome."

Situated on the outskirts of Kirkcaldy this hotel stands in magnificent parkland adjacent to Dunnikier Golf Course. The south facing house was designed for James Oswald around 1790 and is ideally located for visiting Fife's fishing villages and the many sporting facilities nearby. The hotel's proprietor, Barry Bridgens, is only too happy to help with the needs of the guest at Dunnikier and promises a warm welcome. This personal attention combined with delicious food, makes for a very comfortable destination, particularly popular with business people.

Open all year
- Rooms: 14 en suite
- DB&B £62.50–£80   B&B £60
- Special rates available
- Food available all day £
- Lunch ££
- Dinner £££
- Vegetarians welcome
- Children welcome
- No smoking in restaurant

Grilled fillet of locally-caught mackerel served with smoked salmon and cucumber spaghetti with a mussel and dill cream sauce. Medallions of wild boar served with a red onion marmalade and pepper mash on an apple and rosemary sauce. Glenfiddich cup: dark chocolate cup filled with Glenfiddich liqueur and orange cream served with an orange coulis.

STB ★★★ Hotel
- Credit cards: Mastercard/Eurocard, American Express, Visa, Diners Club, Switch, Delta
- Partner: Barry Bridgens

AULD ALLIANCE RESTAURANT

Castle Street
Kirkcudbright DG6 4JA
Tel: 01557 330569

Kirkcudbright town, opposite the castle.

Small restaurant in Kirkcudbright.

- A Listed stone terraced cottage.
- French/Scottish cooking.
- "This establishment offers truly excellent cooking of fresh Scottish produce."

This is a converted tradesman's cottage built from stones quarried from Kirkcudbright Castle on the other side of the street. The restaurant is unfussy, plain and simple inside which is appropriate, as the dishes cooked by Alistair Crawford will focus your attention. They are a wonderful mixture of fresh local foods cooked in opulent, classical French style – the style in which Alistair was trained. The spirit of the establishment echoes the ancient union between Scotland and France – and what better way to express the bond than through the confluence of technique and supply.

Open Easter to 31 Oct
- ✗ Sun lunch only £
- ✗ Dinner £££
- Ⓥ Vegetarians welcome
- ☆ Children welcome
- ♿ Facilities for disabled visitors

Kirkcudbright Bay king scallops, sauteed in garlic butter, syboes, fish velouté and baked in pastry. Kirkcudbright Bay queen scallops with smoked Ayrshire bacon, finished with Galloway cream. Home-made brandy jumble basket filled with apple and Drambuie 'witches foam'.

- 💳 Mastercard/Eurocard, Visa, Switch, Delta, JCB
- Ⓜ Proprietors: Alistair & Anne Crawford

THE SELKIRK ARMS HOTEL

High Street
Kirkcudbright
Dumfries & Galloway DG6 4JG
Tel: 01557 330402
Fax: 01557 331639

At the east end of the High Street in the old part of the town.

A gourmet restaurant in a small town hotel.

- Historic hotel in a pretty town.
- Innovative Scottish.
- "Quality, innovative cuisine in a friendly and relaxed atmosphere."

This place is a gem. Chef Adam McKissock's cuisine is excellent, innovative and inspired and the dishes presented are of superb quality. This is enhanced by professional and courteous service. This is a small town hotel with good facilities but with a restaurant which is worth going out of your way to enjoy. Selkirk Arms has 1 AA Rosette.

Open all year except Christmas night
- 🛏 Rooms: 16 en suite
- 🛏 DB&B £60–£65   B&B £45–£60
- 🆂🅿 Special rates available
- ✗ Lunch £
- ✗ Dinner £££
- Ⓥ Vegetarians welcome
- ☆ Children welcome
- ♿ Facilities for disabled visitors
- 🚭 No smoking in restaurant

Pan-fried breast of pigeon on a bed of roast vegetables and a red wine jus. Seared local king scallops on a herb salad with a dill and elderflower cream. White chocolate cheesecake flavoured with Glayva set on a chocolate shortbread.

STB ★★★★ Hotel
- 💳 Credit cards: Mastercard/Eurocard, American Express, Visa, Diners Club, Switch, Delta, JCB
- Ⓜ Partners: John & Susan Morris

THE GLENISLA HOTEL
Kirkton of Glenisla, By Blairgowrie
Perthshire PH11 8PH
Tel: 01575 582223 Fax: 01575 582203
E-mail: glenislahotel@sol.co.uk
Web: www.glenisla-hotel.co.uk

From south take A93 to Blairgowrie then A926 to Alyth (4 miles). Bypass Alyth to roundabout, follow signs for Glenisla (11 miles). From north take B951 off A93, follow signs for Glenisla (7 miles).

A 17th century coaching inn.

- Whitewashed coach house.
- Traditional Scottish cooking.
- "The Glenisla offers a relaxed and informal atmosphere for its guests."

The Glenisla Hotel is located on the boundary of Angus and Perthshire amidst splendid countryside and yet within easy striking distance of Perth, Dunkeld, Blairgowrie and the many interesting attractions in this area. The hotel is run by Steve Higson and Shona Carrie who, as new owners, have invested much effort and enthusiasm into the upgrading of Glenisla and have already achieved much success. The cooking, by head chef Heather Peggie, is traditional Scottish, well-executed and skilful and is presented in a style which suits the inn. Guests may also enjoy regular malt whisky tasting and 'fruits of the forest' guided walks.

Open all year except Christmas Day and Boxing Day
🏠 Rooms: 6 with private facilities
🛏 DB&B £42.50–£49.50   B&B £33–£39
SP Special rates available
✕ Food available all day Sat Sun only
✕ Lunch ££
✕ Dinner ££
V Vegetarians welcome
🖈 Children welcome
🔥 Facilities for disabled visitors

Home-made farmhouse pâté. Local free-range duck served with a seasonal sauce. Sticky toffee pudding.

STB ★★ Hotel
💳 Credit cards: Mastercard/Eurocard, Visa, Switch, Delta
🖂 Partners: Steve Higson and Shona Carrie

LOCHSIDE LODGE & ROUNDHOUSE RESTAURANT
Bridgend of Lintrathen, By Kirriemuir
Angus DD8 5JJ
Tel: 01575 560340 Fax: 01575 560202

From Kirriemuir take the B951 Glenisla road. Pass through village of Kingoldrum (approx 3 miles). Continue along B951 for 3 miles to Lintrathen. Lochside Lodge signposted 1 mile from turn-off.

Delightful restaurant with rooms in attractive hamlet.

- Converted farm steading/roundhouse.
- Modern/traditional Scottish cuisine of a very high standard.
- "Worth a detour for this charming restaurant – this is my kind of place!"

Original stone walls and small wooden paned windows of the converted steading are a most attractive feature of this lodge and restaurant. The building is surrounded by mature trees and the loch is encircled by beech hedge and makes a delightful setting for a very special dining experience. It is expertly run, and the interior has been thoughtfully restored in keeping with the character of the building. The atmosphere is relaxed. The style of cooking is modern, with excellent local produce well-cooked, using interesting combinations on menus that present something for everyone and offering excellent value for money. Lochside Lodge has 2 AA Rosettes.

Open all year except Boxing Day + New Year's Day
Closed Mon
🏠 Rooms: 2 with private facilities
🛏 B&B £25–£35
SP Special rates available
✕ Lunch except Mon ££
✕ Dinner except Mon ££
V Vegetarians welcome
🖈 Children over 12 years welcome
🔥 Limited facilities for disabled visitors
🚭 No smoking in restaurant
🐄 Member of the Scotch Beef Club

Sauteed scallops, monkfish and asparagus spears with filo wafers and a rhubarb dressing. Seared Angus beef with horseradish crust on a pesto mash with a balsamic jus. Strawberry and raspberry millefeuille with lemon curd ice cream.

💳 Credit cards: Mastercard/Eurocard, Visa, Switch, Delta
🖂 Proprietors: Stephen & Jackie Robertson

DOUNE
Knoydart, by Mallaig
Inverness-shire, PH41 4PL
Tel/Fax: 01687 462667
E-mail: atibbetts@clara.net
Web: www.home.clara.net/atibbetts/index.htm

At Mallaig go to the public steps at the small boat pier (not the Skye ferry pier) to meet Doune's boat at the time arranged when booking made.

A magical place in a magical spot.

- Terraced rooms with wooden deck verandah.
- Fine dining with skilled seafood cooking.
- "A magical spot with a very hospitable family who offer expert help with trips and walks and feed you very well."

Doune consists of a group of stone lodges which are located right on the waterfront and from which you can listen to the Sound of Sleat lapping over the pebbles. The verandah leads to the dining room which doubles as the information office where you can obtain all the advice you need on walking routes, boat trips etc. This is a now thriving community in a part of the Highlands which had been deserted for so long and it is a delight to be able to enjoy good hospitality and cooking in this very special place.

Open 15 April to 30 Sept
🏠 Rooms: 3 with private facilities
🛏 DB&B £45–£52 (incl packed lunch) min 3 night stay
✗ Lunch by arrangement ££
✗ Dinner ££
Ⓥ Vegetarians welcome
🧒 Children welcome

Fresh Doune Bay crab with mixed leaf and herb salad from the garden. Freshly baked granary rolls. Honey and mustard roasted saddle of venison with red cabbage relish, roast potatoes and garden vegetables. Home-made lemon curd pavlova.

💳 No credit cards
👤 Partner: Liz Tibbetts

CONCHRA HOUSE
nr Dornie, by Kyle of Lochalsh
Ross-shire IV40 8DZ
Tel: 01599 555233 Fax: 01599 555433
E-mail: reservations@conchra.co.uk
Web: www.conchra.co.uk

From south continue westwards 1km on A87 past Dornie/Eilean Donan Castle. Follow hotel signposts turning right for ¾ mile (Sallachy/Killilan Road). 8 miles out of Kyle on A87.

An historic 18th century hunting lodge.

- A family-run guest house.
- Good fresh food, plainly cooked.
- "A comfortable country house set in lovely surroundings."

Conchra House was built in the 1760s to house the government's agent in Kintail, following the seizure of Jacobite estates after the '45 Rising. The house is most attractive, fits into the landscape well and enjoys a lovely situation overlooking Loch Long. It is full of interesting antiques and period details. Conchra means 'a fold' or 'haven' and the stated aim of Colin and Mary Deans, resident owners, is to provide just this for their guests. They succeed in full measure. The place is wonderfully peaceful; guests are made to feel very much at home; the food is simple but intelligently cooked and appetising. A gem of a place.

Open all year except 24, 25, 31 Dec + 1, 2 Jan
🏠 Rooms: 6, (5 en suite, 1 with private facilities)
🛏 DB&B £37.50–£57.50   B&B £25–£40
SP Special rates available
✗ Open to non-residents – by arrangement
❢ Restricted licence
✗ Lunch – by prior arrangement ££
Ⓥ Vegetarians welcome
🧒 Children welcome
🚭 No smoking throughout

Cream of celery and cashew nut soup served with crusty bread. Monkfish tails served in a garlic butter sauce with new potatoes and fresh vegetables. Freshly baked nectarine cheesecake.

STB ★★★★ Guest House
💳 Credit cards: Mastercard/Eurocard, American Express, Visa, Switch
👤 Proprietors: Colin & Mary Deans

THE SEAFOOD RESTAURANT

Railway Station, Kyle of Lochalsh
Ross-shire IV40 8XX
Tel: 01599 534813

At Kyle of Lochalsh railway station on platform 1.
Parking on slipway to station.

An informal bistro and cafe in an unusual setting.

- Converted station waiting room.
- Freshly cooked, good quality food.
- "Good food - making the best of local produce."

A railway platform is not the obvious choice of location for a restaurant but it is worth taking the trouble to track down The Seafood Restaurant for you will not be disappointed. The station is right next to the harbour in Kyle of Lochalsh close to the ferry terminal which, before the bridge, was the main crossing point to Skye. The food here is cooked with flair and imagination with only the finest of local produce, everything is sourced locally. The menu consists mainly of fish and shellfish with Jann's husband landing his catch daily. There is also an interesting selection of meat and vegetarian dishes and a daily blackboard special. In the peak season there is a breakfast and lunch menu with a selection of simple, home-cooked fare which changes to give a more sophisticated à la carte choice in the evening. You are advised to check opening hours as they vary depending on the time of year.

Open Easter to Oct
🍷 Table licence
✕ Lunch except Sun Sat £
✕ Dinner ££
Ⓥ Vegetarians welcome
🏃 Children welcome
♿ Limited facilities for disabled visitors
🚭 No smoking in restaurant

Queen scallops in oatmeal: Lochcarron queenies rolled in oatmeal, deep-fried and served with lemon. Seafood kebabs: fresh monkfish, scallops and langoustines grilled and served with a dill and orange sauce. Home-made ice cream: Skye whisky and honey ice cream served with shortbread.

💳 Credit cards: Mastercard/Eurocard, Visa
👤 Owners: Jann Macrae & Andrea Matheson

SEAGREEN RESTAURANT & BOOKSHOP

Plockton Road
Kyle of Lochalsh IV40 8DA
Tel: 01599 534388

Just immediately outside Kyle on the Duirinish to Plockton visitor route.

A relaxed, informal bistro combined with bookshop and gallery.

- Charming stone-built bistro restaurant.
- Modern Scottish cooking, innovative and of good quality.
- "Freshly cooked wholefoods and local seafood - what a combination!"

Situated on the outskirts of Kyle of Lochalsh this is a very attractive complex of an open-plan kitchen and large, spacious dining area with a bookshop. The evening dining room exhibits works of local painters and photographers. Outside there is a sheltered sunny garden and terrace, popular with guests. An all-day counter service offers delicious salads, soups, home baking, etc., all made on the premises from fresh local ingredients. The restaurant offers very good wholefood but the emphasis is increasingly on fish and shellfish. In the evening a full à la carte dinner menu is served. The style of the food is different from that served during the day with a more sophisticated continental/European influenced menu. Investor in People Award.

Open all year except 25, 26 Dec,
1 Jan + 6 Jan – Easter
✕ Lunch £
✕ Dinner ££-£££ reservations preferred
Ⓥ Vegetarians welcome
🏃 Children welcome
♿ Facilities for disabled visitors
🚭 No smoking in restaurant

Local goats cheese soufflé, walnut dressed salad. Sole fillets filled with Lochalsh crabmeat, coriander, lime with foaming red pepper hollandaise. Cock o' the North liqueur ice cream with blaeberries.

💳 Credit cards: Mastercard/Eurocard, Visa, Switch
👤 Chef/Proprietor: Fiona Begg

THE OLD SMIDDY GUEST HOUSE
WINNER OF THE MACALLAN
TASTE OF SCOTLAND AWARD
1999 – SMALL RESIDENCE
Laide, nr Gairloch
Wester Ross IV22 2NB
Tel/Fax: 01445 731425
E-mail: oldsmiddy@aol.com
Web: www.s-h-systems.co.uk/hotels/oldsmid.html

On the main road at Laide, on the A832 Gairloch – Braemore road.

Unique cottage guest house with small restaurant in the tiny village of Laide.

- Small guest house.
- Imaginative, creative, Scottish home cooking.
- "A genuine Scottish welcome awaits you here, matched by the extremely high culinary skills of Kate and Steve."

Just ten minutes from the famous subtropical Inverewe Gardens sits a delightful Highland retreat – the Old Smiddy. It is a warm and friendly little cottage with a well-appointed restaurant with beautiful views over the hills. Absolutely everything is thought of for the rooms in order to make the guests stay more enjoyable. Proprietors, Kate and Steve Macdonald are very skilled breadmakers, and their home baking is excellent with great attention to flavours. The best quality Scottish produce is sourced for taste as well as calibre. Kate has a wealth of local knowledge.

Open Apr until Nov
🏠 Rooms: 3 en suite
🛏 DB&B £50–£54   B&B £26–£30
SP Special rates available
UL Unlicensed – guests welcome to take own wine
✕ Dinner – early booking advisable for non-residents £££
V Vegetarians welcome
♿ Facilities for non-resident disabled visitors
🚭 No smoking throughout

Grilled red pepper and saffron soup with chilli cream. Trio of monkfish, turbot and salmon with langoustine and fennel sauce, served with Parmesan and lovage potatoes and rocket and oakleaf salad leaves. Fresh garden strawberry ice cream and raspberry almond torte.

STB ★★★★ Guest House
💳 Credit cards: Mastercard/Eurocard, Visa
🅽 Proprietors: Kate & Steve Macdonald

THE LODGE AT CARFRAEMILL
Lauder, Berwickshire
TD2 6RA
Tel: 01578 750750 Fax: 01578 750751
E-mail: enquiries@carfraemill.co.uk
Web: www.carfraemill.co.uk

Situated at the junction of the A68/A697, just 21 miles south of Edinburgh, 80 miles north of Newcastle and 70 miles from Glasgow.

Relaxed, informal atmosphere and stylish home cooking – you will not leave hungry.

- A former coaching inn - recently renovated.
- Well-balanced traditional home cooking
- " A great place to visit and ideally located for a good meal on a journey."

Originally a coaching inn, Carfraemill has been a hotel for many years. It was taken over by its present owner in 1997 and has undergone extensive renovation and modernisation since then which has truly transformed the place. Jo Sutherland has made sure that this is a most welcoming place for visitors, diners, locals and travellers which offers comfortable surroundings, and good food. The menus, with a strong emphasis on local produce, change regularly and meals are presented with flair.

Open all year
🏠 Rooms: 10 en suite
🛏 DB&B £50–£70   B&B £35–£55
SP Special rates available
✕ Food available all day £
✕ Lunch £
✕ Dinner ££
V Vegetarians welcome
🧍 Children welcome
♿ Facilities for disabled visitors
🚭 No smoking area in restaurant + no smoking in bedrooms

Award-winning haggis in a filo parcel surrounded by a Drambuie cream. Herb-crusted Border lamb fillet with a balsamic dressing accompanied by a potato mint purée. Raspberry and oatmeal cranachan served with Carfraemill shortbread.

STB ★★★★ Hotel
💳 Credit cards: Mastercard/Eurocard, American Express, Visa, Diners Club, Switch, Delta
🅽 Owner: Jo Sutherland

LIVINGSTON'S RESTAURANT
High Street
Linlithgow, West Lothian
EH49 7AE
Tel: 01506 846565

At eastern end of the High Street opposite the Post Office.

Outstanding small restaurant – special in many ways.

- Restaurant in old stone cottage.
- Modern Scottish cooking.
- "A very special restaurant which prides itself rightly in the extra attention put into little details."

This is a delightful little cottage tucked behind the High Street. Exposed stone walls and assorted tables and chairs provide a charm and warmth which is enhanced by dark red candles, table mats and napkins. The atmosphere is friendly and informal and the food and service is of the highest quality. There is also a conservatory which overlooks a pleasant little attractive garden. Chef David Williams is enthusiastic and is a skilful and imaginative cook who provides interesting menus with much evidence of fresh Scottish produce. Livingston's has 2 AA Rosettes.

Open Feb to Dec except 1 week Oct
Closed Sun Mon
✘   Lunch except Sun Mon £
✘   Dinner except Sun Mon £££
Ⓥ   Vegetarians welcome
⚘   Children over 8 years welcome – evenings
&.   Facilities for disabled visitors
⚬   Smoking permitted in conservatory
🐄   Member of the Scotch Beef Club

Crêpe of West Lothian black pudding with balsamic infused shallots. Roast saddle of venison served with a miniature Forfar bridie and bramble jus. Crème brûlée with iced rhubarb sherbet.

⊞   Credit cards: Mastercard/Eurocard, Visa, Switch
⋈   Manager: Fiona Livingston

CAMERON HOUSE HOTEL AND COUNTRY ESTATE
Loch Lomond, Alexandria
Dunbartonshire G83 8QZ
Tel: 01389 755565   Fax: 01389 759522
E-mail: devere.cameron@airtime.co.uk
Web: www.cameronhouse.co.uk

On A82 near Balloch, on the banks of Loch Lomond. At Balloch roundabout follow signs for Luss. Approx 1 mile, first right.

Luxury hotel and leisure complex on the shores of Loch Lomond.

- Ancestral country house with time-share lodges and a state-of-the-art leisure complex.
- Modern contemporary cooking.
- "Wake up to spectacular views and enjoy the best of Scottish cooking."

A luxury hotel resort on the southern shore of Loch Lomond, standing in 108 acres of parkland. Executive Chef Peter Fleming presents a highly sophisticated and imaginative menu in the hotel's main restaurant, the elegant Georgian Room. The bright and airy Smolletts Restaurant has a more relaxed atmosphere and offers a wide variety of dishes from an à la carte menu; bar snacks are available in the Breakers Restaurant at the Marina. The Georgian Room restaurant has 3 AA Rosettes. Shortlisted and Commended for The Macallan Taste of Scotland Awards 1999.

Open all year
🏠   Rooms: 96 en suite
🛏   DB&B £200–£265   B&B £180–£245
✘   Food available all day £-££££
✘   Lunch except Sat ££
✘   Dinner ££££
Ⓥ   Vegetarians welcome
⚘   Children welcome
&.   Facilities for disabled visitors
⚬   Smoking in public areas only
🐄   Member of the Scotch Beef Club

Roast langoustine tails, beside a crab risotto surrounded by a shellfish cream. Roast saddle of Scottish lamb accompanied by a sweet potato galette on onion chutney and port essence. Hot passion fruit soufflé served with exotic fruit sorbet.

STB ★★★★ Hotel
⊞   Credit cards: Mastercard/Eurocard, American Express, Visa, Diners Club
⋈   Executive Chef: Peter Fleming

COACH HOUSE COFFEE SHOP
Luss, Loch Lomond
Argyll G83 8NN
Tel: 01436 860341 Fax: 01436 860336

Turn off A82 (Glasgow to Crianlarich) at signpost for Luss. Park in car park and walk towards church.

Coffee house with gift shop.

- Stone-fronted large coach house.
- Home baking and light meals.
- "King-size scones, muffins and cakes all made daily."

Set in the heart of the conservation village of Luss, a warm welcome is extended by the kilted Mr Groves whilst his wife supervises the making of delicious hearty snacks, home-made soups, light meals and good home baking. Hand made soft bread rolls are filled with chunky ham, honey-roasted on the premises and other fillings include eggs from their own free-range Black Rock hens. A wide range of teas and coffees complement the giant scones, muffins and cakes – and if that is not enough try the original Orkney ice creams. In fair weather all this may be enjoyed outside in the secluded garden area and in the winter in front of a roaring log fire. The Coach House is a member of the Tea Council's Guild of Teashops.

Open all year except Christmas Day
Unlicensed
Food available all day £
Lunch £
Vegetarians welcome
Children welcome
Facilities for disabled visitors
No smoking throughout
Dogs welcome

Carrot and parsnip soup served with a hunk of bread. Leek and cheese quiche served with salad, coleslaw and fresh or garlic bread. Victoria sandwich. Caffe latte: single espresso with steamed milk and a little frothed milk.

Credit cards: Mastercard/Eurocard, Visa, Switch, Delta, Solo
Proprietors: Gary and Rowena Groves

THE LODGE ON LOCH LOMOND HOTEL & RESTAURANT
Luss, Argyll & Bute G83 8PA
Tel: 0143 686 0201 Fax: 0143 686 0203
E-mail: lusslomond@aol.com
Web: www.loch-lomond.co.uk

In the village of Luss on the A82 main route along Loch Lomond side. Well-sign posted.

A modern, purpose-built hotel on the shores of Loch Lomond.

- Modern stylish hotel.
- Modern Scottish cooking.
- "With food to suit all tastes and pockets, sit back and enjoy the views."

The Lodge on Loch Lomond is set in a particularly stunning location on the shores of Loch Lomond offering panoramic views with the mountains in the distance. The hotel is set in delightful gardens beside the conservation village of Luss and whilst it is a modern building it is very stylish and welcoming. The interior is very much in keeping with a hunting lodge with much quality pine in both the decor and furnishings making a warm and appealing place to enjoy all that this area has to offer. Every bedroom has its own sauna! The bar and restaurant overlook the loch and present menus which offer something to suit every taste. Cooking is skilled, presentation is attractive, and imaginative use is made of local produce. The restaurant has 1 AA Rosette. *See advert page 21.*

Open all year
Rooms: 29 en suite
DB&B £55–£85 B&B £30–£63
Special rates available
Food available all day ££
Lunch ££
Dinner ££
Vegetarians welcome
Children welcome
Facilities for disabled visitors
No smoking in restaurant

Loin of rabbit, Dunkeld black pudding, lambs lettuce and beetroot chutney. Monkfish wrapped in crispy cabbage and smoked bacon, paprika-spiced whitebait. Apricot bread and butter pudding with orange-flavoured custard.

STB ★★★ Hotel
Credit cards: Mastercard/Eurocard, American Express, Visa, Switch, Delta
Manager: Niall Colquhoun

ROCKVILLA HOTEL & RESTAURANT

Main Street, Lochcarron
Ross-shire IV54 8YB
Tel: 01520 722379
Fax: 01520 722844
E-mail: rockvillahotel@btinternet.com
Web: www.smoothhound.co.uk/hotels/rockvill.html

Situated in centre of village, c. 20 miles north of Kyle of Lochalsh.

Little hotel in centre of village.

- Small family-run hotel.
- Traditional Scottish cooking.
- "Wonderful views where all the seasons come and go."

This is an attractive little restaurant with bar and four comfortable rooms above, which has an open outlook to the loch and hills. Rockvilla holds a huge welcome for all its guests, and good food comes naturally. Ken and Lorna Wheelan, proprietors, have chosen some of the local produce to enhance their menus, which will appeal to everyone . An à la carte dinner menu offers excellent value and gives a good choice of starters, main courses and puddings. Local specialities and traditional favourites also appear. After a hearty breakfast guests are well set up for a day's walking, fishing or exploring the West Highlands with its dramatic scenery.

Open all year except Christmas Day + 1 Jan
🏠 Rooms: 4, 3 en suite
🛏 B&B £22–£30
SP Special rates available
✗ Lunch £
✗ Dinner ££
Ⓥ Vegetarians welcome
🧒 Children welcome
🚭 No smoking in restaurant

Salad of hot-smoked venison, sweet charentaise melon and quails eggs, with juniper berry chutney. Saddle of Scottish lamb stuffed with black pudding, with roasted root vegetables and a tomato and basil sauce. Sweet pancakes with citrus and Grand Marnier sauce and an orange marmalade ice cream.

STB ★★★ Hotel
💳 Credit cards: Mastercard/Eurocard, American Express, Visa, Switch, Delta, JCB
👤 Proprietors: Lorna & Kenneth Wheelan

THE ALBANNACH

Lochinver, Sutherland IV27 4LP
Tel: 01571 844407 Fax: 01571 844285

From Lochinver follow signs for Baddidarroch. After ½ mile, pass turning for Highland Stoneware, turn left for the Albannach.

An excellent small restaurant overlooking Lochinver.

- Restaurant with rooms.
- Contemporary Scottish cooking.
- "The Albannach recaptures the flavours of real food – an exceptional experience."

The Albannach is a 19th century house of considerable architectural character standing in a small glen overlooking Lochinver and the wild country beyond. It has been tastefully decorated by Colin Craig and has a Victorian feel and a cosy atmosphere. Drinks are available in the conservatory, which has a paved patio and stone balustrade beyond it. Dinner is served in the wood-panelled, candlelit dining room. Lesley Crosfield presents a set, four course dinner menu sourced from the finest free-range produce. The cooking is creative and the flavours are a revelation to any palate. Colin Craig serves at table resplendent in kilt and Jacobean shirt, and some nights a piper plays outside before dinner. Winner of The Macallan Taste of Scotland Award For Overall Excellence 1998 and Best Restaurant With Rooms 1998.

Open last 2 weeks Mar to 27 Dec
🏠 Rooms: 5 en suite
🛏 DB&B £59–£70
SP Special rates available
✗ Non-residents welcome – booking essential
🍷 Table licence
✗ Dinner 5 course menu £££
Ⓥ Vegetarians welcome – by prior arrangement
🧒 Children over 10 years welcome
🚭 No smoking throughout

Roast cod on braised leeks with sauce vierge. Fillet of hill-fed Highland lamb with Puy lentils and a spinach and pine nut tartlet with port sauce. Aniseed parfait with Scottish berry fruits and blackberry coulis.

STB ★★★ Hotel
💳 Credit cards: Mastercard/Eurocard, Visa, Switch, Delta, JCB
👤 Chef/Proprietors: Lesley Crosfield & Colin Craig

INVER LODGE HOTEL
Iolaire Road, Lochinver
Sutherland IV27 4LU
Tel: 01571 844496 Fax: 01571 844395
E-mail: inverlodge@compuserve.com
Web: www.inverlodge.com

A837 to Lochinver, first turn on left after village hall.
½ mile up private road to hotel.

West Highland hotel in the 'grand hotel' tradition.

- A modern luxury hotel with outstanding views.
- Traditional Scottish.
- "Modern hotel with grand traditions."

Inver Lodge stands on the hill above Lochinver village and bay, and enjoys panoramic views across the Minch and the wild country of Assynt. The building itself is long, low and plain – even spartan. Inside, however, it is comfortably and tastefully appointed, with a 'highland shooting lodge' theme (it has good private fishing for salmon and trout); public rooms and bedrooms are spacious and airy, and all share the terrific view. It has a snooker room, solarium and sauna. Members of staff are uniformed in tartan, well-trained and courteous. À la carte and table d'hôte menus feature Lochinver-landed fish and shellfish and Assynt venison. The cooking is highly professional, and the presentation and service is in the 'grand hotel' style. Great care and effort goes into every aspect of Inver Lodge's hospitality. Inver Lodge has 1 AA Rosette. *See advert page 258.*

Open 10 Apr to 1 Nov
🏠 Rooms: 20 en suite
🛏 DB&B £75–£100   B&B £60–£100
ᴾ Special rates available
✕ Lunch £
✕ Dinner £££
Ⅴ Vegetarians welcome
☆ Children welcome
✗ No smoking in dining room
🐄 Member of the Scotch Beef Club

Crab cakes with lemon and ginger served with a dill sauce. Highland venison served on a bed of red cabbage and served with a rowanberry sauce. Cranachan and seasonal fruits.

STB ★★★★ Hotel
💳 Credit cards: Mastercard/Eurocard, American Express, Visa, Diners Club, Switch, Delta, JCB
👤 General Manager: Nicholas Gorton

DRYFESDALE HOTEL
Lockerbie
Dumfriesshire DG11 2SF
Tel: 01576 202427
Fax: 01576 204187
E-mail: dryfesdalehotel@adunbobbin.freeserve.co.uk
Web: www.dryfesdalehotel.co.uk

Junction 17 on M74. Head towards Lockerbie at first roundabout take first left. Hotel entrance is 100 yards on left.

Delightful family-run hotel, set in its own grounds which overlook breathtaking countryside.

- Former manse - now country house hotel.
- Modern Scottish cooking.
- "A comfortable, friendly hotel with a reputation locally for good food."

Built in 1782, Dryfesdale was converted into a country house hotel in the early 1950s. Only one mile from Lockerbie, the hotel is set in delightful grounds (5 acres) which are well-kept and afford superb views of the countryside. This is an elegant and informal hotel which is run by the Dunbobbin family who took over in 1995. They aim to provide a very high standard of experience for their guests, from the quality of the accommodation to the excellent food – and they succeed.

Open all year, except Christmas Day night and Boxing Day
🏠 Rooms: 15 en suite
🛏 DB&B £75–£85 B&B £55–£65
✕ Food available all day ££
✕ Lunch ££
✕ Dinner £££
Ⅴ Vegetarians welcome
☆ Children welcome
♿ Facilities for disabled visitors
✗ No smoking in dining room
🐕 Dogs welcome on ground floor only

Dryfesdale tartlett filled with haggis and mushrooms, topped with a poached egg and a creamy whisky sauce and deep-fried onions. Galloway shank of lamb sat on boulangere potatoes with baby vegetables and red wine gravy. Sticky toffee pudding smothered in butterscotch sauce and served with ice cream.

STB ★★★ Hotel
💳 Credit cards: Mastercard, American Express, Visa, Switch, Delta
👤 Owners: The Dunbobbin Family

SOMERTON HOUSE HOTEL
Carlisle Road
Lockerbie DG11 2DR
Tel: 01576 202583
Fax: 01576 204218

Follow High Street eastwards towards M74, 1 mile from town centre.

Small, family hotel on the edge of the town.

- Sandstone mansion.
- Classic contemporary.
- "Warm, friendly hotel producing fine home-cooked food."

Situated on the outskirts of town with views to open countryside, yet within easy striking distance of the M74, the hotel stands in its own spacious grounds facing the road with well-kept pretty gardens to one side and ample private parking. Inside, this attractive merchant's villa/mansion has retained, in excellent order, many of its superb original features. These are combined expertly with all the best of modern comforts, making the hotel a relaxing and charming place to stay. Diners have the choice of eating in the extensive cosy lounge where a bar menu is available; the conservatory; and in the delightful dining room where a full à la carte is served. The food is hearty and the dishes familiar but served with some style in these pleasant surroundings. Popular with locals and visitors alike, a warm welcome awaits guests at the Somerton.

Open all year
- ⊞ Rooms: 11 en suite
- 🛏 B&B £26–£30
- ✗ Lunch £
- ✗ Dinner ££-£££
- Ⓥ Vegetarians welcome
- 🕏 Children welcome
- 🚭 No smoking in dining room

Lowland Ham and Haddie: a local speciality of smoked haddock and ham in a cream sauce topped with croûtons, tomato and cheese. Fillet of ostrich with a creamy tarragon sauce. Meringue and mango roulade.

STB ★★★ Hotel
- 🆔 Credit cards: Mastercard/Eurocard, American Express, Visa, Diners Club
- 🅗 Proprietors: Alex & Jean Arthur

THE FISH MARKET
Station Road, Mallaig
Inverness-shire PH41 4QS
Tel: 01687 462299 Fax: 01687 462623

In the centre of village overlooking the harbour. A 2 minute walk from railway station and 5 minutes from ferry terminal.

Fresh seafood in informal surroundings.

- Modern corner building near the harbour.
- Imaginative Scottish cooking.
- "Lovely fresh seafood by the harbour."

The Fish Market restaurant is in a new building with downstairs restaurant and more eating space upstairs, which is occasionally used for private meetings/lunches. The restaurant is relatively young and everything is fresh and clean. Items from large white bowls of prawns to fresh haddock and fries are served, with home baking for teas and coffees. The restaurant is run by Sandra McLean who makes the very best of the plentiful supplies of fresh produce to ensure diners enjoy her cooking at its best.

Open all year except Christmas Day, 31 Dec + New Year's Day
- ✗ Lunch £-££
- ✗ Dinner £-££
- Ⓥ Vegetarians welcome
- 🕏 Children welcome
- ♿ Facilities for disabled visitors

Creamy smoked haddock soup. Grilled whole sea bass with plum and star anise compote. Chocolate truffle torte.

- 🆔 Credit cards: Mastercard/Eurocard, Visa, Switch, Delta
- 🅗 Proprietor: Sandra McLean

MARINE HOTEL
Mallaig
Inverness-shire PH41 4PY
Tel: 01687 462217 Fax: 01687 462821
E-mail: marinehotel@btinternet.com

Adjacent to railway station. First hotel on right off A830, and a 5 minute walk from ferry terminal.

A family-run hotel in the fishing port of Mallaig.

- Long established local small town hotel.
- Traditional cooking.
- "Good home-cooking using some of the local catch."

Mallaig is at the end of the famous West Highland Railway Line and also marks the termination of The Road to the Isles. Once the busiest herring port in Britain, the town has still a busy fishing harbour and is the main ferry terminal to the Hebrides. The exterior of the Marine does not complement the refurbished interior which offers well-appointed, comfortable bedrooms. The menus, which are offered in both the lounge bar and the restaurant, take full advantage of freshly landed fish and shellfish. The staff are friendly, attentive and efficient. The hotel is popular with both locals and tourists alike. Good selection of malt whiskies available. Investor in People Award.

Open all year except Christmas Day + New Year's Day
Note: Restricted service Nov to Mar
🏠 Rooms: 19 (18 en suite, 1 with private facilities)
🛏 DB&B £40–£45   B&B £26–£32
[SP] Special rates available
✗ Lunch ££
✗ Dinner ££
[V] Vegetarians welcome
⽊ Children welcome
& Limited facilities for disabled visitors
⽏ No smoking in restaurant

Grilled whole langoustines with garlic butter. Roast monkfish with julienne of carrot and leek on a seafood sauce. Caramelised lemon tart.

STB ★★★ Hotel
⊞ Credit cards: Mastercard/Eurocard, Visa
⋈ Proprietor: Dalla Ironside

LADYBURN
by Maybole, Ayrshire KA19 7SG
Tel: 01655 740 585
Fax: 01655 740 580
E-mail: jhdh@ladyburn.freeserve.co.uk
Web: www.ladyburn.co.uk

A77 (Glasgow-Stranraer) to Maybole then B7023 to Crosshill. Turn right at War Memorial (Dailly-Girvan). After exactly 2 miles, turn left and follow signs. 5 miles south of Maybole.

Country house hotel.

- 17th century country house.
- Home cooking.
- "Ladyburn's atmosphere and standard of cooking are of a very high standard."

Ladyburn is an historic house set deep in 'the most beautiful valley in Ayrshire' and is the family home of Jane and David Hepburn. There is a homely authenticity about the food served in the dining room, reflecting Jane Hepburn's commitment to produce genuine dishes cooked with original touches of flavours and textures; neither overbearing nor trendily understated. Substantial well-tried recipes cooked with care are the order of the day. Dining room open at all times for residents. Italian and French spoken.

Open all year except 2 weeks Nov + 4 weeks during Jan to Mar
🏠 Rooms: 5 en suite
🛏 DB&B £90–£120   B&B £70–£100
[SP] Special rates available
⚱ Restricted licence
✗ Reservations essential for non-residents
✗ Lunch except Mon ££
✗ Dinner except Sun Mon £££
[V] Vegetarians welcome
⽊ Children over 16 years welcome
& Facilities for disabled visitors
⽏ No smoking in dining room, drawing room + bedrooms

Broccoli soufflé with a fresh tomato and basil sauce. Poêle of pheasant breasts served in a sauce of white wine, cream and pomegranate juice, surrounded by fresh grapes and orange segments. Lemon layer pudding with fresh whipped cream.

⊞ Credit cards: Mastercard/Eurocard, American Express, Visa
⋈ Proprietors: Jane & David Hepburn

BURTS HOTEL
Market Square, Melrose
Roxburghshire TD6 9PN
Tel: 01896 822285 Fax: 01896 822870
E-mail: burtshotel@aol.com
Web: www.burtshotel.co.uk

A6091, 2 miles from A68, 38 miles south of Edinburgh.

Family-run town house hotel.

- Delightful 18th century restored inn.
- Modern Scottish cooking.
- "A family-run hotel offering warm Border's hospitality and good Scottish food."

Burts Hotel is a delightful 18th century town house hotel offering warm hospitality and innovative cooking using the best of produce from Scotland's natural larder. It is run by Graham, Anne and Nicholas Henderson, professional and friendly hosts, who ensure that the hotel is maintained to a very high standard and is comfortable with a most relaxing atmosphere. Their restaurant has a good local reputation. The daily changing lunch and dinner menus are ambitious and display imaginative combinations, creative confidence and a sound appreciation of appropriate flavours. The cooking and presentation is akin to that which you would expect to find in a refined country house. Burts Hotel has 2 AA Rosettes. *See advert page 25.*

Open all year except Boxing Day
🏠 Rooms: 20 en suite
🛏 DB&B £60–£69   B&B £44–£50
SP Special rates available
✘ Lunch except Christmas Day + Boxing Day ££
✘ Dinner except Christmas Day + Boxing Day £££
Ⓥ Vegetarians welcome
⚘ Children welcome
🚭 No smoking in restaurant
🐄 Member of the Scotch Beef Club

Carpaccio of fresh tuna complemented with a gâteau of Parmesan crisps. Medallion of Scotch beef fillet served with seared scallops in a filo tartlet with creamed leeks and basil salsa. Marbled white and dark chocolate timbale wrapped in a chocolate overcoat served with a minted Mascarpone cream.

STB ★★★★ Hotel
💳 Credit cards: Mastercard/Eurocard, American Express, Visa, Diners Club, Switch, Delta, JCB
🕴 Manager: Nicholas Henderson

DRYBURGH ABBEY HOTEL
Dryburgh, Melrose
Roxburghshire TD6 0RQ
Tel: 01835 822261
Fax: 01835 823945
E-mail: enquiries@dryburgh.co.uk

Off A68 at St Boswells onto B6404. 2 miles turn left onto B6356. Continue for 1½ miles, hotel signposted.

A luxury hotel, with swimming pool, owned by a family with 100 years experience.

- Scottish baronial red sandstone mansion on the banks of the River Tweed.
- International and modern Scottish cuisine.
- "Dryburgh Abbey is set in beautiful well-tended gardens on the banks of the Tweed."

In a most romantic and tranquil setting on the banks of the River Tweed, adjacent to the ruins of the historic abbey, this hotel offers quiet peace and a restful stay, overlooking the ancient abbey. Dryburgh Abbey has been restored and converted into a first class hotel, including indoor heated swimming pool. The Tweed Restaurant is situated on the first floor, with views over the lawns and gardens to the river. It is a spacious, elegant room with decorative cornicing and ornate chandeliers. The head chef, Carl Morgan, offers a table d'hôte menu (lunch and dinner) which changes daily, and uses only fresh local produce. During the day and evening a range of light meals is also available, served in the lounge or bar.

Open all year
🏠 Rooms: 37 en suite
🛏 DB&B £52–£93   B&B £38–£70.50
SP Special rates available
✘ Food available all day £
✘ Lunch from £-££
✘ Dinner from £££
Ⓥ Vegetarians welcome
⚘ Children welcome
♿ Facilities for disabled visitors
🚭 No smoking in restaurant

Steamed sole and salmon mousseline with white wine and lobster cream. Pan-fried pigeon breast carved onto a julienne of vegetables with port wine jus. Lavender and peach crème brûlée.

STB ★★★★ Hotel
💳 Credit cards: Mastercard/Eurocard, American Express, Visa, Switch, Delta, JCB
🕴 General Manager: Matthew Grose

HOEBRIDGE INN RESTAURANT

Gattonside, Melrose
Roxburghshire TD6 9LZ
Tel/Fax: 01896 823082
E-mail: hoebridge@easynet.co.uk

From A68 take sign to Gattonside. First left on
entering the village of Gattonside.

Country restaurant.

- Village restaurant.
- Modern Scottish cooking.
- "A memorable meal cooked and prepared with
  great care and attention, and refreshingly
  imaginative."

The Hoebridge dates back to 1840 when the original
building was a bobbin mill. It has a friendly, relaxed
atmosphere with simple yet tasteful decor in
keeping with the building's white walls, wooden
beams and wooden tables. The food here is good
quality Scottish fare, presented and cooked by
Maureen Rennie in a modern style. Attention to
detail is excellent, imaginative food combinations
impressively executed. The restaurant has the buzz
and general atmosphere found in traditional village
inns and is well worth seeking out. A real find.

Open Mar to Jan except Boxing Day + New
Year's Day
Closed Mon
✗ Christmas Day lunch
✗ Dinner ££
Ⓥ Vegetarians welcome

**Seared salmon fillet with wilted spinach and
langoustine vinaigrette. Char-grilled saddle of roe
deer with cardomom-roasted pears and coriander
oil. Fine gooseberry crumble tart with elderflower
Champagne sorbet.**

🖾 Credit cards: Mastercard/Eurocard, Visa,
  Switch, Delta
🄽 Proprietors: Tony & Maureen Rennie

WELL VIEW HOTEL

Ballplay Road, Moffat
Dumfriesshire DG10 9JU
Tel: 01683 220184
Fax: 01683 220088
Web: www.wellview.co.uk

Leaving Moffat take A708. At crossroads, left into
Ballplay Road – hotel on right.

Family-run hotel offering first class cuisine.

- Victorian town house with gardens.
- Modern Scottish cooking.
- "An excellent blend of natural cooking and the
  tastes of Scottish produce."

Janet and John Schuckardt run this traditional
hotel, which has a peaceful garden and stands on
the outskirts of Moffat. It is within easy walking
distance of the centre of this charming town which
sits in a fertile plain below the dramatic Devil's Beef
Tub. John has a good knowledge of wine and has
over 100 Bins available. The six course taster menu
demonstrates an inventive approach to more
familiar dishes, accompanied by light fruity sauces
and dressings. The meat is served pink and the
vegetables al dente, which is a good sign of use of
fresh produce. The owners go out of their way to
look after their guests every need. Prior reservation
essential for both lunch and dinner. German and a
little French spoken. Well View has 2 AA Rosettes.

Open all year
🛏 Rooms: 6 en suite
🛌 DB&B £62–£90   B&B £34–£65
🆂🅿 Special rates available
✗ Lunch except Sat ££
✗ Dinner 6 course menu £££
Ⓥ Vegetarians welcome
🧒 Children over 5 years welcome at dinner
🚭 No smoking throughout

**Filo casket of Kirkcudbright queenies and wild
mushrooms on a bed of wilted baby spinach. Roast
saddle of Annandale venison on a bed of cous cous
with a gin and juniper sauce.**

STB ★★★★ Hotel
🖾 Credit cards: Mastercard/Eurocard, American
  Express, Visa
🄽 Owners: Janet & John Schuckardt

ORD HOUSE HOTEL

Muir of Ord
Ross-shire IV6 7UH
Tel/Fax: 01463 870 492
E-mail: eliza@ord-house.com

On A832 Ullapool-Marybank, ½ mile west of Muir of Ord.

A relaxed and friendly small country house hotel in beautiful surroundings.

- Country house hotel.
- Good country cooking.
- "An old manison house offering good hospitality, good food and lots of character and charm."

John and Eliza Allen offer their guests the unhurried peace of a bygone age in this 17th century laird's house. Open fires and an elegant drawing room match the calm beauty of the hotel's 50 acres of grounds. Bedrooms are tastefully decorated and well-appointed. The dining room offers unpretentious and reasonably-priced honest country cooking that uses fresh meat, game and fish and vegetables in season from the hotel's own garden. Service is attentive without being fussy. The wine list is sound and inexpensive. Fluent French is spoken.

Open 1 May to 20 Oct
🏠 Rooms: 10 en suite
🛏 DB&B £57–£68   B&B £36–£48
✕ Lunch £
✕ Dinner 4 course menu ££
Ⓥ Vegetarians welcome
🕊 Children welcome
🚭 No smoking in dining room

Salad of quails eggs, artichoke hearts and smoked salmon. Pan-fried strips of venison fillet with redcurrant and port sauce. Sticky gingerbread pudding with ginger wine and brandy sauce.

STB ★★ Hotel
💳 Credit cards: Mastercard/Eurocard, American Express, Visa
🔖 Proprietors: John & Eliza Allen

BOATH HOUSE

Auldearn, Nairn
IV12 5TE
Tel: 01667 454896 Fax: 01667 455469
E-mail: wendy@boath-house.demon.co.uk
Web: www.boath-house.demon.co.uk

On A96, 2 miles east of Nairn.

Magnificence without pretention, in this fine Georgian hotel set in 20 acres of woodlands.

- Classical Georgian mansion.
- Innovative Scottish with European influences.
- "A little piece of heaven with excellent cuisine, and a gym to bring one back to earth!"

Boath House is the epitomé of style and elegance, coupled with commendable service, friendliness and superb cuisine. Wendy and Don Matheson are delightful hosts and their exquisite home has been lovingly restored, mainly by Wendy. The menus are original and well-balanced, the presentation sophisticated and visually appealing. Healthy option meals are offered as an alternative. Chef Charles Lockley's dedication to freshness is conspicuous in his blend of innovative ingredients and home-grown produce. The meal experience at Boath House is truly memorable.

Open all year except Christmas Day + Boxing Day
Closed to non residents Mon Tue
🏠 Rooms: 7 en suite
🛏 DB&B £82.50–£110   B&B £55–£80
SP Special rates available
✕ Lunch booking required ££
✕ Dinner £££
Ⓥ Vegetarians welcome
🕊 Children welcome
♿ Facilities for disabled visitors
🚭 No smoking in restaurant
🐕 Residents dogs only by agreement
🐄 Member of the Scotch Beef Club

Seared fillet of sea bass on a citrus cous cous, tapenade and a basil-infused oil. Roasted saddle of venison with a sweet potato purée, sauted foie gras, potato crisps and a Madeira and thyme sauce. Nectarine crème brûlée served with strawberry sorbet-filled tuille basket.

STB ★★★★ Hotel
💳 Credit cards: Mastercard/Eurocard, American Express, Visa, Diners Club, Switch, Delta
🔖 Proprietor: Wendy Matheson

CAWDOR TAVERN
The Lane, Cawdor
Nairn-shire IV12 5XP
Tel/Fax: 01667 404777
E-mail: cawdort@aol.com

Turn off A96 to Cawdor. Tavern is clearly signposted.

Traditional village inn with friendly atmosphere.

- An historic inn.
- Modern freshly prepared cooking.
- "A bustling little tavern with good food and friendly hospitality."

Cawdor Tavern is a traditional country pub and restaurant located in the quiet conservation village by Cawdor Castle. The building itself was originally the old castle workshop which has been tastefully refurbished. An open log fire in the oak-panelled lounge and a wood burning stove in the bar provide diners with a warm welcome to enjoy some quality bar meals. The restaurant offers modern Scottish cuisine using fresh, local produce. Elegant surroundings with a relaxed atmosphere make this a popular place for the traveller and locals alike.

Open all year, except 25 + 26 Dec
✕ Lunch £
✕ Dinner ££
Ⓥ Vegetarians welcome
✫ Children welcome
♿ Facilities for disabled visitors
✳ No smoking area in restaurant

Venison sausage on a bed of red onion marmalade with rosemary jus. Fillet of Ayrshire pork sliced over a pillow of clapshot and served with an Arran grain mustard sauce. Butterscotch tart with Blairgowrie raspberry cream.

💳 Credit cards: Mastercard/Eurocard, American Express, Visa, Diners Club, Switch
👤 Proprietor: Norman Sinclair

THE GOLF VIEW HOTEL & LEISURE CLUB
Seabank Road
Nairn IV12 4HD
Tel: 01667 452301 Fax: 01667 455267
E-mail: info@morton-hotels.com
Web: www.morton-hotels.com

At west end of Nairn. Seaward side of A96. Turn off at large Parish Church. Hotel on right-hand side at end of street.

A large sporting hotel with a leisure club.

- 19th century seafront mansion converted into a modern hotel, leisure club and terrace restaurant.
- Modern Scottish cooking.
- "A friendly and relaxing hotel offering excellent sports facilities and food."

Adjacent to the Nairn Golf Club, the appropriately named 'Golf View' is also within an hour's drive of 25 further courses. The hotel has a fully equipped leisure club with a magnificent swimming pool and multi-gym. The restaurant offers a nightly changing, invitingly descriptive, table d'hôte menu. Fish and shellfish are featured strongly, as well as locally sourced meat and game. Creative and well-made sauces complement the dishes and demonstrate the chef's expertise. Vegetarian dishes show skill and imagination, and delicious fresh bread is baked every day. The Conservatory serves food all day.

Open all year
🛏 Rooms: 47 en suite
🛏 DB&B £70–£86   B&B £50–£65
SP Special rates available
✕ Food available all day ££
✕ Lunch £
✕ Dinner 4 course menu £££
Ⓥ Vegetarians welcome
✫ Children welcome
♿ Facilities for disabled visitors
✳ No smoking in restaurant + conservatory

West Coast scallop and prawn risotto with leeks and freshly shaved Parmesan. Char-grilled lamb carved over baked Provençal vegetables and basil pesto dressing. Bourbon croissant bread and butter pudding with toffee sauce.

STB ★★★★ Hotel
Green Tourism 🌿🌿 SILVER Award
💳 Credit cards: Mastercard/Eurocard, American Express, Visa, Diners Club, Switch
👤 General Manager: Greta Anderson

THE NEWTON HOTEL
Inverness Road
Nairn, Nairnshire IV12 4RX
Tel: 01667 453144 Fax: 01667 454026
E-mail: info@morton-hotels.com
Web: www.morton-hotels.com

West of Nairn town centre on A96.

A country house hotel set in secluded grounds with views over the Moray Firth.

- Country house with brand new conference facilities.
- Modern Scottish.
- "A popular hotel for weddings and conferences offering a wide range of facilities."

The Newton Hotel is set in 21 acres of secluded grounds with magnificent views over the Moray Firth and the Ross-shire Hills beyond. The hotel building is an interesting combination of Georgian and Scottish baronial styles and is furnished in a style which is in keeping with the building. The restaurant offers interesting menus which focus on best use of local produce which are treated skilfully and imaginatively by the chef. Their sister hotel, The Golf View Hotel & Leisure Club in Nairn, offers use of excellent leisure facilities to guests. A very appealing place to explore the beauty of this particular part of Scotland. The Newton also offers conference facilities for up to 400 people.

Open all year
🏩 Rooms: 57 en suite
🛏 DB&B £75–£95 B&B £55–£75
SP Special rates available
✗ Food available all day £££
✗ Lunch £
✗ Dinner £££
Ⓥ Vegetarians welcome
⚘ Children welcome
♿ Facilities for disabled visitors
✗ No smoking in restaurant

A warm crab and scallop sausage with a vine tomato dressing. Collops of venison topped with a shallot and parsnip marmalade and ribboned with a creamy mild green peppercorn sauce. Bramble tart served with a frosted elderflower yoghurt.

STB ★★★★ Hotel
Green Tourism 🍃🍃 SILVER Award
💳 Credit cards: Mastercard/Eurocard, American Express, Visa, Diners Club, Switch
👤 General Manager: Kevin Reid

SUNNY BRAE HOTEL
Marine Road
Nairn, Nairnshire IV12 4EA
Tel: 01667 452309 Fax: 01667 454860
E-mail: sunnybrae@easynet.co.uk
Web: www.vacations-scotland.co.uk/sunnybrae.html

Follow A96 Aberdeen-Inverness road through Nairn, at roundabout carry straight onto Marine Road, hotel on left.

An attractive small hotel with stunning view overlooking the Moray Firth.

- Small town hotel.
- Scottish cooking with European flair.
- "Excellent quality is offered at Sunnybrae with views out over the Moray Firth."

Sunny Brae Hotel is run by Sylvia and Ian Bochel and has been extensively and tastefully refurbished over the last five years. Sylvia who is German is the chef, the menus have a distinct European influence with a strong emphasis on quality local produce. Sunny Brae has nine charming bedrooms, five with sea view, all are attractively appointed with quality furniture and fittings. This is a stylish and welcoming small hotel offering an excellent overall standard.

Open Mar to Oct
🏩 Rooms: 9 en suite
🛏 DB&B £49–£56 B&B £32–39
SP Special rates available
✗ Non-residents booking essential
✗ Lunch ££
✗ Dinner ££
Ⓥ Vegetarians welcome
⚘ Children welcome
♿ Limited facilities for disabled visitors
✗ Smoking in lounge only

Sautéed king scallops served on bed of mixed salad leaves with lemon, basil and white wine dressing. Braised Nairnshire lamb shank with red wine and rowanberry sauce, infused with rosemary and served with aubergine risotto and ratatouille. Cranachan with Royal Brackla malt whisky and Scottish summer berries.

STB ★★★★ Hotel
Green Tourism 🍃🍃 SILVER Award
💳 Credit cards: Mastercard/Eurocard, Visa, Switch, Delta, JCB
👤 Owners: Sylvia & Ian Bochel

NEW LANARK MILL HOTEL
Mill One, New Lanark
Lanarkshire ML11 9DB
Tel: 01555 667200 Fax: 01555 667222
E-mail: hotel@newlanark.org
Web: www.newlanark.org

From the town of Lanark, follow signs for New
Lanark south for ½ mile. Hotel is through the gates
and 100 metres to the right.

18th century restored cotton mill.

• Converted 18th century cotton mill.
• Modern Scottish.
• "Unique building on the banks of the Clyde
  situated in the heart of a World Heritage Village."

New Lanark Mill Hotel has a magnificent location on
the banks of the River Clyde in the heart of a popular
world heritage village. Over 200 years ago it rose to
fame as a model village, under the management of
social pioneer Robert Owen. The hotel has been
cleverly modernised combining the original features
with all the contemporary facilities required in a
modern hotel. Staff have been trained to a high
standard and are welcoming and professional. In
the kitchen fresh Scottish produce is respectfully
prepared in modern style by head chef Martin Ross
and his team. A most interesting and appealing
place.

   Open all year
🛏 Rooms: 38 en suite
🛏 DB&B £37.50–47.50 B&B £30–£37.50
SP Special rates available
✕ Food available all day £
✕ Lunch ££
✕ Dinner ££
V Vegetarians welcome
☆ Children welcome
♿ Facilities for disabled visitors
✔ No smoking in restaurant
🐾 Dogs welcome

**Goats cheese grilled on fresh asparagus with a
Dijon mustard dressing. Baked fillet of Scottish
salmon on a potato and celeriac mash, served on a
chive cream sauce. Caramelised apple tart served
with lemon curd ice cream.**

STB ★★★★ Hotel
💳 Credit cards: Mastercard/Eurocard, American
   Express, Visa, Diners Club, Switch, Delta
🗒 General Manager: Stephen Owen

UDNY ARMS HOTEL
Main Street, Newburgh, Aberdeenshire AB41 6BL
Tel: 01358 789444
Fax: 01358 789012
E-mail: enquiry@udny.co.uk
Web: www.udny.com

On A975, 2½ miles off A92 Aberdeen-Peterhead,
15 minutes from Aberdeen in Newburgh.

**Long standing hotel in the centre of Newburgh
village with function suite and cafe bar and
overlooking the golf course .**

• A traditional Victorian stone-built house with the
  style and character of an old village inn.
• Creative Scottish cooking.
• "Relax at the Udny Arms and take in the
  wonderful views over the Ythan."

The Udny Arms Hotel overlooks the Ythan Estuary and
has attracted sportsmen, nature lovers and tourists to
the Aberdeenshire village of Newburgh for over 100
years. It is an unpretentious and intimate hotel, run by
the Craig family, and the service is cheerful and
efficient. There is a cosy residents lounge and dining
is in the bistro, a split-level restaurant overlooking the
lovely Sands of Forvie. The extensive à la carte menu
changes every six weeks, and includes a handful of
'specials' which change daily. Meat and game come
from Bain of Tarves – and fish is a speciality. The
hotel also has a brasserie-style restaurant, in the
Parlour, with table d'hôte menu. Udny Arms has an
AA Rosette and is a member of the Certified
Aberdeen Angus Scheme.

   Open all year except Christmas Night +
   Boxing Night
🛏 Rooms: 26 en suite
🛏 DB&B £43–£72 B&B £35–£64
SP Special rates available
✕ Lunch £-££
✕ Dinner £-££
V Vegetarians welcome
☆ Children welcome
♿ Facilities for disabled visitors

**Warm goats cheese tartlet with red onion and baby
Caesar salad. Pan-seared, hand-dived scallops
with wilted spinach and a saffron butter sauce. The
original sticky toffee pudding.**

STB ★★ Hotel
💳 Credit cards: Mastercard/Eurocard, American
   Express, Visa, Diners Club, Switch, Delta
🗒 Proprietors: Denis & Jennifer Craig

CORSEMALZIE HOUSE HOTEL
Port William
Newton Stewart
Wigtownshire DG8 9RL
Tel: 01988 860254
Fax: 01988 860213
Web: www.galloway.co.uk

Halfway along B7005 Glenluce-Wigtown, off A714 Newton Stewart-Port William or A747 Glenluce-Port William.

Victorian mansion house with strong sporting links.

- Victorian country mansion.
- Modern, Scottish cooking.
- "Much of the produce used in the kitchen is taken from the hotel's own sporting lands."

This 19th century house with its own 40 acre estate is a popular venue for those who enjoy the countryside. It has its own small burn, The Malzie Burn, within its garden and also lovely woodland walks. Corsemalzie has a traditional Scottish country mansion-style and feel to it. It is very secluded, very rural, peaceful and quiet. A cosy bar serves lighter meals and lunches while the dining room is more formal and looks out onto the well-tended gardens. The hotel has recently extended its kitchen garden which offers fresh vegetables to complement all meals. Corsemalzie has its own fishing, both on the river and loch, and fresh game from its estate. *See advert page 27.*

Open 1 Mar to 20 Jan except Christmas Day + Boxing Day
- 🏠 Rooms: 14 en suite
- 🛏 DB&B from £59.50 B&B £37–£47
- 🆂🅿 Special rates available
- ✘ Lunch £-££
- ✘ Dinner £££
- Ⓥ Vegetarians welcome
- ⚘ Children welcome
- ♿ Facilities for disabled visitors – ground floor only
- ⚥ No smoking in dining room

Smoked haddock soufflé with lemon and chive sauce. Loin of lamb with black pudding stuffing and served with bramble and port sauce. Warm butterscotch tart with malt whisky ice cream.

STB ★★★★ Hotel
- 💳 Credit cards: Mastercard/Eurocard, American Express, Visa, Switch, Delta
- 🅜 Proprietor: Peter McDougall

CREEBRIDGE HOUSE HOTEL
Minnigaff, Newton Stewart
Wigtownshire DG8 6NP
Tel: 01671 402121 Fax: 01671 403258
E-mail: creebridge.hotel@daelnet.co.uk
Web: www.creebridge.co.uk

From roundabout signposted Newton Stewart on A75, through the town, cross bridge over river to Minnigaff. 250 yards – hotel on left.

1760 Scottish country mansion in grounds beside the river Cree, formerly owned by the Earls of Galloway.

- An old, Galloway family house with character and charm.
- Imaginative country house cooking.
- "Great pride is taken in using the very best of fresh local produce to create excellent modern dishes."

Chris and Sue Walker have sensitively decorated and refurbished Creebridge to reflect the elegant past of the house itself. There is a choice of eating during the day; the Bridges, a welcoming bar/brasserie, or the Garden Restaurant, which is more formal and is approached from a very spacious drawing room. Tea/coffee is available on the terrace in the mature and well-tended gardens. Chef/proprietor Chris Walker and his head chef Paul Sommerville present imaginative table d'hôte menus and outstanding à la carte bar menus. The staff here are warm and welcoming. *See advert page 27.*

Open all year except 24 to 26 Dec
- 🏠 Rooms: 19 en suite
- 🛏 DB&B £45–£60 B&B £30–£42
- 🆂🅿 Special rates available
- ✘ Lunch £
- ✘ Dinner ££
- Ⓥ Vegetarians welcome
- ⚘ Children welcome
- ♿ Facilities for disabled visitors
- ⚥ No smoking in restaurant
- 🐄 Member of the Scotch Beef Club

Home-cured Gravadlax with Kirkudbright smoked greenie scallops and a raspberry vinaigrette. Seared fillet of Solway salmon set on an apple mash, finished with a sweet chilli and tomato sauce. Warm summer fruit risotto with crème anglaise.

STB ★★★ Hotel
- 💳 Credit cards: Mastercard/Eurocard, American Express, Visa, Switch, Delta
- 🅜 Proprietor: Chris Walker

KIRROUGHTREE HOUSE
Newton Stewart
Wigtownshire DG8 6AN
Tel: 01671 402141 Fax: 01671 402425
E-mail: kirroughtree@n-stewart.demon.co.uk
Web: www.mcmillanhotels.com

From A75 take A712 New Galloway road, hotel 300 yards on left.

Delightful, grand Scottish country hotel set in attractive grounds.

- 18th century mansion converted into a stylish, family-run country house hotel.
- Gourmet Scottish cooking.
- "A hotel that strives for perfection and achieves excellent results."

Kirroughtree has all the grandeur and opulence of an historical mansion. It is sumptuously furnished and elegantly decorated, yet it has an atmosphere which is welcoming and considerate rather than over-formal. There are two dining rooms, reached from the panelled lounge. Head chef, Ian Bennett, was trained by the celebrated Michel Roux, and his cooking is highly-accomplished. The menus are short (three main courses at dinner, two at lunch), creative and well-balanced. Everything at Kirroughtree is done to the highest standards and the service is polished and professional without being stuffy. Kirroughtree has 3 AA Rosettes. *See advert page 259.*

	Open mid Feb to 3 Jan
🏨	Rooms: 17 en suite
🛏	DB&B £70–£100 B&B £60–£85
SP	Special rates available
✗	Lunch – booking essential ££
✗	Dinner 4 course menu £££
Ⓥ	Vegetarians welcome – prior notice required
🧒	Children over 10 years welcome
🚭	No smoking in dining rooms
🐂	Member of the Scotch Beef Club

Mille feuille of wood pigeon, lentils and toasted brioche with juniper sauce. Fillet of sea bass with herb risotto, asparagus tips, tomato confit and a crayfish sauce. White chocolate bavarois with a tuille horn filled with a summer berry compote.

STB ★★★★ Hotel
💳 Credit cards: Mastercard/Eurocard, Visa, Switch
👤 Manager: James Stirling

CHANNEL RESTAURANT
17 Main Street
North Queensferry
Fife KY11 1JG
Tel: 01383 412567
Fax: 01383 415460

From north take Junction 1 M90, follow B891 into North Queensferry. From south take A90 across Forth Road Bridge, take first exit left, follow B981 into North Queensferry.

Relaxed, informal restaurant.

- Small restaurant.
- Modern Scottish.
- "A delightful small and informal restaurant where you can enjoy good modern Scottish cooking."

The Channel Restaurant is a small, modern bistro-style restaurant where diners can enjoy innovative Scottish cooking whilst enjoying views of the Forth. The restaurant is situated in the unique location under the shadow of the Forth Bridge. It was originally a post office building and has been attractively converted with tiled floors, wooden tables, and modern paintings on the walls. It is run by Samantha and Andrew Oliver; Samantha is the chef whilst Andrew takes care of matters front-of-house. An excellent addition to Taste of Scotland.

	Open all year except 24, 26 Dec + first week in Jan
	Closed Sun Mon
✗	Lunch by prior arrangement only
✗	Dinner except Sun Mon £££
Ⓥ	Vegetarians by arrangement
🚭	Smoking at coffee stage only

Seared West Coast scallops on herb risotto with Parmesan, rocket and balsamic vinegar. Gressingham duck breast on celeriac mash with port and rowanberry sauce and crispy parsnips. Glazed lime tart with Cointreau cream.

💳 Credit cards: Mastercard/Eurocard, American Express, Visa, Switch, Delta
👤 Owner: Andrew Oliver

ARDS HOUSE

Connel, by Oban
Argyll PA37 1PT
Tel: 01631 710255
E-mail: jb@ardshouse.demon.co.uk

On main A85 Oban–Tyndrum, 4½ miles north
of Oban.

Small family-run hotel overlooking Loch Etive.

- Victorian villa.
- Traditional Scottish cooking.
- "Scottish hospitality at its best – good food, warm and friendly hosts."

This is a comfortable small hotel standing on the shores of a loch, with views over the Firth of Lorn and the Morvern Hills. Six of the seven bedrooms are en suite, and there is a happy air of the family home here. This is encouraged by the owners John and Jean Bowman. John, who is an innovative cook, along with Jean, an exceptionally warm and friendly hostess, who treat their guests like friends. The daily changing set menu is displayed in the afternoon and any special requirements are easily catered for. The dishes rely on local produce where possible, combining a taste for detail and fresh home cooking.

Open Feb to mid Nov
🏠 Rooms: 7 (6 en suite, 1 with private facilities)
🛏 DB&B £40–£54 B&B £30–£45
SP Special rates available
✗ Non-residents – by arrangement
❢ Restricted licence
✗ Dinner 4 course menu £££
Ⓥ Vegetarians – by arrangement
✶ Children over 14 years welcome
🚭 No smoking throughout

Tomato, pear and tarragon soup with home-baked bread. Fettucine of local grey sole and smoked salmon roulade with a curry and coriander velouté. Almond and prune tart with an angelica and camomile syrup.

STB ★★★ Hotel
💳 Credit cards: Mastercard/Eurocard, Visa, Switch, Delta
🧑 Proprietors: John & Jean Bowman

DUNGALLAN HOUSE HOTEL

Gallanach Road, Oban
Argyllshire PA34 4PD
Tel: 01631 563799 Fax: 01631 566711

In Oban, at Argyll Square, follow signs for Gallanach. ½ mile from Square.

A sweeping elegant driveway leads you to a fine old Victorian house offering a tranquil, country atmosphere.

- A small and friendly country house hotel.
- Traditional fresh Scottish/home cooking.
- "Great attention to quality and freshness is shown in Janice Stewart's culinary skills."

Set in its own five acres of mature woodland yet close to Oban's bustling centre, Dungallan House was built in 1870 by the Campbell family. It was used as a hospital in the First World War and as HQ for the Flying Boat Squadrons in the Second. Now owned and refurbished by George and Janice Stewart, Dungallan House enjoys magnificent panoramic views over Oban Bay to the Island of Mull, Lismore and the Hills of Morvern. As is appropriate for this prime West Coast port, menus take full advantage of the range of fresh fish and shellfish available locally. Janice Stewart does the cooking. The well-balanced table d'hôte menu offers four/five choices for each course. The wine list offers something to match each dish on Dungallan's rounded menu. Dungallan has 1 AA Rosette. *See advert page 257.*

Open all year except Nov Feb
🏠 Rooms: 13, 11 en suite
🛏 DB&B £58–£73 B&B £33–£48
SP Special rates available
✗ Lunch by arrangement £
✗ Dinner £££
Ⓥ Vegetarians welcome
✶ Children welcome
♿ Limited facilities for disabled visitors
🚭 No smoking in dining room
🐄 Member of the Scotch Beef Club

Roasted onion, tomato and Gruyere tartlets. Baked sea bass with a squat lobster sauce. Hazelnut meringue torte with sweet chestnut and chocolate filling.

STB ★★★ Hotel
💳 Credit cards: Mastercard/Eurocard, Visa
🧑 Directors: Janice & George Stewart

THE GATHERING RESTAURANT AND O'DONNELL'S IRISH BAR

Breadalbane Street, Oban
Argyll PA34 5NZ
Tel: 01631 565421/564849/566159
Fax: 01631 565421

Entering Oban from A85 (Glasgow) one-way system. Turn left at Deanery Brae into Breadalbane Street (signs for swimming pool etc.) then right at bottom of Deanery Brae.

An authentic Victorian banqueting hall with an informal Irish pub below.

- A popular restaurant and bar with a Celtic theme.
- Good, plain cooking with lots of imagination.
- "Warm and interesting restaurant with excellent choice of menu."

First opened in 1882 as a supper room for the famous annual Gathering Ball, the Gathering has a distinguished pedigree and is rightly popular with Oban's many tourists. The menu offers first-class, straightforward dishes made from local meat and seafood, as well as a range of imaginative starters and popular 'lighter bites'. The wine list is well-chosen and fairly priced. Portions are generous, prices modest and service cheerful. Staff are friendly and helpful. During July to September live music is available every night in O'Donnell's Irish Bar e.g. ceilidhs, folk music and local musicians. Live music at weekends off-season.

Open Easter to New Year except Christmas Day, New Year's Day + some Suns
Closed Sun off-season – please telephone
Note: closed to public last Thu in Aug
✘ Bar lunch £-££: Bar evening meals £ – off-season by reservation
✘ Dinner (Restaurant) ££-£££
Ⓥ Vegetarians welcome
‡ Children welcome
♿ Facilities for disabled visitors
🚭 No smoking in restaurant

Combination plate of local seafood: mussels, oysters, langoustines, herring, salmon, smoked trout. Fillet of Highland venison, char-grilled with a port and wild berry jus. Highlander ice cream: whisky, honey, oatmeal and ice cream, finished with toasted oatmeal and honey whisky sauce.

💳 Credit cards: Mastercard/Eurocard, American Express, Visa, Switch, Delta, JCB
Ⓝ Owner/Chef: Elaine Cameron

ISLE OF ERISKA

Ledaig, by Oban, Argyll PA37 1SD
Tel: 01631 720 371 Fax: 01631 720 531
E-mail: office@eriska-hotel.co.uk
Web: www.eriska-hotel.co.uk

A85 north of Oban, at Connel Bridge take A828 for 4 miles. North of Benderloch village follow signs to Isle of Eriska.

An exceptional hotel by any standards.

- An impressive, grey granite Scottish baronial house built in 1884, romantically situated on an island reached by a short road bridge.
- Gourmet country house cuisine.
- "Excellent ambience and impeccabale service combined with delicous food – guests return year after year and it is easy to see why!"

The Buchanan-Smith family have run their home on the island of Eriska as a hotel for over 20 years and manage to combine the intimate atmosphere of a family-run country house with the highest standard of professional service. In the dining room, chef Robert MacPherson has a well-established cooking style, and his enthusiasm and skill are evident in the menus and dishes presented. The hotel has a leisure complex with swimming pool, gymnasium – making it a totally secluded resort with style. Isle of Eriska has 3 AA Rosettes. Winner of The Macallan Taste of Scotland Hotel of the Year Award 1994.

Open all year except Jan + Feb
🛏 Rooms: 17 en suite
🛏 B&B £210–£260
✘ Open to non-residents for dinner only
✘ Lunch – residents only
✘ Dinner 7 course menu ££££
Ⓥ Vegetarians welcome
‡ Children over 10 years old welcome at dinner
♿ Facilities for disabled visitors
🚭 No smoking in dining room
🐮 Member of the Scotch Beef Club

Wild rabbit and courgette timbale with squab pigeon, morels and a Puy lentil velouté. Fresh langoustines set around an open ravioli of squat lobsters and seared scallops together with spring vegetables and a Champagne sauce. Agen prunes poached in red wine and served with a claret sauce.

STB ★★★★★ Hotel
💳 Credit cards: Mastercard/Eurocard, American Express, Visa, Switch
Ⓝ Partner: B Buchanan-Smith

KNIPOCH HOTEL
By Oban
Argyll PA34 4QT
Tel: 01852 316251
Fax: 01852 316249
E-mail: reception@knipochhotel.co.uk
Web: www.knipochhotel.co.uk

On the A816 south of Oban. ½ mile along Loch Feochan (6 miles) on left-hand side.

Country house hotel offering good food and relaxation.

• Rambling painted building.
• Modern Scottish.
• "A most relaxing country house in tranquil surroundings."

In 1592 this lovely house was owned by a member of the Campbell Clan and has a wonderful history dating to this, including the assassination of 'Thane of Cawder'. Today, however, it is owned by the Craig family who offer a house of tranquillity, good dining and solace for the traveller. Recent additions include a smokehouse, with produce incorporated into their menus, and a mail order service. The wine list is extensive, as is the range of malts and Cognacs.

Open mid Feb to mid Dec
🏨 Rooms: 16 en suite
🛏 DB&B £66–£101.50   B&B £37–£72
SP Special rates available
✗ Lunch ££
✗ Dinner £££
Ⓥ Vegetarians welcome
⚘ Children welcome
✄ No smoking in restaurant
🐕 Dogs welcome

Knipoch-smoked salmon: salmon cured and marinated then smoked for three days. Fillet of Aberdeen Angus beef, roasted whole then served sliced with a bearnaise sauce. Whisky crêpes served with whisky caramel sauce and vanilla ice cream.

STB ★★★★ Hotel
💳 Credit cards: Mastercard/Eurocard, American Express, Visa, Diners Club, Switch, Delta
👤 Director/Owner: Mr Nicky Craig

LOCH MELFORT HOTEL AND RESTAURANT
Arduaine, by Oban
Argyll PA34 4XG
Tel: 01852 200233
Fax: 01852 200214
Web: www.loch-melfort.co.uk

On A816, 19 miles south of Oban.

A country house with spectacular views and gardens.

• Stylish and friendly hotel with the emphasis on welcome.
• Fresh, imaginative Scottish cuisine.
• "A mesmerising spot where time slips by...."

Under its owners Philip and Rosalind Lewis, the Loch Melfort Hotel deserves its growing reputation . It is dramatically situated with panoramic views across Asknish Bay to the islands. Originally the home of the Campbells of Arduaine, the hotel has been sensibly and tastefully extended to take maximum advantage of the magnificent land and seascape. The renowned Arduaine Gardens are adjacent to the hotel grounds. Both in its dining room and Skerry Bistro, the hotel offers the best of fresh local produce – particularly seafood and shellfish – skilfully presented and cheerfully served – with imaginatively balanced wine list. The hotel has 2 AA Rosettes. *See advert page 259.*

Open all year except mid Jan to mid Feb
🏨 Rooms: 26 en suite
🛏 DB&B £45–£85   B&B £35–£55
SP Special rates available
✗ Food available all day from £
✗ Lunch (Skerry Bistro) £
✗ Dinner ££££
Ⓥ Vegetarians welcome
⚘ Children welcome
♿ Some facilities for disabled visitors
✄ No smoking in dining room

Celery and Dunsyre Blue soup. A seafood confection: local fish and crustaceans in a vermouth and leaf coriander sauce with fresh pasta spirals. Pecan roulade with autumn fruits: a light sponge filled with a drunken cream, blueberries, redcurrants and brambles.

STB ★★★★ Hotel
💳 Credit cards: Mastercard/Eurocard, American Express, Visa, Switch
👤 Proprietors: Rosalind & Philip Lewis

THE MANOR HOUSE

Gallanach Road, Oban
Argyll PA34 4LS
Tel: 01631 562087
Fax: 01631 563053

From Argyll Square, Oban, follow signs for Gallanach and the car ferry. Continue for approx ½ mile. Hotel on right-hand side of road.

An historic house overlooking Oban Bay.

- Elegant country house hotel.
- Modern Scottish with French influences.
- "A place to come and be pampered by the outstanding service and culinary delights."

Situated on the southern tip of Oban Bay, the Manor House was built in 1780 by the Duke of Argyll, and was first a factor's residence and then a dower house. In 1826 Oban's first bank, 'The National', opened here and in 1845 Admiral Otter used it as his base which conducted hydrographic surveys on the West Coast. The house retains much of the charm and atmosphere of the past. The five course table d'hôte dinner menu (three/four starters, three/four main courses) changes every day, according to what is available and seasonal. The cooking is fresh and creative. The Manor House has 2 AA Rosettes. *See advert page 260.*

Open all year
N.B. From mid Nov to end Feb closed Mon Tue
⊞ Rooms: 11 en suite
🛏 DB&B £50–£80 B&B £30–£60
ⓈⓅ Special rates available
✖ Lunch 3 course menu from £
✖ Dinner 5 course menu £££
Ⓥ Vegetarians welcome
🚭 No smoking in dining room + bedrooms

Sauteed scallops, bacon and pine nut salad with a sesame oil and chilli dressing. Canon of venison with braised red cabbage, caramelised prunes and a kumquat basil glaze. Meringue nest with cassis sorbet and strawberries and a lime crème anglaise.

STB ★★★★ Hotel
💳 Credit cards: Mastercard/Eurocard, American Express, Visa, Switch
𝕄 Manageress: Gabriel Wijker

THE WATERFRONT RESTAURANT

No 1 Railway Pier
Oban, Argyll PA34 4LW
Tel: 01631 563110

Approaching Oban from north or south. Look out for the clock tower – park wherever you can and head for railway and ferry pier. Restaurant is well-signposted from start of pier.

Originally Fisherman's Mission building.

- High building of several storeys, which dominates the pier.
- Bold and skilled seafood.
- "Distinctive and talented seafood treatment in casual environment."

The Waterfront is a bright, airy and spacious restaurant with well-set tables. The theme is positively 'fish'. The chef is 'on view' preparing fresh seafood for lunch/dinner. All produce is carefully cooked to order and presented professionally in a relaxed atmosphere. The flavour and balance of ingredients is excellent. The motto here is 'from the pier to the pan as fast as you can'!

Open Easter to Christmas
✖ Lunch – depending on choice £-££££
✖ Dinner ££-£££
Ⓥ Vegetarians welcome
🧒 Children welcome
🦮 Guide dogs welcome

Seared scallop salad with pancetta and croûtons. Grilled local sole with char-grilled potatoes and warm leek vinaigrette. Sticky toffee pudding.

💳 Credit cards: Mastercard/Eurocard, American Express, Visa, Switch
𝕄 Head Chef: Alex Needham

WILLOWBURN HOTEL
Clachan Seil
By Oban, Argyll PA34 4TJ
Tel: 01852 300276 Fax: 01852 300597
E-mail: willowburn.hotel@virgin.net
Web: www.willowburn.co.uk

On the Island of Seil, near Oban, just a few 100 yards from 'The bridge over the Atlantic'.

Small, privately-owned hotel offering excellent food and comfort.

- Country hotel in a lovely and unique part of Argyll.
- Outstanding Scottish cooking.
- "Excellent food - and the attention to small details is second to none."

The lovely little Island of Seil is noted for its wildlife, and for being connected to the mainland by the bridge over the Atlantic, built in 1792. Willowburn stands in one and a half acres of garden which lead down to the still waters of Clachan Sound and offers spectacular views from all the public rooms and bedrooms. Guests are made very welcome by owners Jan Wolfe and Chris Mitchell who subscribe to the highest standards of hospitality. Menus change every day and offer a generous choice of local produce all served with fresh garden vegetables. Guests all agree on the peace, tranquillity and relaxing location of Willowburn. The hotel has 2 AA Rosettes.

    Open 1 Mar to 2 Jan
🏠 Rooms: 7 en suite
🛏 DB&B £50–£60
SP Special rates available for longer stays
✗ Lunch – residents only £
✗ Dinner £££
Ⓥ Vegetarians welcome
🧒 Well-behaved children welcome
🚭 Smoking permitted in bar only

Hot salmon and scallop soufflé en croûte. Minted pea and pear soup. Medallions of venison marinated in oak leaf wine and wild herbs, pan-fried and served with a bitter sweet sauce. Lemon, honey and Lagavulin ice cream.

STB ★★★★ Hotel
💳 Credit cards: Mastercard/Eurocard, Visa, Switch, Delta
👤 Proprietors: Jan Wolfe & Chris Mitchell

YACHT CORRYVRECKAN
Dal an Eas
Kilmore, nr Oban
Argyll PA34 4XU
Tel/Fax: 01631 770246
E-mail: yacht.corryvreckan@virgin.net
Web: www.corryvreckan.co.uk

Magnificent, stylish yacht exclusively designed for West Coast cruising and gourmet eating.

- Charter yacht.
- Best fresh home cooking.
- "After a day's sailing, gather round the table for a glass of wine, a wonderful freshly cooked dinner and some good stories."

Douglas and Mary Lindsay have been offering chartered cruises on the West Coast for many years and brought all their experience to bear when they designed Corryvreckan (strictly speaking Corryvreckan II, since their earlier vessel had the same name). She is 65 feet overall, 16 feet in the beam and has a wonderfully spacious feel – standing room is available throughout. This is a really unique experience – to enjoy participating in the art of sailing whilst experiencing excellent cuisine from an expert cook. Douglas and Mary make a really tremendous team – their stamina is to be commended! Not only does Mary provide a dinner to be proud of, but also home-made soups every lunchtime and freshly baked scones and chocolate cake for that afternoon refreshment on the ocean wave. Fresh delicacies already on board are supplemented by locally gathered mushrooms, mussels and mackerel harvested en route, and are all part of the memorable experience. Guests are members of the crew and help with washing up as well as actually sailing the ship.

    Open Apr to Oct
⚓ Cabins: 5 twin berth cabins, 3 heads with shower
🛏 DB&B £445–£495 per person for 1 week cruise – all incl
SP Special rates available for whole boat charter
UL Unlicensed – wine available with dinner
🚭 No smoking below deck
🚗 Parking available

Arbroath smokies baked in cream with basil and tomato. Ragoût of venison with toasted walnuts. Bramble whisky syllabub.

💳 No credit cards
👤 Proprietors: Douglas & Mary Lindsay

SAPLINBRAE HOUSE HOTEL
Old Deer, Mintlaw
Aberdeenshire AB42 4LP
Tel: 01771 623515 Fax: 01771 624472

12 miles west of Peterhead and 1 mile west of Mintlaw on A950 New Pitsligo Road. ¾ mile from Aden Country Park.

Charming small country house hotel.

• Dower house built in 1756.
• Modern Scottish cuisine.
• "Saplinbrae offers good food in the most relaxing surroundings."

Saplinbrae House Hotel is a wonderful building with beautifully-kept gardens. It combines the character of the past with a high standard of modern day comforts in a highly picturesque setting. There are two dining areas here, the bar offering a more relaxed dining experience and the brasserie where one can relax in more formal surroundings. Menus are appealing and offer an interesting modern Scottish theme using best local produce.

Open all year except Christmas Day + Boxing Day
🏠 Rooms: 7 en suite
🍴 DB&B £50–£75   B&B £33–£55
SP Special rates available
✖ Food available all day £
✖ Lunch £
✖ Dinner £££
Ⓥ Vegetarians welcome
🕇 Children welcome

Grilled mussels with a herb and garlic crust and smoked Portsoy cheddar. Pot-roast haunch of venison in a roast onion and green peppercorn sauce. Saplinbrae clarty pudding with a dual caramel toffee sauce and wild berry compote.

STB ★★★ Hotel
💳 Credit cards: Mastercard, Visa, Switch
👤 Owners: Julia & Andrew Brown

MELDRUM HOUSE
Oldmeldrum
Aberdeenshire AB51 0AE
Tel: 01651 872294
Fax: 01651 872464

Main gates on A947 (Aberdeen to Banff road). 1 mile north of Old Meldrum. 13 miles north of Aberdeen airport.

An historic house in rural Aberdeenshire.

• Scottish baronial mansion, now a country house hotel with its own 18 hole golf course.
• Creative Scottish cooking.
• Meldrum House offers a step back in history."

Local tradition maintains that King Charles I spent part of his childhood here, when a ward of the Seton family of nearby Fyvie Castle. The historic atmosphere of the house is enhanced by antiques, portraits and faded furniture. The house stands in 15 acres of lawns and woodland, with its own small loch. The resident proprietors are Douglas and Eileen Pearson, attentive and courteous hosts who make you very welcome to their home. Residents and non-residents can enjoy an imaginative and well-constructed four course table d'hôte menu carefully overseen by enthusiastic chef Mark Will. Meldrum House now has its own 18-hole golf course.

Open all year
🏠 Rooms: 9 en suite
🍴 DB&B £114–£124   B&B £105–£115
SP Special rates available
✖ Lunch ££
✖ Dinner £££
Ⓥ Vegetarians welcome
🕇 Children welcome
♿ Facilities for disabled visitors
🚭 No smoking in restaurant

Cod and rosemary fish cakes with saffron and lime sauce. Breast of duck with ginger and grapefruit sauce. White and dark chocolate mousse with caramelised sugar.

STB ★★★ Hotel
💳 Credit cards: Mastercard/Eurocard, Visa, Switch
👤 Proprietors: Douglas & Eileen Pearson

ALLT-NAN-ROS HOTEL

Onich, by Fort William
Inverness-shire PH33 6RY
Tel: 0185 582 1210
Fax: 0185 582 1462
E-mail: allt-nan-ros@zetnet.co.uk
Web: www.allt-nan-ros.co.uk

On A82, 10 miles south of Fort William.

Quality highland hotel on the shore of Loch Linnhe.

- Lochside Victorian house.
- Modern Scottish cooking.
- "The best of Scottish produce prepared with flair and imagination."

Situated halfway between Ben Nevis and Glencoe, Allt-nan-Ros is an attractive 19th century shooting lodge standing in an elevated position above the loch and commanding spectacular views: a most picturesque situation. The Gaelic name means 'Burn of the Roses', and derives from the cascading stream which passes through the gardens of the hotel. The decoration is modern, rooms are comfortably furnished and service is personal. Dinner is served in a new conservatory. The menus offer a range of familiar Scottish dishes, prepared from locally sourced ingredients. Presentation is imaginative and innovative. The style of the cooking has French influences. Allt-nan-Ros has 2 AA Rosettes.

Open 1 Jan to 10 Nov
🏠 Rooms: 20 en suite
🛏 DB&B £60–£80   B&B £38–£55
SP Special rates available
✗ Lunch from £
✗ Dinner 5 course menu from £££
Ⓥ Vegetarians welcome
🚭 No smoking in dining room

Roulade of Guinea fowl and wild forest mushrooms. Steamed Mallaig king scallops, sorrel sabayon, home-grown herbs and roast fennel. Strawberry and heather honey tart.

STB ★★★★ Hotel
💳 Credit cards: Mastercard/Eurocard, American Express, Visa, Diners Club, Switch
Ⓜ Proprietor: James Macleod

CUILCHEANNA HOUSE

Onich
by Fort William
Inverness-shire PH33 6SD
Tel: 01855 821226
E-mail: relax@cuilcheanna.freeserve.co.uk

Signposted 300m off A82 in village of Onich
– 9 miles south of Fort William.

Friendly and welcoming small hotel.

- Small country house.
- Creative Scottish fayre.
- "Innovative food with a warm welcome."

This is an old farmhouse (17th century foundation) now a small hotel personally run by Russell and Linda Scott, who are most welcoming hosts. It stands in its own grounds overlooking Loch Linnhe, peacefully situated with views towards Glencoe and the Isle of Mull. It is pleasantly furnished and features piles of books of local interest and a cosy log fire in the lounge. The set four course dinner menu changes daily, and is complemented by a hand-picked and personally tested wine list, as well as a fine selection of quality malt whiskies. The emphasis is on genuine creative cooking and Linda makes good use of prime local produce and fresh Scottish-grown herbs. The comprehensive breakfast choice includes local favourites such as venison sausage, haggis, herring in oatmeal and Mallaig kippers.

Open Easter to end Oct
🏠 Rooms: 7 en suite
🛏 DB&B £43–£46   B&B £26–£28
SP Special rates available
✗ Residents only
✗ Dinner 4 course menu ££
Ⓥ Vegetarians welcome
🚭 No smoking throughout

Lochaber smoked haggis with a carrot and swede slaw and whisky cream. Fillet of Scottish salmon with a tarragon, lime and avocado crème fraîche. Chocolate and apricot tart.

STB ★★★ Guest House
💳 Credit cards: Mastercard/Eurocard, Visa, Switch, Delta
Ⓜ Proprietors: Linda & Russell Scott

FOUR SEASONS BISTRO & BAR
Inchree, Onich
by Fort William
Inverness-shire PH33 6SD
Tel: 01855 821393
Fax: 01855 821287

8 miles south of Fort William. Take Inchree turn-off,
¼ mile south of Corran Ferry, then 250 yards.

Casual dining in a pine clad chalet-style building.

* Log cabin.
* Modern home style Scottish cooking.
* "Attractively furnished bistro with good Scottish food."

Four Seasons Bistro and Bar is a warm and welcoming haven in lovely leafy surroundings with views of Loch Linnhe and Ardgour. It is a family business and the staff are all pleasant, exuding a happy atmosphere. The interior is unusual but suits the timber of the building and the furniture and decor is pleasing, complementing the style of the establishment. The menus are interesting, food well-cooked with much evidence of fresh, locally caught seafood prepared and presented with care and attention to detail.

Open Christmas + New Year period
Winter limited opening until Easter
Closed Tue except Jul + Aug
✗ Dinner except Tue ££
Ⓥ Vegetarians welcome
☆ Children welcome
⅋ Facilities for disabled visitors
⊬ No smoking in eating areas

Salad of langoustine with hot garlic butter and lemon and parsley dressing. Rack of lamb with a honey, chilli and soy sauce glaze served with steamed rice and stir-fried vegetables. Caramelised banana tart with vanilla custard.

⊞ Credit cards: Mastercard/Eurocard, American Express, Visa
Ⓚ Manageress: Susan Heron

THE LODGE ON THE LOCH HOTEL
Onich, by Fort William
Inverness-shire PH33 6RY
Tel: 0185 582 1237
Fax: 0185 582 1238
E-mail: reservations@freedomglen.co.uk
Web: www.freedomglen.co.uk

On A82, 1 mile north of the Ballachulish Bridge.

A well-appointed hotel in beautiful gardens.

* Victorian country hotel, with modern additions.
* Traditional Scottish cooking.
* "A luxury hotel with homely atmosphere."

The Lodge on The Loch Hotel is a granite Victorian villa with new additions. It stands within yards of Loch Linnhe and enjoys good views towards the hills of Morvern. Guests of the Lodge on The Loch Hotel have automatic membership of a sister hotel's swimming pool, sauna, steam room, turbo pool, sunbed and exercise room. A traditional, comfortable hotel with friendly, helpful staff. The decor reflects the beauty of the surrounding gardens and countryside. Bedrooms are comfortable and the dining room has delightful loch views. The table d'hôte menus feature several Scottish dishes.

Open all year except 5 Jan to 26 Mar
🏨 Rooms: 20, 18 en suite
🛏 DB&B £48–£85 B&B £33–£59
SP Special rates available
✗ Light lunch £
✗ Dinner 4 course menu £££
Ⓥ Vegetarians welcome
☆ Children over 10 years welcome
⅋ Facilities for disabled visitors
⊬ No smoking in dining room

Sauté Banffshire chicken livers with fine herbs, grilled with a gratin of wholemeal breadcrumbs and seasoned with paprika. Sauté fillets of Mallaig monkfish tails with a courgette and onion compote accompanied by light court bouillon. Lemon mousse with mango and raspberry sauces accompanied by cookie spoons.

STB ★★★★ Hotel
⊞ Credit cards: Mastercard/Eurocard, Visa, Switch, Delta
Ⓚ Manager: Mr Ian Shaw

ONICH HOTEL
Onich, nr Fort William
Inverness-shire PH33 6RY
Tel: 01855 821 214
Fax: 01855 821 484

On A82 in the village of Onich on the shores of Loch Linnhe – 12 miles south of Fort William.

Well-appointed hotel on the shores of Loch Linnhe.

- White-washed hotel.
- Blends of traditional and contemporary Scottish.
- "All the luxuries of a hotel with a personal touch."

The Onich Hotel is ideally located on the shores of Loch Linnhe with stunning views across to the mountains of Glencoe in the East and to Morvern and the Isle of Mull in the west. It offers an ideal location to explore this beautiful part of the Highlands. The hotel is owned and run by Stewart Leitch whose commitment to all aspects of the hotel is evident – from the calibre of staff to the quality of produce and cooking from the kitchen.

	Open all year except Christmas week
🏠	Rooms: 25 en suite
🛏	DB&B £54–£78 B&B £32–£52
SP	Special rates available
✘	Bar meals available all day ££
✘	Dinner £££
V	Vegetarians welcome
🧒	Children welcome
♿	Facilities for disabled visitors
✗	No smoking in restaurant
🐕	Dogs welcome

Loch Linnhe langoustine raviolis with grilled goats cheese. Roast loin of Rannoch Moor venison with braised red cabbage, glazed apples and a juniper and thyme jus. Hot Drambuie soufflé and marmalade ice cream.

STB ★★★★ Hotel
- 💳 Credit cards: Mastercard/Eurocard, American Express, Visa, Diners Club, Switch, Delta
- 👤 Proprietor: Stewart Leitch

OBINAN CROFT
Laide
Wester Ross IV22 2NU
Tel: 01445 731548 Fax: 01445 731635
E-mail: rj&mc.beeson@obinan.co.uk
Web: www.obinan.co.uk

Turn off the A832 Braemore junction-Gairloch road at Laide Post Office. Continue to Mellon Udrigle then Opinan. Obinan Croft is last house by the shore - keep right to the end of the road.

Small remote family-run croft with wonderful panoramic views.

- White-washed seashore house.
- Skilled and stylish Scottish cooking.
- "Croft on the outside - inside stylish and trendsetting decor with wonderful food."

Obinan Croft occupies a solitary position on a headland – you can see it long before you reach it. Innovative furnishings, a mix of old and new blend well together and make for very comfortable, homely and interesting surroundings, the sitting room is full of interesting books and pictures. The food here is excellent – Mairi is a self-taught and talented cook and Roger cooks breakfasts, makes sauces etc whilst both also being genial hosts. All that Taste of Scotland could ask for is offered here – excellent fresh local produce, lovingly prepared and presented in warm convivial surroundings.

	Open 1 Mar to 31 Oct
🏠	Rooms: 4 en suite
🛏	DB&B £65
✘	Residents only
🧺	Packed lunch £
♿	Facilities for disabled visitors
✗	No smoking in dining room + bedrooms

Orkney cheddar rarebit and red onion relish tartlets with cucumber pickle salad. Grilled rainbow trout with caper sauce, glazed shallots and carrot and potato cake. Gloag's gin and lemon jelly with a compote of rhubarb and strawberries and shortbread.

STB ★★★★ Hotel
- 💳 Credit cards: Mastercard/Eurocard, Visa, Switch
- 👤 Proprietors: Roger & Mairi Beeson

MAKERSTON HOUSE
19 Park Road
Renfrewshire PA2 6JP
Tel/Fax: 0141 884 2520

Less than 5 miles from Glasgow Airport. Follow signs to Paisley University then to shopping centre, turn right into Falside Road, continue uphill until Park Road and house is on right hand side.

Family guest house.

* Tudor-style mansion.
* Scottish home cooking.
* "A family welcome offering the 'Natural Cooking of Scotland'."

Makerston is a Tudor mansion located in a residential area of Paisley. The house dates back to 1905 and until the 1980s belonged to Coates Viyella. The present owner, Mary McCue, was housekeeper at Makerston in the past and now welcomes guests in her amicable style making them feel part of the family. Food is prepared and presented in simple style with attention to flavour and quality of ingredients. There is also much home baking here to be enjoyed 'in the jewel in Paisley's crown'. Quiet comfort is offered here in the suburbs of Paisley.

Open 3 Jan to 24 Dec
🏠 Rooms: 11, 7 en suite
🍴 DB&B £37.50–£55   B&B £25–£35
SP Special rates available
✗ Food available all day – by arrangement after 8.30 pm £££
✗ Lunch – pre booking for private functions ££
✗ Dinner – pre booking necessary
Ⓥ Vegetarians welcome
☀ Children welcome
🚭 No smoking in dining room

Red pepper soup. Roast leg of lamb and poached minted pear with gratin dauphinoise, courgette and carrot batons and rosemary and thyme. Pavlova.

STB ★★★ Guest House
💳 Credit cards: Eurocard, Visa
🗿 Owner: Mrs Mary McCue

THE PEAT INN
Peat Inn, by Cupar, Fife KY15 5LH
Tel: 01334 840206 Fax: 01334 840530
Web: www.standrews.co.uk/hotelspeatinn.htp

At junction of B940/B941, 6 miles south west of St Andrews.

Delightful first-class restaurant with luxury accommodation.

* Restaurant with rooms in a converted village inn.
* Unpretentious top quality modern cuisine.
* "Delightful, world-renowned restaurant with luxury accommodation."

Food and style writers have waxed lyrical about the Peat Inn since the day it opened its doors. Chef and owner David Wilson has literally re-written the rule book on Scottish cooking and has created a world-class restaurant whose name is synonymous with good food. His bold imaginative cooking style has gained him all the top food and wine awards. All ingredients are of the utmost freshness and quality and, with tremendous flair, they are transformed into truly memorable dishes. His wine list is formidable but provides great choice even in the lowest price range. Menus are table d'hôte, à la carte and a tasting menu of six or seven courses which must be ordered for a complete table. The Peat Inn has 3 AA Rosettes.

Open all year except Christmas Day + New Year's Day
Closed Sun Mon
🏠 Suites: 8 en suite
🍴 DB&B £90–£98, £65–£95
✗ Lunch except Sun Mon 3 course menu ££
✗ Dinner except Sun Mon 3 course menu £££
Ⓥ Vegetarians welcome
☀ Children welcome
♿ Facilities for disabled visitors
🚭 No smoking in dining rooms
🐄 Member of the Scotch Beef Club

Roasted scallops on leek, potato and smoked bacon with pea purée. Peat Inn 'cassoulet' of lamb, pork and duck with flageolet beans. Caramelised banana on a banana cake with coconut ice cream.

STB ★★★★★ Restaurant with Rooms
💳 Credit cards: Mastercard/Eurocard, American Express, Visa, Diners Club, Switch, JCB
🗿 Partners: David & Patricia Wilson

CRINGLETIE HOUSE HOTEL
Peebles
EH45 8PL
Tel: 01721 730 233 Fax: 01721 730 244
Web: www.wrensgroup.com

From Peebles take A703, hotel 2 miles on left.

Built in 1861 this is a traditional Borders family home.

- Country mansion house.
- Modern Scottish cooking.
- "Enjoy well-presented, good quality food in an elegant and historic setting."

Cringletie is set in a 28 acre garden which encompasses woodlands, formal gardens and a wonderful walled garden – something to suit every taste. There is also an extensive vegetable and flower garden which supplies all the fresh vegetables and flowers for the house daily. The house has been carefully restored to retain its 19th century features, retaining family portraits in the main room. The atmosphere here is both relaxing and romantic with attention to detail in both service and carefully designed menus. Shortlisted and Commended for The Macallan Taste of Scotland Awards 1999. *See advert page 27.*

Open all year
- 🏨 Rooms: 13 en suite
- 🛏 DB&B £89.50–£109.50 B&B £60–£80
- ⑤ᴾ Special rates available
- ✕ Lunch ££
- ✕ Dinner £££
- Ⓥ Vegetarians welcome
- ✝ Children welcome
- ✗ No smoking in restaurant
- 🐂 Member of the Scotch Beef Club

Open ravioli of garden herb-marinated St Andrews cheese with char-grilled artichokes. Collops of red deer upon garlic mashed potatoes with date dumplings and thyme jus. Iced honey and Macallan whisy parfait served with a toffee and roasted almond sauce.

STB ★★★★ Hotel
- ⒺⒷ Credit cards: Mastercard/Eurocard, American Express, Visa, Switch, Delta
- 🛅 General Manager: Charles Cormack

PEEBLES HOTEL HYDRO
Innerleithen Road
Peebles EH45 8LX
Tel: 01721 720602 Fax: 01721 722999
Web: www.peebleshotelhydro.co.uk

Within Peebles boundaries, hotel is signposted.

A resort offering a full range of both indoor and outdoor activities.

- An Edwardian-style hotel.
- Modern Scottish cooking.
- "Contemporary Scottish cooking catering for all ages, along with superb hotel facilities."

Peebles Hotel Hydro was custom built and opened in 1907 with gracious style and most features are retained today. The format for providing facilities and entertainment for the new born to great-grandparents has been fine tuned over the years to create a wonderful resort for all the family. Facilities include outdoor tennis, croquet, pitch and putt, and pony-trekking with most other sports available nearby. Indoors there are daily activities for children, a newly opened leisure complex and badminton. Whilst 'live' music is organised at weekends, the comfortable lounges and bars offer quiet relaxation to the less energetic. There is also Lazels coffee shop to add to the extensive options.

Open all year
- 🏨 Rooms: 133 en suite
- 🛏 DB&B £66–£99.25 B&B £52–£84
- ⑤ᴾ Special rates available
- ✕ Food available all day £
- ✕ Lunch £
- ✕ Dinner £££
- Ⓥ Vegetarians welcome
- ✝ Children welcome
- ♿ Facilities for disabled visitors
- ✗ Smoking is permitted in the restaurant after 8.45 pm only

Timbale of Achiltibuie smoked salmon with a mousse of broad beans on a strawberry vinaigrette. Loin of Stobo lamb baked in a spinach and raspberry farce, surrounded by a whisky cream. An individual Heather Honey bavarois on a Drambuie sabayon.

STB ★★★★ Hotel
- ⒺⒷ Credit cards: Mastercard/Eurocard, American Express, Visa, Diners Club, Switch
- 🛅 General Manager: Gerard Bony

BALLATHIE HOUSE HOTEL
Kinclaven, by Stanley, Perthshire PH1 4QN
Tel: 01250 883268 Fax: 01250 883396
E-mail: email@ballathiehousehotel.com
Web: www.ballathiehousehotel.com

Off A9, 2 miles north of Perth – turn off at Stanley
and turn right at sign to Kinclaven.

Individual and unique country house hotel.

• A Victorian baronial house on the River Tay.
• Award-winning modern and classic Scottish
  cooking.
• "Modern comfort, Victorian elegance
  combined with award-winning cooking!"

An elegant turreted mansion, well-seated in superb
shooting country on one of the best salmon beats
on the mighty River Tay. Chris Longden, Ballathie's
Manager, is very experienced, and his Chef, Kevin
MacGillivray, presents lunches and dinners which
one inspector described as "exceptional." His
menus change daily, use local produce and offer
subtle variations on classic Scottish dishes.
Ballathie has 2 AA Rosettes. Winner of The
Macallan Taste of Scotland Country House Hotel of
the Year Award 1994 and Winner of The Macallan
Taste of Scotland Special Merit Award for Best
Lunch 1997. Winner (Category 1) in The Taste of
Scotland Scotch Lamb Challenge Competition 1999.

Open all year
🏠 Rooms: 27 en suite
🛏 DB&B £95–£140　B&B £70–£120
SP Special rates available
✘ Food available all day ££
✘ Lunch ££
✘ Dinner ££££
Ⓥ Vegetarians welcome
🕏 Children welcome
♿ Facilities for disabled visitors
🚭 No smoking in dining rooms
🐂 Member of the Scotch Beef Club

Ballathie home-cured salmon in citrus and dill
marinade with Arran mustard cream. Roast rack of
Perthshire lamb with rosemary and garlic served
with a confit of shallots, smoked bacon and thyme.
Warm poached pear with fudge sauce, brandy
snap basket with toffee ice cream.

STB ★★★★ Hotel
💳 Credit cards: Mastercard/Eurocard, American
Express, Visa, Diners Club, Switch, Delta, JCB
🍴 Manager: Christopher J Longden

EXCEED
65 South Methven Street
Perth PH1 5NX
Tel: 01738 621189 Fax: 01738 445758
E-mail: exceed@btconnect.com

Situated between South Street and High Street.

**Excellent local produce, skilfully presented in this
restaurant.**

• Tastefully converted seed store.
• Skilful Scottish cooking with international
  influence.
• "A very fine restaurant which exceeds
  expectations!"

Exceed is chef proprietor Willie Little's second
restaurant, having already achieved recognition
with Cargills Restaurant in Blairgowrie. The
restaurant was formerly a florists and seed store
and has been tastefully converted with wooden
tables and floor. The atmosphere reflects the buzz
of Perth city centre and the menus are modern,
offering excellent local produce in a style which has
taken the best from around the world and
successfully married them with Scotland's best.
Exceed is now established as one of Perth's finest
restaurants. Shortlisted and Commended for The
Macallan Taste of Scotland Awards 1999.

Open all year except Christmas Day + New
Year's Day
🍷 Table licence
✘ Lunch ££
✘ Dinner £££
Ⓥ Vegetarians welcome
🕏 Children welcome
♿ Facilities for disabled visitors
🚬 Smoking areas in restaurant

Duck and roast pine kernel sausage with wilted
spinach and ginger-braised rhubarb. Loin of pork
stuffed with mixed dried fruits and clove jus.
Caramel and almond tart with a nut brittle ice
cream.

💳 Credit cards: Mastercard/Eurocard, American
Express, Visa, Switch, Delta, Solo
🍴 Chef Proprietor: Willie Little

HUNTINGTOWER HOTEL

Crieff Road
Perth PH1 3JT
Tel: 01738 583771
Fax: 01738 583777

Signposted off A85 (nr Perth Mart), 1 mile west of Perth, towards Crieff.

Fine country mansion in landscaped gardens.

- Mock Tudor.
- Country house cuisine.
- "Splendid setting, relaxing atmosphere and good country house cooking."

Huntingtower is an Edwardian mansion standing in four acres of landscaped gardens, located in the country yet only ten minutes drive from Perth city centre. There is a choice of two restaurants – the Garden conservatory with a light informal menu; Drew Heron, Master Chef Great Britain also displays his talents in the fine dining Oak Room. Huntingtower has 1 AA Rosette.

Open all year
🛏 Rooms: 34 en suite
🍴 DB&B £45–£49.50 B&B £45–£50
SP Special rates available
✗ Lunch £
✗ Dinner ££
V Vegetarians welcome
♁ Children welcome
♿ Facilities for disabled visitors

Mille feuille of scallops and smoked salmon with fine leaves and provençal dressing. Saddle of local venison, red onion confit, Boudin noir and bitter sweet port wine sauce. Iced soufflé of Drambuie marmalade sauce, fresh raspberries and chocolate.

STB ★★★★ Hotel
💳 Credit cards: Mastercard/Eurocard, American Express, Visa, Diners Club, Switch
🗝 Operations Director: Michael Lee

THE LANG BAR & RESTAURANT, PERTH THEATRE

185 High Street, Perth PH1 5UW
Tel: 01738 472709 Fax: 01738 624576
E-mail: theatre@perth.org.uk

Perth city centre in pedestrian zone at middle section of High Street.

Restaurant, bar and cafe within Perth Theatre.

- Theatre restaurant.
- Innovative/traditional Scottish cooking.
- "A high standard of home-made food in theatrical setting."

Perth Theatre was built in 1900. The bar, restaurant and coffee bar benefits both from its situation and its period reproduction feel. The menus are changed to suit the current production (a novel touch!). However being theatrical, when the stage is 'dark' so is the restaurant. The food is of a high standard and covers the range of Scottish meat, fish and game in really rather interesting dishes with continental touches. There is a creative touch in the more traditional dishes which demonstrates Chef Colin Potter's culinary energy. This place is understandably popular with locals and visitors.

Open all year except Christmas Day +
Public Holidays
Closed Sun
Note: Please telephone to ensure Restaurant is open in the evening
✗ Food available all day ££
✗ Lunch except Sun £
✗ Dinner except Sun – booking advised ££
V Vegetarians welcome
♁ Children welcome
♿ Facilities for disabled visitors
⊬ Smoking areas in restaurant + coffee bar

Smoked cod and prawn cannelloni baked with mozzarella cheese and sun-dried tomatoes. Roast loin of Perthshire lamb stuffed with minted vegetables and rosemary and served with a mustard sauce. Bread and butter pudding with apricots marinaded in brandy, served with vanilla custard.

💳 Credit cards: Mastercard/Eurocard, American Express, Visa, Diners Club, Switch, Delta
🗝 Front of House & Catering Manager: Peter Hood

LET'S EAT
77/79 Kinnoull Street
Perth PH1 5EZ
Tel: 01738 643377
Fax: 01738 621464

Restaurant stands on corner of Kinnoull Street and Atholl Street, close to North Inch. 3 minutes walk from High Street.

An exceptional city bistro restaurant.

- Attractive town centre restaurant.
- Modern Scottish cooking with a continental influence.
- "Quite simply – an exceptional restaurant!"

Under the skilled hands of Tony Heath and Shona Drysdale, Let's Eat is enjoying growing success. Shona's expertise is front of house and between them they have a very successful blend of hospitality, comfortable welcoming surroundings and superb food. The style of food is bistro in style with classic influences, the atmosphere relaxed. Consistent popularity and high standards are maintained here. Let's Eat has 2 AA Rosettes. Winner of The Macallan Taste of Scotland Restaurant of the Year Award 1997 and Winner of The Macallan Taste of Scotland Restaurant of the Year (Joint Winners) Award 1998.

Open all year except 2 weeks mid Jul
Closed Sun Mon
✗ Lunch except Sun Mon ££
✗ Dinner except Sun Mon ££
Ⓥ Vegetarians welcome
⚲ Children welcome
♿ Facilities for disabled visitors
⚬ No smoking in restaurant area
🐂 Member of the Scotch Beef Club

Salad of pan-roasted dived scallops with a sweet chilli dressing and crème fraîche. Seared fillets of halibut and sea bass with an asparagus, prawn and queen scallop risotto, spinach and pesto butter sauce. Warm pineapple and almond upside down pudding with mango ice cream and an orange caramel sauce.

⊞ Credit cards: Mastercard/Eurocard, American Express, Visa, Switch, Delta
⋈ Partners: Tony Heath & Shona Drysdale

LET'S EAT AGAIN
33 George Street, Perth
Perthshire PH1 5LA
Tel: 01738 633771
Fax: 01738 621464

Town centre – one-way traffic in George Street. Restaurant is halfway up on right-hand side.

Bistro in city centre.

- Within row of shops.
- Modern Scottish.
- "I would eat here again, and again and....!"

This bistro-style restaurant is situated in the shopping area of the city of Perth. The green and burnt orange decor creates a relaxed and cool atmosphere. Staff are trained by proprietors, Tony Heath and Shona Drysdale, who own sister restaurant 'Let's Eat', also in Perth. Chef Neil Simpson prepares food in classic style while manageress Laura Harper looks after front of house. The ambience is less formal here than Let's Eat but the food is just as dynamic.

Open all year except Christmas Day + Boxing Day, 2 weeks Jan + 2 weeks Jul
Closed Sun Mon
✗ Lunch except Sun Mon ££
✗ Dinner except Sun Mon ££
Ⓥ Vegetarians welcome
⚲ Children welcome
⚬ No smoking in restaurant
🐂 Member of the Scotch Beef Club

Chowder of Arbroath smokie, bacon and sweetcorn. Neil's fish cakes with a herb butter sauce and side salad. Home-made sticky toffee pudding with toffee sauce, whipped cream and hazelnut praline.

⊞ Credit cards: Mastercard/Eurocard, American Express, Visa, Switch, Delta
⋈ Manager: Laura Harper

ACARSAID HOTEL
8 Atholl Road
Pitlochry
Perthshire PH16 5BX
Tel: 01796 472389 Fax: 01796 473952
E-mail: acarsaid@msn.com

On main road at the south end of Pitlochry occupying a prominent position.

An attractively furnished town hotel ideal for theatre-goers.

- Victorian villa with later additions.
- Traditional home cooking with imagination.
- "A comfortable hotel near Pitlochry town centre."

Comfort of guests and attention to detail are priorities here. Attractively furnished throughout, the hotel is comfortable with care given to small details, and residents receive complementary afternoon tea upon arrival. Of the public rooms one is 'smoking' and one 'non-smoking'. Good visibility of Scottish produce on menus. Ina and Sandy MacArthur are attentive hosts who care for their guests comfort and this is evident throughout.

Open all year except 2 Jan to 12 Mar
- 🏠 Rooms: 19 en suite
- 🛏 DB&B £39–£54 B&B £25–£36
- SP Special rates available
- ✗ Lunch – residents only £
- ✗ Dinner ££
- V Vegetarians welcome
- 🏃 Children over 10 years welcome
- 🚭 No smoking in dining room

Home-smoked chicken breast presented with heather honey dressing. Baked fillet of Tay salmon wrapped in spinach and lattice puff pastry, enhanced by a grape and white wine velouté. Marshmallow roulade filled with Perthshire raspberries and freshly whipped cream.

STB ★★★ Hotel
- 💳 Credit cards: Mastercard/Eurocard, Visa, Switch, Delta
- 🅽 Partners: Sandy & Ina MacArthur

EAST HAUGH COUNTRY HOUSE HOTEL & RESTAURANT
Pitlochry, Perthshire PH16 5JS
Tel: 01796 473121 Fax: 01796 472473
E-mail: easthaugh@aol.com
Web: www.vacations-scotland.co.uk/easthaugh.html

1½ miles south of Pitlochry on old A9 road.

Charming country house hotel.

- 17th century turreted stone house.
- Elegant Scottish cuisine.
- "A popular hotel near Pitlochry with high cooking standards."

East Haugh is a turreted stone house, standing in its own gardens and is run by Neil and Lesley McGown. Both Neil and Lesley are keen fishermen and Neil also shoots and stalks – these are encouraging pastimes for Neil who is the chef, since the bag or catch often appear on the menu. There is a great deal of food on offer at East Haugh, with children's menus, lunchtime and evening bistro style menus plus those offered in The Gamekeeper's Restaurant for dinner. The lunch dishes are very wide-ranging and are prepared to order; dinner in the restaurant is a more formal affair, with a well-composed menu which changes every two days and features local produce. Traditional roast, Sunday lunch menu, a speciality. Winner of The Macallan Taste of Scotland Special Merit Award for Best Informal Lunch 1996.

Open all year except 20 to 26 Dec
N.B. Closed Mon to Thu for lunch during Nov, Dec, Jan + Mar – unless by prior arrangement
- 🏠 Rooms: 13, (12 en suite + 2 family with shared bathroom)
- 🛏 DB&B £49–£79 B&B £25–£55
- SP Special rates available
- ✗ Lunch ££
- ✗ Dinner ££-£££
- V Vegetarians welcome
- 🏃 Children welcome
- 🚭 No smoking in restaurant

Fillet of new season lamb cooked pink and seared scallops with rosemary and lime jus. Warm salad of sweet peppers, smoked pigeon breast and herb croûtons. Belgian chocolate tart with whisky cream.

STB ★★★ Hotel
- 💳 Credit cards: Mastercard/Eurocard, Visa
- 🅽 Proprietors: Neil & Lesley McGown

THE GREEN PARK HOTEL

Clunie Bridge Road
Pitlochry, Perthshire
PH16 5JY
Tel: 01796 473248
Fax: 01796 473520
E-mail: bookings@thegreenpark.co.uk
Web: www.thegreenpark.co.uk

Following Atholl Road through Pitlochry, the hotel is signposted to the left at the town limits.

Comfortable hotel with breathtaking views overlooking Loch Faskally.

- White building dating from 1800s.
- Traditional/classical cooking.
- "A traditional hotel offering comfort, tranquillity and excellent service."

The Green Park Hotel is delightful and overlooks Loch Faskally. Alistair and Diane McMenemie know their customers well and make every effort to ensure that their stay is a special one. The cooking is classical with great attention to detail and the best use is made of local produce to ensure that the flavours dominate. The dining room is very tastefully decorated and overlooks the gardens.

Open all year
🍴 Rooms: 39 en suite
🛏 DB&B £39–£64 B&B £25–£42
SP Special rates available
✗ Lunch £-££
✗ Dinner £££
V Vegetarians welcome
&. Facilities for disabled visitors
✗ No smoking throughout

Marinated fillet of red mullet with green olives and sesame croûtons. Suprême of Guinea fowl with blue cheese mousse and a port wine sauce. Dark and white chocolate terrine with a vanilla sauce and ice cream.

STB ★★★ Hotel
💳 Credit cards: Mastercard/Eurocard, Visa, Switch
Ⓜ Proprietors: The McMenemie Family

THE KILLIECRANKIE HOTEL

Killiecrankie, by Pitlochry
Perthshire PH16 5LG
Tel: 01796 473220 Fax: 01796 472451
E-mail: killiecrankie.hotel@btinternet.com
Web: www.btinternet.com/~killiecrankie.hotel/

B8079 on old A9, 3 miles north of Pitlochry.

An attractive country house overlooking the River Garry.

- Small country house hotel.
- Modern Scottish cooking with classic influences.
- "A deservedly popular hotel offering excellent informal bar lunches, and gourmet dinners in the evening."

This is a former manse built in 1840 and stands in four acres of well-kept gardens and woodland above the River Garry and the historic Pass of Killiecrankie, where a notable battle was fought in 1689. The surrounding country abounds with wildlife and the hotel has the atmosphere of a sporting lodge. Its resident owners, Colin and Carole Anderson, have decorated and furnished the house very tastefully, and have provided a high standard of comfort. Head chef Mark Easton's cooking is highly professional and imaginative, and his table d'hôte menus (four starters, four main courses) are well-balanced and appetising. A most attractive and well-run establishment. Killiecrankie has 2 AA Rosettes.

Open 7 Mar to 3 Jan except 1 week mid Dec
🍴 Rooms: 10 en suite
🛏 DB&B £80
SP Special rates available
✗ Lunch ££
✗ Dinner 5 course menu £££
V Vegetarians welcome
🧒 Children welcome
✗ No smoking in dining room
🐂 Member of the Scotch Beef Club

Cream of celery, Stilton and wine soup. Pan-fried loin of lamb served with potato rösti and mange tout, and redcurrant flavoured jus. Dark chocolate flan with fruit coulis and white chocolate sauce.

STB ★★★★ Hotel
💳 Credit cards: Mastercard/Eurocard, Visa, Switch, Delta
Ⓜ Owner/Proprietors: Colin & Carole Anderson

KNOCKENDARROCH HOUSE HOTEL

Higher Oakfield, Pitlochry
Perthshire PH16 5HT
Tel: 01796 473473 Fax: 01796 474068
E-mail: info@knockendarroch.co.uk
Web: www.knockendarroch.co.uk

In a commanding position, 3 minutes walk from the town centre. Take Bonnethill Road and then take first right turn.

An imposing Victorian villa with a period atmosphere.

- Victorian mansion in Pitlochry.
- Excellent classic cooking.
- "Gentle comfort and relaxation, and traditional hospitality and food."

Knockendarroch, an elegant Victorian mansion buit in Pitlochry in 1880, enjoys wonderful views up the Tummel Valley to the south, and of Ben Vrackie to the north. The house is well-proportioned, the public rooms well-appointed and comfortable and the bedrooms all individually furnished. The cooking is excellent in a traditional style and your hosts, Tony and Jane Ross, make every effort to make you feel at home – and succeed. Knockendarroch has 1 AA Rosette.

Open 1 Feb to 16 Nov
- Rooms: 12 en suite
- DB&B £41–£59 B&B £30–£41
- Special rates available
- Non-residents – prior booking essential
- Dinner £££
- Vegetarians welcome
- Children over 10 years welcome
- No smoking throughout

A roulade of home-smoked salmon and cream cheese. Roast breast of pheasant filled with a mousseline of spinach and lemon set on a cranberry and red wine jus. Ecclefechan butter tart with toffee cream.

STB ★★★★ Hotel
- Credit cards: Mastercard/Eurocard, American Express, Visa, Switch, Delta
- Owners: Tony & Jane Ross

THE OLD ARMOURY

Armoury Road
Pitlochry
Perthshire PH16 5AP
Tel: 01796 474 281 Fax: 01796 474 447

Situated on Armoury Road close to Loch Faskally on the way down to the Dam and Fishladder. Signposted at Northern end of main road through town.

A charming restaurant in the converted old Black Watch armoury.

- Renovated traditional farm cottage and armoury.
- Accomplished modern Scottish.
- "Skilfully cooked fresh food available all day."

This restaurant has many original armoury features including wooden panelled walls now painted white (displaying to good effect some of the sculptures of co-owner Alison Rollo, a well-known Scottish sculptor). A large stone log fire takes up one wall of the restaurant and the rest of the furniture has been carefully selected to make a cosy and comfortable space. The restaurant is run by Alison and her husband George who spend six months each year in New Zealand – there are some welcome New Zealand influences particularly evident on the wine list! The cooking here is fresh, skilled and innovative with good food available throughout the day.

Open Easter Friday to 7 Oct
- Comfortable 3 bed self-catering cottage in restaurant grounds
- Food available all day £
- Lunch ££
- Dinner £££
- Vegetarians welcome
- Children welcome
- Facilities for disabled visitors
- No smoking throughout
- Dogs welcome in the tea garden

Terrine of local wild pigeon encased in bacon with a raspberry and walnut dressing. Spicy vale of Athol lamb enhanced by garlic-infused tomatoes on a bed of cous cous, with citrus yoghurt topped with crispy leek. Drambuie parfait on a shortbread base with bramble coulis.

- Credit cards: Mastercard/Eurocard, Visa
- Proprietors: Alison & George Rollo

PITLOCHRY FESTIVAL THEATRE RESTAURANT

Portnacraig, Pitlochry
Perthshire PH16 5DR
Tel: 01796 484600
Fax: 01796 484616
E-mail: admin@pitlochry.org.uk
Web: www.pitlochry.org.uk

On south bank of the River Tummel, approx ¼ mile from centre of town. Clearly signposted.

For theatre-goers, an informal restaurant with a relaxed atmosphere.

- Restaurant and coffee bar.
- Modern Scottish cooking enlivened with imaginative touches.
- "Wonderful elevated views onto the River Tummel – a great place for an informal pre-theatre meal."

The Pitlochry Festival Theatre is beautifully situated on the banks of the River Tummel at the gateway to the Highlands. The theatre's restaurant and coffee bar are a boon to theatre patrons as well as Pitlochry locals who drop in regularly to enjoy the home baking which is such a feature of the coffee bar in the foyer. At lunchtime the restaurant is buffet style with a choice of hot and cold dishes, including local fish from the 'Summer Festival Buffet'. Portions are generous with lots of healthy eating options. In the evening table d'hôte dinner is served at 6.30 pm to accommodate theatre-goers. Booking is essential.

Open 28 July – due to restaurant extension being built
✘ Lunch £
♨ Dinner – booking essential ££-£££
Ⓥ Vegetarians welcome
⚹ Children welcome
⚹ Facilities for disabled visitors
⚹ No smoking in restaurant
⚹ Smoking area in Coffee Bar

Trio of local smoked meats on a bed of rocket. Cushion of cod fillet with tapenade and Parmesan in herb crust on a red pepper coulis. Home-made terrine of dark and white chocolate on a Cointreau and orange sauce.

⊞ Credit cards: Mastercard/Eurocard, American Express, Visa
⋈ Catering Manager: John Anderson

THE POPLARS

Lower Oakfield
Pitlochry
Perthshire PH16 5DS
Tel: 01796 472129
Fax: 01796 472554
E-mail: enquiries@poplars-hotel.co.uk
Web: www.poplars-hotel.co.uk

Between Lower Oakfield and Higher Oakfield Roads. Follow sign at south end of the town, up the hill.

Restored and extended Victorian villa in an elevated position.

- Comfortable hotel close to Pitlochry town centre.
- Scottish cooking to order, promoting traditional flavours.
- "Relaxing hotel – good value for money!"

Poplars is a friendly and comfortable hotel in Pitlochry. Beautifully situated in a very quiet yet town-centre convenient location in Pitlochry. The panoramic vista from the hotel across the Tummel Valley is quite stunning. Poplars is convenient for theatre-goers, as the Pitlochry Festival Theatre is nearby. The accommodation is comfortable and pleasant. Breakfast and dinner are served in the restaurant. Owners Kathleen Shepherd and Ian Goodlet are friendly and hospitable hosts whose local area and activity knowledge can greatly enhance your stay. The hotel concentrates exclusively on the provision of a truly memorable experience to its resident guests. Service is good, courteous and attentive.

Open all year
🛏 Rooms: 11
🛏 DB&B £36–£49 B&B £24–£35
SP Special rates available
✘ Dinner ££
Ⓥ Vegetarians welcome
⚹ Children welcome
⚹ Facilities for disabled visitors
⚹ No smoking in restaurant
🐕 Dogs welcome

Whiting marinated in lime and coriander, served with tortilla crisps and onion salad. Pan-fried venison with a rich wine and blackcurrant sauce. Fresh summer fruit pavlova with a red berry coulis.

STB ★★★ Hotel
⊞ Credit cards: Mastercard/Eurocard, Visa, Switch
⋈ Owners: Kathleen & Ian

PORTNACRAIG INN AND RESTAURANT
Portnacraig
Pitlochry
Perthshire PH16 5ND
Tel: 01796 472777
E-mail: portnacraig@talk21.com

Directly below the Pitlochry Festival Theatre on the banks of the River Tummel.

Charming inn with a wonderful riverside location.

- Delightful stone built inn.
- Modern Scottish cooking.
- "Scottish cooking with modern style, and an informal, friendly, atmosphere."

Portnacraig is a bistro-style restaurant with windows looking out onto the River Tummel from where you can watch the fishermen in waders; the ducks flying over and skimming the water; and the fish jumping; whilst you enjoy a candlelit dinner. It is one of the oldest buildings in Pitlochry, dating back some 300 years, both the inn and the restaurant have been lovingly restored. The restaurant has a buzz about it – it is busy with friendly staff and the sort of place where you can dress up or down depending upon the occasion. Cooking is excellent with good quality food and interesting menus presented with imagination and flair. Weather permitting, you may dine alfresco on the patio which is situated on the banks of the River Tummel.

Open 14 Mar to 30 Nov + private parties available during off season
- **ℍ** Rooms: 2 en suite
- **⇔** DB&B £35–£45 B&B £20–£30
- **SP** Special rates available
- **✕** Food available all day ££
- **✕** Lunch £
- **✕** Dinner ££
- **Ⅴ** Vegetarians welcome
- **ⵊ** Children welcome
- **⛬** Facilities for disabled visitors

Salmon and cod fish cakes with a spring onion and tomato salsa. Confit of duck leg with a pearl barley risotto and a warm blueberry vinaigrette. Warm chocolate tart with crème anglaise.

STB ★★★ Inn
- **⊞** Credit cards: Mastercard/Eurocard, Visa, Switch, Delta
- **ℕ** Partners: Bill & Andrew Bryan

WESTLANDS OF PITLOCHRY
160 Atholl Road, Pitlochry
Perthshire PH16 5AR
Tel: 01796 472266 Fax: 01796 473994
E-mail: info@westlandshotel.co.uk

A924 into Pitlochry, Westlands at north end of town on right-hand side.

Attractive stone building in own grounds.

- Country town hotel.
- Imaginative traditional cooking.
- "Good quality food freshly prepared."

An attractive stone building with an extension, built in keeping with the rest. The lawn, which is bordered by mature trees, slopes down to the main road, and Westlands has attractive views. The hotel is personally run by its resident partners – Andrew and Sue Mathieson, and Ian and Allison Robertson. There is an interesting table d'hôte menu and an à la carte menu which offers a wide range of Scottish dishes. Both are reasonably priced. Meals are served in the Garden Room Restaurant, which has pleasant views of the Vale of Atholl. Bar meals are also available.

Open all year except 25 + 26 Dec
- **ℍ** Rooms: 15 en suite
- **⇔** DB&B £55.50–£63.50 B&B £37–£45
- **SP** Special rates available
- **✕** Lunch £
- **✕** Dinner ££
- **Ⅴ** Vegetarians welcome
- **ⵊ** Children welcome
- **⚭** No smoking in restaurant

Creamed smoked Scottish haddock on a crisp croûton with lambs leaves and cherry tomatoes. Highland Lamb Wellington set on a pool of minted red wine sauce. Caramelised rhubarb and ginger tart tatin with a Glayva and vanilla ice cream.

STB ★★★ Hotel
- **⊞** Credit cards: Mastercard/Eurocard, Visa
- **ℕ** Partners: Andrew & Sue Mathieson/ Ian & Allison Robertson

THE HAVEN HOTEL

Innes Street, Plockton, Ross-shire IV52 8TW
Tel: 01599 544223
Fax: 01599 544467

In the village of Plockton.

A small West Highland hotel.

- Converted 19th century merchant's house.
- Stylish Scottish cooking.
- "A quality, family-run hotel."

Plockton is known as the 'jewel of the Highlands.' With its palm trees along the waterfront and shining views out over the sea, it is really one of the country's loveliest villages. The Haven was built for a Victorian merchant and has a pleasing simplicity in its architecture, whinstone-fronted and harled sides and rear. Although detached, it stands in the terrace of traditional houses in Plockton, only yards from the beach. The hotel offers two suites, one with a four-poster bed. It continues to offer the same high standard of cuisine for which it has long had such a good reputation. Dinner menus are table d'hôte (six choices of main course) and combine fresh local produce with interesting sauces, changing daily. The Haven has 1 AA Rosette, and is a member of the Certified Aberdeen Angus Scheme.

Open 1 Feb to 20 Dec incl
🏨 Rooms: 15, 12 en suite
🛏 DB&B £53–£60 B&B £35–£37
🆂🅿 Special rates available
❗ Restricted licence
✕ Lunch – 24 hours notice required ££
✕ Dinner 5 course menu £££
Ⓥ Vegetarians welcome
🕏 Children over 7 years welcome
♿ Facilities for disabled visitors
🚭 No smoking in restaurant

Chilled turbot and salmon mousse sitting in a crispy salad, accompanied by blue cheese and greek yoghurt dressing. Roast rack of Highland lamb decorated with minted pear and glazed with a redcurrant jelly gravy. A choice of home-made sweets.

STB ★★★★ Hotel
💳 Credit cards: Mastercard/Eurocard, Visa, Switch, Delta
👤 Owners: Annan & Jill Dryburgh

THE PLOCKTON HOTEL

Harbour Street, Plockton
Ross-shire IV52 8TN
Tel: 01599 544274
Fax: 01599 544475

In the centre of Harbour Street, Plockton.

A popular family-run hotel on the seafront.

- Traditional village hotel.
- Good quality bar food specialising in fish and shellfish.
- "Bustling family hotel with friendly atmosphere."

At the Plockton Hotel hosts Tom and Dorothy Pearson aim to make sure that your stay is a memorable one. They are charming hosts and obviously very popular with their guests. The hotel seems to continuously bustle with folk wanting to sample some of the local dishes and there is really something for everyone on the menu. Demand has dictated that the business expand and so there will be extended facilities next door from early 2000. A small garden on the shore makes this a very restful spot to reflect on your day.

Open all year except New Year's Day
🏨 Rooms: 10 en suite
🛏 B&B from £27.50
🆂🅿 Special rates available
✕ Food available all day ££
✕ Lunch £
✕ Dinner 5 course menu ££
Ⓥ Vegetarians welcome
🕏 Children welcome
♿ Facilities for disabled visitors
🚭 No smoking in dining room
🐕 Dogs by arrangement only

Talisker whisky pâté: a rough country style pâté flavoured with local malt whisky. Fillet of monkfish and Plockton prawn provençal, baked and topped with prawns bound in garlic, basil and sun-dried tomato sauce. Iced cranachan parfait with raspberry and blackcurrant coulis.

STB ★★ Inn
💳 Credit cards: Mastercard/Eurocard, American Express, Visa, Switch, Delta
👤 Partners: Dorothy, Tom & Alan Pearson

POOL HOUSE HOTEL
(by Inverewe Garden), Poolewe
Wester Ross IV22 2LD
Tel: 01445 781 272 Fax: 01445 781 403
E-mail: poolhouse@inverewe.co.uk
Web: www.inverewe.co.uk

6 miles north of Gairloch on A832. The hotel is
situated by the bridge, alongside the River Ewe
where it meets the sea and overlooks Inverewe
Gardens.

**The former home of Osgood Mackenzie, founder of
the famous Inverewe Gardens.**

- White-washed hotel on shorefront at River Ewe.
- Assured cooking specialising in seafood and
  game.
- "An ideal place to experience breathtaking
  scenery while enjoying the comforts of this
  lavishly furnished house."

Pool House Hotel is richly furnished and sits on the
waterfront overlooking Loch Ewe. The owner is a
keen collector of art, much of which is displayed in
the house, and also has a wealth of information to
offer on the subject of paintings and antiques. All
the family are involved in the business which has a
bright, friendly atmosphere. Chef John Moir goes to
a lot of trouble to source only the best fresh local
seafood and produce – his speciality being Loch
Ewe scallops. Chef also enjoys discussing with
guests what the catch of the day is and how it will
appear on the menu in the evening. *See advert page
262.*

Open 1 Mar to 31 Dec
🏠 Rooms: 10 en suite
🛏 DB&B £65–£100 B&B £45–£80
SP Special rates available
✗ Lunch ££
✗ Dinner £££
V Vegetarians welcome
≠ No smoking in dining room

**Dived scallops wrapped in bacon and roasted,
served with pesto dressing and roast tomato. Roast
venison medallion crowned with a pigeon breast
served on haggis mash with a whisky sauce.
Caramel and banana tart with caramel ice cream
encased in spun sugar.**

STB ★★★★ Hotel
Green Tourism PPP GOLD Award
ⓔ Credit cards: Mastercard/Eurocard, American
  Express, Visa, Switch, Delta, JCB
Ⓜ General Manager: Elizabeth Miles

FERNHILL HOTEL
Heugh Road, Portpatrick
DG9 8TD
Tel: 01776 810220 Fax: 01776 810596
E-mail: fernhill@portpatrick.demon.co.uk
Web: www.mcmillanhotels.com

On entering Portpatrick take first right – Heugh
Road – and hotel is c. 300 yards on left.

**A very comfortable hotel overlooking the pretty
seaside village and sea.**

- Victorian house with modern conservatory
  extension.
- Modern Scottish cooking.
- "A well run and comfortable hotel with a prime
  seaside location in this pretty Galloway village."

Fernhill is now under the professional ownership of
the McMillan family, who also own Kirroughtree
House at Newton Stewart. The terraced hotel
gardens fall away below the hotel and a large and
delightful conservatory makes a pleasant dining
room with the best sea views. The hotel
successfully blends modern extensions with an
original Victorian core and nearly every room takes
advantage of the fabulous elevated sea views. Don't
miss out on the house speciality – locally-caught
lobster – now always available fresh from the
hotel's new sea water holding tank. The staff are
very friendly and relaxed and try hard to make your
stay a most enjoyable experience. *See advert page
28.*

Open all year
🏠 Rooms: 20 en suite
🛏 DB&B £67.50–£80 B&B £47.50–£60
SP Special rates available
✗ Lunch ££
✗ Dinner £££
V Vegetarians welcome
☆ Children welcome
♿ Facilities for disabled visitors
≠ There is a smoking dining room

**Fernhill speciality: Mull of Galloway lobsters,
freshly cooked to order. Gravadlax with freshly
baked brown bread. Brandy snap basket filled
with home-made whisky, honey and oatmeal ice
cream.**

STB ★★★★ Hotel
ⓔ Credit cards: Mastercard/Eurocard, American
  Express, Visa, Switch
Ⓜ Manageress: Nicola Murchie

KNOCKINAAM LODGE
Portpatrick, Dumfries & Galloway DG9 9AD
Tel: 01776 810471 Fax: 01776 810435

From the A77 or the A75, follow signs for
Portpatrick. 2 miles west of Lochans, Knockinaam
sign on right. Take first left turning, past
smokehouse. Follow signs for 3 miles to lodge.

Luxury country house hotel.

- A 19th century hunting lodge converted into a
  first class country house hotel.
- Best modern British cooking.
- "Consistently exceptional standards – a role
  model for the hospitality industry."

This is a private, exclusive, elegant and yet
unpretentious country house. The welcome is warm
and personal, your every desire met and your
gourmet cravings utterly satisfied – the luxury of a
well-run hotel where nothing matters more than
your needs. The rooms are sumptously stylish yet
sympathetic to the building – each one individually
furnished and with its own idiosyncracies. Very
addictive! Knockinaam has a stunning cellar and
vast selection of malts. Knockinaam has 3 AA
Rosettes. Winner of The Macallan Taste of Scotland
Country House Hotel of the Year Award 1997 and
The Macallan Taste of Scotland Award for
Excellence 1997.

Open all year
- 🏨 Rooms: 10 en suite
- 🛏 DB&B from £80–£160
- 🆂🅿 Special rates available
- ✗ Food available all day ££
- ✗ Lunch £££
- ✗ Dinner ££££
- Ⓥ Vegetarians welcome
- 🕏 Children welcome
- ♿ Facilities for disabled visitors – restaurant only
- 🚭 No smoking in dining room
- 🐄 Member of the Scotch Beef Club

**Terrine of duck foie gras with ice wine jelly and
honey brioche. Steamed Drummore turbot with
langoustine ravioli and buttered spring cabbage.
Hot Sambuca soufflé with white chocolate ice
cream.**

STB ★★★★ Hotel
- 💳 Credit cards: Mastercard/Eurocard, American
  Express, Visa, Diners Club, Switch, Delta
- 🅺 Proprietors: Michael Bricker
  & Pauline Ashworth

THE GRANGE INN
Grange Road, St Andrews
Fife KY16 8LJ
Tel: 01334 472670 Fax: 01334 472604
Web: www.yell.co.uk/sites/grange-inn

From centre of town follow A917 Crail road past
hospital to double mini-roundabout. Take middle
road signposted Grange – ¾ mile to Inn.

**A charming country Inn overlooking St Andrews
Bay.**

- 17/18th century buildings.
- Modern and traditional Scottish cooking.
- "A country inn with a relaxed atmosphere."

Charming restaurant dating back to the 17th/18th
century situated on a hillside overlooking St
Andrews Bay. A short distance from the historic old
town of St Andrews, The Grange offers fresh
Scottish produce imaginatively prepared and
cooked to order. Under the capable management of
Proprietors Peter and Agnes Aretz, the Grange has
prospered and grown busy yet still managed to
retain much of its old-fashioned charm and
atmosphere. There are three separate dining areas
where you'll find high standards of hospitality with
uncomplicated, tasty, home-cooked food. A range of
draught and bottled beers, spirits and liqueurs are
available in the cosy, stone-flagged Caddies Bar,
with a personally selected wine list.

Open all year but closed Mon Tue Nov to
April incl
- 🏨 Rooms: 2 en suite
- 🛏 B&B £35–£40
- ✗ Lunch £-££
- ✗ Dinner £££
- Ⓥ Vegetarians welcome
- 🕏 Children welcome
- 🚭 No smoking in Patio Room + Bay Room

**Terrine of chicken and smoked venison with
caramelised fig and apple sauce, served with
angel toast. Medallions of pork with apricots and
dates, set on a Calvados cream sauce. Chocolate
and raspberry crème brûlée**

STB ★★ Restaurant with Rooms
- 💳 Credit cards: Mastercard/Eurocard, American
  Express, Visa, Diners Club, Switch, Delta
- 🅺 Proprietors: Peter & Agnes Aretz

"INN TOWN" AT THE MERCHANT'S HOUSE
49 South Street, St Andrews
Fife KY16 9QR
Tel: 01334 472595 Fax: 01334 472495
E-mail: inntown@theinn.co.uk
Web: theinn.co.uk/inntown

Situated on the north side of South Street, at the East end near to Abbey Street.

French-style cafe bistro in historical merchant's house.

- Bistro in historical surroundings.
- Classic French brasserie/style food.
- "Old historical house, full of character, serving simple French-style brasserie food."

The history of the Merchant's House dates back to the 16th century when it was built at the time of wood and thatch. It is the most imposing historical house in St Andrews, having the only original wooden floor and painted ceiling in the area. Today it is a charming French brasserie/cafe, oozing with character, simply furnished with oak and pine furniture. The perfect place to enjoy an intimate meal by candlelight. Nick White, the owner, prides himself on sourcing as much produce locally as possible. The pastry chef bakes all the pastries, bread and cakes on the premises which are hard to resist!

Open all year except Christmas Day
Closed Sun toThur evenings Jan/Feb
✘ Food available all day £
❢ Table licence only
✘ Lunch £
✘ Dinner ££
Ⓥ Vegetarians welcome
⅄ Children welcome
⅃ Facilities for disabled visitors

Salad Niçoise with locally-caught crispy trout. Roast rack of lamb with rosemary and virgin olive oil jus. Fresh fruit French tartlets.

⊞ Credit cards: Mastercard/Eurocard, American Express, Visa, Diners Club, Switch, Delta
Ⓜ Manager: Violet Innes

THE OLD COURSE HOTEL
GOLF RESORT & SPA
St Andrews, Kingdom of Fife KY16 9SP
Tel: 01334 474371 Fax: 01334 477668
E-mail: oldcoursehotel@st.andrews.co.uk
Web: www.oldcoursehotel.co.uk

A91 to St Andrews on outskirts of town.

A modern resort hotel standing on the edge of the most famous golf course in the world.

- Grand resort hotel.
- Modern Scottish.
- "Excellent food, and luxurious surroundings."

The hotel is set in a spectacular location, overlooking the infamous 17th Road Hole and the historic Royal and Ancient Clubhouse. By May 2000 the hotel will offer 148 bedrooms, including 33 suites. At the Old Course there is quiet elegance, excellent service, luxurious facilities and a warm welcome in the finest traditions of Scottish hospitality. The hotel offers its guests a unique choice of dining experiences – fine dining in the Road Hole Grill; Sands, a contemporary brasserie-style restaurant; and the Jigger Inn, originally a 19th century cottage, now a popular golfing pub serving real ale and good wholesome food. The hotel has 2 AA Rosettes. Runner-up (Category 2) in The Taste of Scotland Scotch Lamb Challenge Competition 1998.

Open all year
🛏 Rooms: 148 en suite
🛌 DB&B from £285 B&B from £245
SP Special golf and spa rates available
✘ Food served all day £-££
✘ Lunch ££
✘ Dinner ££££
Ⓥ Vegetarians welcome
⅄ Children welcome
⅃ Facilities for disabled visitors
⅄ Pipe and cigar smoking not permitted in restaurants
🐂 Member of the Scotch Beef Club

Pan-fried diver scallops with a sweet chilli and infused red pepper. Fillet of Buccleuch beef with truffle baked potatoes, white and green asparagus, cracked Parmesan wafer, bearnaise sauce and a thyme jus. Poached tamarillo with raspberry meringue and crème fraîche ice.

STB ★★★★★ International Resort Hotel
⊞ Credit cards: Mastercard/Eurocard, American Express, Visa, Diners Club, Delta, JCB
Ⓜ Executive Assistant Manager: Andrew Phelan

RUFFLETS COUNTRY HOUSE & GARDEN RESTAURANT

Strathkinness Low Road, St Andrews
Fife KY16 9TX
Tel: 01334 472594 Fax: 01334 478703
E-mail: reservations@rufflets.co.uk
Web: www.rufflets.co.uk

On B939, 1½ miles west of St Andrews.

Stylish country house by historic St Andrews.

- Enchanting country house hotel.
- Highly accomplished Scottish cooking.
- "Excellent – as always."

Rufflets is one of the oldest established country house hotels in Scotland, and has the distinction of being privately owned and managed by the same family since 1952. The house itself was built in 1924 and stands in formal gardens; furnishings are extremely tasteful (a mix of antique and contemporary country house). The attractive Garden Restaurant has 2 AA Rosettes, among other awards. The daily changing menus are table d'hôte and the cooking combines the fresh seafood available from the East Neuk and good local meats and vegetables with imaginative sauces and stuffings. Chef's signature dishes are highlighted on menu.

Open all year
🏠 Rooms: 22 en suite
🛏 DB&B from £105 B&B from £85
🆂🅿 Special rates available
✕ Lunch (Restaurant) Sun from ££
✕ Dinner from ££££
Ⓥ Vegetarians welcome
ⵁ Children welcome
& Facilities for non-residential disabled visitors
🐄 Member of the Scotch Beef Club

Pan-seared king scallops with a collage of seasonal leaves and garden herbs, drizzled with an Arran mustard and lime dressing. Grilled collop of Rannoch venison, pan-seared duck liver with dauphinoise potatoes, fresh asparagus and raspberry tea syrup glaze. Mille feuille of wafer thin orange blossom biscuits and lemon cream, iced lemon parfait and candied citrus fruits.

STB ★★★★ Hotel
💳 Credit cards: Mastercard/Eurocard, American Express, Visa, Diners Club, Switch
🅽 Proprietor: Ann Russell

ST ANDREWS LINKS CLUBHOUSE

West Sands Road, St Andrews
Fife KY16 9XL
Tel: 01334 466666 Fax: 01334 466664
E-mail: linkstrust@standrews.org.uk
Web: www.standrews.org.uk

From M90 take A91 to St Andrews (25 miles). In St Andrews follow signs to West Sands and golf courses. At beginning of Golf Place proceed ½ mile along road, towards beach. Clubhouse is on left.

Golf complex.

- Modern golf clubhouse with magnificent views.
- Informal creative cooking.
- "Adjacent to the St Andrews golf courses. It meets the needs of golfer and visitor alike."

St Andrews Links has become the largest golf complex in Europe, the Links Clubhouse is its latest addition. The dining room has been tastefully decorated with modern quality furniture and fittings. A fixed price menu and an extensive wine list are available here. Breakfast and light meals can be obtained in the lounge, which is also ideal for drinks as it permeates a relaxing atmosphere.

Open all year except Christmas Day
✕ Food available all day £
✕ Lunch £
✕ Dinner ££
Ⓥ Vegetarians welcome
ⵁ Children welcome
& Facilities for disabled visitors

Parcels of haggis wrapped in filo pastry served with home-made red onion chutney. Pan-fried suprême of chicken, fanned and served with a fresh raspberry vinegar. Traditional crème brûlée.

💳 Credit cards: Mastercard/Eurocard, Visa, Switch
🅽 Food & Beverage Manager: Sue Hutchison

AITHERNIE RESTAURANT AT OLD MANOR HOTEL
Leven Road, Lundin Links
nr St Andrews, Fife KY8 6AJ
Tel: 01333 320368 Fax: 01333 320911
E-mail: enquiries@oldmanorhotel.co.uk
Web: www.oldmanorhotel.co.uk

On A915 Kirkcaldy–St Andrews, 1 mile east of
Leven, on right overlooking Largo Bay.

**An excellent comfortable and friendly hotel in a
golfer's paradise.**

- Country house restaurant.
- Contemporary Scottish cuisine.
- "Stunning views, excellent hospitality and very
  good food."

Owned and run by the Clark family, their
commitment to what they do here is obvious. The
Clarks are a mine of information and advice on the
game of golf. Their Aithernie Restaurant serves both
à la carte and table d'hôte dishes, based on fresh
local meat and fish, imaginatively prepared and
presented. The wine list is sound and reasonably
priced. The restaurant's success has been reflected
by a number of awards for chef Alan Brunt. The Old
Manor has 2 AA Rosettes.

Open all year except Boxing Day +
New Year's Day
- ⌂ Rooms: 23 en suite
- ⛄ DB&B £45.50–£105 B&B £30–£90
- SP Special rates available
- ✗ Food available all day ££
- ✗ Lunch ££
- ✗ Dinner £££
- V Vegetarians welcome
- ⅄ Children welcome
- ⅄ Facilities for disabled visitors
- ⅄ No smoking in restaurant
- 🐂 Member of the Scotch Beef Club

Trio of salmon topped with a crisp herb pastry on a
chive butter sauce garnished with keta. Roast loin
of marinated venison set around a gâteau of apple
and black pudding on a woodland mushroom jus.
Heather honey and whisky-flavoured crème brûlée
with Tayside raspberries.

STB ★★★★ Hotel
- 💳 Credit cards: Mastercard/Eurocard, American
  Express, Visa, Diners Club, Switch, Delta, JCB
- 🗲 Owners: Clark Family

THE INN AT LATHONES
Lathones, By Largoward
Kingdom of Fife KY9 1JE
Tel: 01334 840494 Fax: 01334 840694
E-mail: lathones@theinn.co.uk
Web: www.theinn.co.uk

5 miles out of St Andrews on the A915 towards
Leven. The inn is on the main road, 1 mile before
Largoward.

Charming 400 year old coaching inn.

- Traditional refurbished coaching inn.
- Excellent Scottish cooking.
- "Delightful food and hospitality awaits the
  traveller at this coaching inn."

The Inn at Lathones is run by Nick and Jocelyn
White. It has, under their watchful eye been
completely refurbished and offers traditional
coaching inn hospitality in elegant surroundings.
Comfort is the main priority here and no effort has
been spared to ensure that guests feel at home.
Staff are friendly without being intrusive and this is
matched by a very high standard of cooking. This is
indeed a very special place on the outskirts of St
Andrews to enjoy good food in comfortable
surroundings.

Open all year except Christmas Day, Boxing
Day + Jan
- ⌂ Rooms: 14 en suite
- ⛄ DB&B £45–£75 B&B £49.50–£65
- SP Special rates available
- ✗ Food available all day Apr to Oct ££
- ✗ Lunch £
- ✗ Dinner ££
- V Vegetarians welcome
- ⅄ Children welcome
- ⅄ No smoking in restaurant
- 🐂 Member of the Scotch Beef Club

Avocado mousse and tempura of mussels with a
gazpacho sauce. Baked wood pigeon and pan-
fried Isle of Skye scallops, served with a dressed
salad and red pepper and olive dressing. A
selection of favourite desserts: french tart, soup of
red fruits, chocolate crème brûlée and poire belle
Helene.

STB ★★★★ Inn
- 💳 Credit cards: Mastercard/Eurocard, American
  Express, Visa, Diners Club, Switch, Delta
- 🗲 Proprietor: Nick White

SANDFORD COUNTRY HOUSE HOTEL
Newton Hill, Wormit
Fife DD6 8RG
Tel: 01382 541802 Fax: 01382 542136
E-mail: sandford.hotel@btinternet.com
Web: www.sandfordhotelfife.com

4 miles south of Dundee on A92 (formerly A914) at junction of B946 signposted Wormit.

An historic 20th century building on the Tay.

- Country house hotel.
- Scottish/French modern cuisine.
- "Elegant hotel set amidst delightful gardens - an ideal venue for fine dining."

The Sandford Country House Hotel is a Listed building and stands in five acres of gardens. It has been carefully and lovingly cared for over the years. Under the ownership of the Cowan family this care continues both in the level of hospitality offered and the standard of cooking which are both excellent. The emphasis is very much on a combination of Scottish and continental flavours and there is also great attention to the small details which take skill and commitment to prepare – like hand-made sweets and petits fours for example. Sandford is also an excellent base from which to enjoy the outdoor pursuits of the Newton Hill Outdoor Centre next door. Sandford Country House Hotel has 1 AA Rosette. *See advert page 263.*

Open all year
- Rooms: 16 en suite
- DB&B £52.50–£85   B&B £35–£70
- Special rates available
- Food available all day £-£££
- Lunch £-£££
- Dinner £-£££
- Vegetarians welcome
- Children welcome
- No smoking in restaurant

Sauté of chicken livers encased in a pastry tartlet nappe, by a grape and red wine jus. Slow-roasted chicken suprême stuffed with a light asparagus mousse, on a bed of fresh egg noodles bordered by a lemon cream sauce. Triple chocolate Marquise placed onto a pool of hazelnut praline anglaise.

STB ★★★★ Hotel
- Credit cards: Mastercard/Eurocard, American Express, Visa, Diners Club, Switch, Delta
- Proprietor: G Cowan

CLINT LODGE
Clinthill, St Boswells
Melrose TD6 0DZ
Tel: 01835 822027 Fax: 01835 822656
E-mail: clintlodge@aol.com

At St Boswells take the B6404, continue for 2 miles across the Mertoun Bridge, turn left onto B6356 through Clint Mains village veering left. Follow this road to Clint Lodge, 1 mile on right.

A 19th century sporting lodge offering superior furnishings, relaxed atmosphere and good home cooking.

- Country sports lodge with spectacular views.
- Traditional Scottish cooking.
- "A quiet, relaxing get-away with real Scottish hospitality and good home cooking."

This is a wonderful stone-built lodge, built by Lord Polwarth and now owned by the Duke of Sutherland. Bill and Heather Walker took a long lease in January 1997 and carefully restored the house paying great attention to the finest of detail. All woodwork has been stripped and even the window shutters are in fine working order. Furnishings are carefully selected to blend into the traditional atmosphere recreated here amongst a treasure trove of family heirlooms and selected antique furniture. A real get-away-haven with excellent hospitality and superb cooking.

Open all year except Christmas
- Rooms: 5 (4 en suite, 1 private facilities)
- DB&B £45–£55   B&B £25–£35
- Special rates available
- Residents only
- Unlicensed – guests welcome to take own wine
- Dinner ££
- Vegetarians welcome
- Children welcome

Home-made lovage soup served with cheese scones. Rolls of beef with garden-herb stuffing in onion and red wine sauce. Lemon and lime meringue roulade with raspberry syrup.

STB ★★★★ B&B
- Credit cards: Mastercard/Eurocard, Visa
- Proprietors: Bill & Heather Walker

THE SEAFOOD RESTAURANT
16 West End, St Monans, Fife KY10 2BX
Tel/Fax: 01333 730 327

From St Andrews drive south to Anstruther (B9131) then turn west along the A917 through Pittenweem to St Monans. Go down to the harbour and turn right.

A delightful seafood restaurant overlooking St Monans harbour.

- 400 year old fisherman's house with purpose-built semi-circular restaurant with panoramic sea views.
- Contemporary Scottish seafood.
- "Fine dining with views to match."

St Monans is a delightful old fishing village situated on the East Neuk of Fife. The Seafood Restaurant adjoins the original fisherman's house – this dates back 400 years. An interesting feature of the restaurant is a 900 year old fresh water well from which drinking water can be taken. Chef Craig Millar has no problem sourcing the freshest of seafood and uses only the best to prepare fish dishes with a contemporary innovative twist. This is obvious on his menus as they are very appealing, with interesting varieties and combinations. The quality of local produce is superb and inspiring. The pleasant attitude of staff is excellent at all times. The bar is part of the original fisherman's house and provides the perfect atmosphere to browse over the menu. In summer cold food is served on the terrace. The restaurant has 1 AA Rosette. Shortlisted and Commended for The Macallan Taste of Scotland Awards 1999.

Open all year except Christmas Day and
3 weeks mid Jan
Closed Mon Oct to Apr
✘ Lunch ££
✘ Dinner £££
Ⓥ Vegetarians welcome
♿ Facilities for disabled visitors
⌲ No smoking in restaurant

Pan-seared, hand-dived scallops with a basil oil and an orange, vanilla and cardamom reduction. Grilled turbot fillet with local chanterelle mushrooms and a meaux mustard dressing. William pear poached in lime and saffron with coconut ice cream.

⊞ Credit cards: Mastercard/Eurocard, American Express, Visa, Switch
Ⓜ Partner: Tim Butler

THE COACH HOUSE RESTAURANT
Glenfintaig
by Spean Bridge, Lochaber
PH34 4DX
Tel: 01397 712 680 Fax: 01397 712 407
E-mail: crann_tara@bigfoot.com
Web: www.sol.co.uk/c/coach_house/

From Spean Bridge take A82 to Inverness. Approx 3 miles on right-hand side.

Small country restaurant in converted coaching inn.

- Stone cottage.
- Innovative, contemporary cooking.
- "Small, cosy restaurant – smart, upmarket food!"

The Coach House has a fascinating history dating back to the time of the Jacobite risings in the 18th century. It is now run as a restaurant by chef proprietors Iain Mac Donald and Tarlika Joshi. The house is very Scottish in style with whitewashed walls, polished mahogany tables decorated with fresh flowers, and a warming log stove combining to make a comfortable and welcoming atmosphere. The owners cook all meals to order using base quality ingredients sourced locally where possible and use their combined skill and expertise to accentuate flavours and textures. Guests can try the recipes for themselves by checking out the restaurant's website! The restaurant is popular locally and, owing to its size, advance booking (particularly in the evenings) is recommended.

Open 30 Apr to 25 Oct
✘ Lunch £
✘ Dinner ££
Ⓥ Vegetarians welcome – prior notice required
♱ Children welcome
⌲ No smoking in restaurant

Castle of angel hair pasta filled with leek and sun-dried tomatoes. Pan-roasted rack of Highland lamb, redcurrant, citrus and port sauce, and a medley of root vegetables with a phyllo basket of dauphinoise potatoes. Praline parfait on a shortcake biscuit surrounded by a loch of raspberries.

⊞ Credit cards: Mastercard/Eurocard, Visa, Switch, Delta, JCB
Ⓜ Chef Proprietors: Iain Mac Donald & Tarlika Joshi

CORRIEGOUR LODGE HOTEL

Loch Lochy, Near Spean Bridge
Inverness-shire PH34 4EB
Tel: 01397 712685 Fax: 01397 712696
E-mail: info@corriegour-lodge-hotel.com
Web: www.corriegour-lodge-hotel.com

Follow A82, 17 miles north of Fort William; 47 miles south of Inverness – between Spean Bridge and Invergarry.

A charming former Victorian hunting lodge on the shores of Loch Lochy.

- A small, personally owned and managed country house hotel.
- Excellent modern Scottish cooking.
- "Set in a wonderfully scenic part of the Highlands this is an ideal place to enjoy relaxed hospitality and good food."

This is a well-established hotel situated on the shores of Loch Lochy with the grounds extending through their own gardens and across the road to a private beach and jetty. The hotel is run by Christian Drew and her family. It is well-maintained and cared for and the addition of a conservatory dining room offers wonderful scenery. The house is full of old comfortable furniture, nice books to read, interesting bits and pieces. The food here is good, using local produce with menus which change often reflecting the availability of the produce. The hotel's wine list is extensive and reasonably priced.

Open 1 Feb to 30 Nov (weekends only 1 Feb to 31 Mar) + special 3/6 day breaks at New Year
- 🏠 Rooms: 9 en suite
- 🛏 DB&B £53–£75 B&B £43–£55
- SP Special rates available
- ✗ Non-residents – dinner only
- ✗ Lunch – by arrangement
- ✗ Dinner £££
- V Vegetarians welcome with prior notice
- ☆ Children over 8 years welcome
- ✗ No smoking in restaurant

Seared scallops in a fresh ginger sauce. Baked lemon sole in a Pernod butter sauce. Chilled caramel and chocolate terrine with poached pear, pecan nuts and Drambuie cream.

STB ★★★★ Hotel
- 💳 Credit cards: Mastercard/Eurocard, American Express, Visa, Switch, Delta
- 🙎 Owner: Christian Drew

OLD PINES RESTAURANT WITH ROOMS

Spean Bridge, by Fort William
Inverness-shire PH34 4EG
Tel: 01397 712324 Fax: 01397 712433
E-mail: goodfood.at.oldpines@lineone.net
Web: www.lochaber.com/oldpines

From Spean Bridge take A82 to Inverness. 1 mile north take B8004 next to Commando Memorial 300 yards on right.

Award-winning cuisine in this restaurant with rooms.

- Scandinavian-style log and stone chalet.
- Outstanding and sophisticated Scottish cuisine.
- "Sukie Barber's attention to detail and commitment to high quality ingredients makes each labour-intensive dish a delightful taste experience."

Old Pines is a little jewel set amongst mature pine trees in the Great Glen. It is the family home of Bill and Sukie Barber, and dinner by crystal and candlelight in the conservatory will certainly be the highlight of your stay. Sukie offers the finest of Scottish food, cooked superbly bringing unlimited enthusiasm and skill to her craft. All ingredients are sourced locally, and Old Pines has its own smokehouse. An unusual, well-researched wine list offering top quality wine at a reasonable price complements Sukie's cooking. Winner of The Macallan Taste of Scotland Best Child Friendly Establishment Award 1998.

Open all year except 2 weeks winter
- 🏠 Rooms: 8 en suite
- 🛏 DB&B £60–£70
- SP Special rates available
- ✗ Food available all day ££
- ✗ Dinner 5 course menu except Sun May to Sept (supper to residents) £££
- V Vegetarians welcome – prior notice appreciated
- ☆ Children welcome
- ♿ Facilities for disabled visitors
- ✗ No smoking throughout
- 🐂 Member of the Scotch Beef Club

Scallops, squat lobsters and mussels with spinach and a vermouth and orange sauce. Roast Mallaig cod with ratatouille and garlic mayonnaise. Lemon feather cake with cardamom ice cream and bramble sauce.

STB ★★★★ Restaurant with Rooms
Green Tourism 🍀🍀🍀 GOLD Award
- 💳 Credit cards: Mastercard/Eurocard, Visa, Switch, Delta
- 🙎 Proprietors: Bill & Sukie Barber

OLD STATION RESTAURANT
Station Road, Spean Bridge
Inverness-shire PH34 4EP
Tel: 01397 712535

In Spean Bridge on A82 to Fort William, follow sign
for railway station on the left-hand side.

**A delightful restaurant in this working Victorian
station in Spean Bridge.**

* Converted station restaurant.
* Creative Scottish home cooking.
* "Superb service, carefully crafted dishes and a
  wonderful ambience."

This is a converted Victorian station which is still in
use today; watch the trains go by as you enjoy your
meal. One can even venture by train from Fort
William for dinner which would make for a most
interesting evening. Richard and Helen Bunney,
proprietors, converted this building to its present
condition and have kept a pictorial record of
progress for interested visitors to peruse. The
restaurant and bar/lounge occupy the centre of the
building and have been sensitively converted and
decorated. Cooking is skilled, making best use of
fresh local produce and presenting dishes in an
attractive style. The Old Station Restaurant has 1 AA
Rosette.

Open 1 Apr to 30 Oct
Closed Mon
✘ Lunch – by prior arangement
✘ Dinner except Mon ££-£££
Ⓥ Vegetarians welcome
⚘ Children over 10 years welcome
♿ Facilities for disabled visitors
✄ Smoking permitted in bar area only
🐄 Member of the Scotch Beef Club

**Warm garlic mushrooms and seafood in a filo shell.
Noisettes of venison with a herb crust and a port
and rowanberry sauce. Fresh strawberry and
vanilla tart with hazelnut shortbread pastry.**

🆔 Credit cards: Mastercard/Eurocard, Visa,
   Switch, Delta, JCB
📋 Proprietors: Richard & Helen Bunney

OLIVIA'S RESTAURANT
Baker Street
Stirling FK8 1BJ
Tel/Fax: 01786 446277

From Stirling town centre follow directions to
Stirling Castle. Restaurant is approx 800 yards from
castle on approach.

**Relaxed informal-style restaurant in historic town
setting.**

* Modern shop in row.
* Modern Scottish.
* "Every effort is taken with the presentation of
  food and the care of the customer."

Set in a row of modern shop fronts, with a large
plate glass window and door, Olivia's is an
appealing modern restaurant located in a historic
part of Stirling centre. Decor is also modern and
reflects the informal style of eating here. The menus
are interesting, featuring good local produce
cooked with flair and imagination. It is advisable to
pre-book.

Open all year except Christmas Day, Boxing
Day, 1 + 2 Jan
Closed Sun
✘ Lunch except Sun £
✘ Dinner except Sun ££
Ⓥ Vegetarians welcome
⚘ Children welcome
♿ Facilities for disabled visitors

**Seared scallops with an orange and cardamom
dressing. Roast loin of venison wrapped in
pancetta with fennel mash and a rosemary and port
gravy. Chocolate cinnamon tuile with Baileys ice
cream and a poached pear.**

🆔 Credit cards: Mastercard/Eurocard, Visa,
   Switch, Delta
📋 Manageress: Becky Spaven

SCHOLARS RESTAURANT
AT STIRLING HIGHLAND HOTEL
Stirling
FK8 1DU
Tel: 01786 272727 Fax: 01786 272829
E-mail: andrews@scottishhighlandhotels.co.uk
Web: www.scottishhighlandhotels.co.uk

From Stirling town centre follow directions to
Stirling Castle. Stirling Highland Hotel is on the hill
approx 500 yards below the castle in Spittal Street
which is a one way street.

**An historic A Listed building, converted from the
old high school.**

- Historic converted town hotel.
- Modern Scottish cooking.
- "Historic converted town hotel offering every
  modern comfort and luxury with good food."

In keeping with the rest of the hotel, Scholars
Restaurant is named with its former use in mind –
namely that of the old high school. The restaurant
adjoins the lounge bar entitled 'Headmaster's
Study' and is a formal restaurant, with fine linen,
cutlery and crockery. Menus are à la carte and
table d'hôte and offer a good selection of freshly
prepared dishes. Chef Ian Hamilton uses fresh local
produce with imagination and flair. Staff are well-
trained and professional yet friendly. Scholars
Restaurant has 2 AA Rosettes.

 Open all year
 Closed Sat lunch
🏫 Rooms: 94 en suite
🛏 DB&B £102.50 B&B £55–£82.50
SP Special rates available
✕ Food available all day
✕ Lunch except Sat £
✕ Dinner ££
Ⓥ Vegetarians welcome
🛉 Children welcome
♿ Facilities for disabled visitors
🚭 No smoking in restaurant

**Tian of fresh and smoked Scottish salmon with an
avocado, dill and lime dressing. Roast Highland
venison set on a sauté of artichoke hearts and
oyster mushrooms. Lemon posset served with
orange sablé.**

STB ★★★★ Hotel
💳 Credit cards: Mastercard/Eurocard, American
 Express, Visa, Diners Club, Switch, JCB
👤 General Manager: Andrew G Swinton

THE TOPPS
Fintry Road, Denny (B818)
Stirlingshire FK6 5JF
Tel: 01324 822471
Fax: 01324 823099

On B818 Denny – Fintry road, off M80. 4 miles from
Denny.

Modern farmhouse with superb open aspect.

- A farmhouse on a working sheep and cashmere
  goat farm.
- Excellent home cooking.
- "The Topps remains consistent in standards."

This is a most informal farm guest house where you
cannot help but share in the day to day
activities of the country. The house itself is a
modern bungalow with splendid views over the
Fintry and Ochil Hills, pleasantly furnished with
plenty of family bric-a-brac. The atmosphere is cosy
and familiar. A popular restaurant complements the
guest house facilities. It has a small bar and a
comfortable dining room. Scottish owners Jennifer
and Alistair Steel both cook. The menus are
straightforward, usually offering a choice of four
main courses. As much produce as possible comes
from the farm itself.

 Open all year
🏫 Rooms: 8 en suite
🛏 B&B £20–£32
✕ Dinner ££
Ⓥ Vegetarians welcome – prior notice required
🛉 Children welcome
♿ Facilities for disabled visitors
🚭 No smoking throughout

**Alistair's gravadlax – herb marinaded salmon.
Lamb fillet with port sauce, fresh raspberries and
wild mushrooms. Lacy crêpes filled with chocolate
and greek yoghurt sauce.**

STB ★★ Guest House
💳 Credit cards: Mastercard/Eurocard, Visa
👤 Owners/Chefs: Jennifer & Alistair Steel

COUL HOUSE HOTEL
Contin, by Strathpeffer
Ross-shire IV14 9EY
Tel: 01997 421487 Fax: 01997 421945
Web: www.milford.co.uk/go/coulhouse.html

North of Inverness, continue on A9 over Moray Firth Bridge. After 5 miles take second left at roundabout on to A835. Follow this road for about 12 miles until you reach the village of Contin. Hotel is ½ mile up private drive to the right.

A country house near Strathpeffer.

• 19th century mansion.
• Country house cooking.
• "Very good dining in country house splendour."

This elegant country house hotel commands fine views over unspoiled Highland scenery, little has changed since its original inhabitants, the Mackenzies of Coul lived here. The spacious public rooms have open log fires and the en suite bedrooms are comfortable and tastefully decorated. Home to Martyn and Ann Hill, whose warm Highland welcome is only matched by their loveable Labradors. The bar lunches are notable – and the 'Kitchen Bar' itself is very popular with locals. Mackenzie's Taste of Scotland Restaurant offers table d'hôte and à la carte lunch and dinner menus which focus on Scottish specialities. There is also the new Tartan Bistro. Coul House Hotel has 1 AA Rosette. *See advert page 27.*

Open all year
🏨 Rooms: 20 en suite
🛏 DB&B £51–£79 B&B £36–£54
SP Special rates available
✗ Lunch £-££ (Restaurant – prior booking only)
✗ Dinner 5 course menu £££
V Vegetarians welcome
🏃 Children welcome
♿ Facilities for disabled visitors
🚭 No smoking in restaurant
🐂 Member of the Scotch Beef Club

Home-smoked venison with avocado fan and pigeon, cranberry parfait. Char-grilled salmon, monkfish and scallops, lemon and watercress cream. Layered apple, raspberry, cinnamon crisp and chantilly cream.

STB ★★★★ Hotel
💳 Credit cards: Mastercard/Eurocard, American Express, Visa, Diners Club, Switch, JCB
👤 Proprietors: Martyn & Ann Hill

CREAGAN HOUSE
RESTAURANT WITH ACCOMMODATION
Strathyre
Perthshire FK18 8ND
Tel: 01877 384638 Fax: 01877 384319
Web: www.milford.co.uk/go/creaganhouse.html

On A84, ¼ mile north of Strathyre.

Family-run restaurant with accommodation.

• 17th century farmhouse.
• Innovative Scottish cooking.
• "Full of charm and elegance, you will find excellent classical French cooking here with a strong Scottish influence."

Creagan House dates from the 17th century, and has been sympathetically restored to provide a 'baronial' dining room and five letting bedrooms. The house is eclectically furnished with all sorts of interesting pieces, and one of the bedrooms has a unique four-poster bed. Guests choose from the 'menu of the day' or the 'chef's favourites menu'. The emphasis of the cooking is to allow the fresh local ingredients to emerge, with herbs from the garden, meats sourced from within Perthshire and interesting Scottish cheeses. The care and attention given to preparation, cooking and presentation is obvious and the overall effect is excellent. Creagan House has 2 AA Rosettes.

Open all year except 3 to 28 Feb + 1 week Oct
🏨 Rooms: 5 en suite
🛏 B&B £40
SP Special rates available
✗ Booking essential for all meals
✗ Lunch parties can be arranged
✗ Dinner ££-£££
V Vegetarians welcome – with prior notice
🏃 Children welcome
🚭 No smoking in dining hall + bedrooms
🐂 Member of the Scotch Beef Club

Seared-dived scallops on tequila and orange-flavoured braised chicory, surrounded by orange vermouth sauce and garnished with coconut prawns. Braised shoulder of lamb on clapshot flavoured with garlic and rosemary oil, served with watercress purée and sherry jus. Apple flapjack pudding with fresh ginger crème anglaise.

STB ★★★★ Restaurant with Rooms
💳 Credit cards: Mastercard/Eurocard, American Express, Visa
👤 Chef/Proprietor: Gordon Gunn
👤 Co-Proprietor: Cherry Gunn

ROSEBANK HOUSE

Main Street, Strathyre, by Callander
Perthshire FK18 8NA
Tel: 01877 384208 Fax: 01877 384201
Web: www.smoothhound.co.uk/hotels/
rosebank.html

On the east side of the main A84 in the village of
Strathyre.

Guest house with restaurant.

- Victorian Highland house.
- Modern Scottish cooking.
- "A family run establishment with a relaxed
  atmosphere."

Rosebank House is a fine example of Victorian
architecture built in 1872. It is run by Jill and Pete
Moor whose philosophy is to offer comfortable and
welcoming surroundings, good food and a place for
guests to relax and enjoy the area. The house is
welcoming with open fires and comfortable
furnishings. Walls are enhanced with wild life
paintings by Jill, whose talents also extend to the
kitchen where she prepares fine dishes using fresh
local produce. Home-made preserves are also a
speciality here.

	Open 1 Mar to 31 Dec
⌂	Rooms: 4, 2 en suite
⇋	DB&B £33–£36 B&B £19–£22
SP	Special rates available
✗	Booking essential for all meals
⅏	Unlicensed – guests welcome to take own wine
⊕	Packed lunch £
✗	Dinner ££
Ⓥ	Vegetarians welcome
⅄	Children welcome
⅍	No smoking throughout
⚲	Dogs welcome

**Home-cured gravadlax with wholegrain mustard
and dill sauce. Local trout with almond and
mushroom stuffing, seasonal local vegetables and
home-grown herbs. Whisky Mac bread and butter
pudding.**

STB ★★★★ Guest House
⊞ Credit cards: Mastercard/Eurocard, Visa, Delta
⋈ Co-Proprietors: Jill & Pete Moor

KILCAMB LODGE HOTEL

Strontian
Argyll PH36 4HY
Tel: 01967 402257
Fax: 01967 402041

On A861, 13 miles from Corran Ferry (A82, 15 miles
south of Fort William).

**Charming, small country house hotel in stunningly
beautiful loch-side setting.**

- Small country house hotel.
- High quality Scottish cuisine.
- "Charming setting, perfect hosts and delicious
  food."

Kilcamb Lodge is a charming, substantial West
Highland dowager house, with extensions at each
end. Its situation is superb – standing in 28 acres of
lawns and woodland, with half a mile of shoreline
along Loch Sunart. The hotel is family-owned and
run by Anne and Peter Blakeway. The excellence of
the food has been recognised by the award of 2 AA
Rosettes. Neil Mellis cooks, presenting a highly
professional table d'hôte menu which changes daily
and uses the best of the produce available that day.
This is a family business with real style – the perfect
setting for any hotel and the way it is run enhances
it further. Investor in People Award.

	Open all year except Jan Feb
	N.B. Open New Year
⌂	Rooms: 11 en suite
⇋	DB&B £75–£100 B&B £45–£70
✗	Light Lunch £
✗	Dinner 4 course menu £££
Ⓥ	Vegetarians welcome – prior notice required
⅄	Children welcome
♿	Facilities for non-residential disabled visitors
⅍	No smoking in restaurant

**Pan-fried veal sweetbreads with olive cake and
truffle essence. Loin of Argyll lamb with a soft herb
crust, vegetable gâteau and a rosemary jus. Hot
passion fruit soufflé with raspberry sorbet.**

STB ★★★★ Hotel
⊞ Credit cards: Mastercard/Eurocard, Visa,
    Switch, Delta
⋈ Directors: Peter & Anne Blakeway

THE WHEATSHEAF HOTEL
Main Street, Swinton
Berwickshire TD11 3JJ
Tel: 01890 860 257
Fax: 01890 860 688

On B6461 Kelso-Berwick-upon-Tweed, 12 miles west of Berwick or a few miles east of A697.

Personally run village inn, in the heart of the Borders.

• A small country inn on the village green.
• Modern Scottish cooking.
• "A well-deserved reputation for good quality cooking."

It is evident that a great deal of care has been taken to preserve the character of a genuine country inn. The result is a welcoming, comfortable and intimate atmosphere, the sort that takes years to acquire. Bedrooms are prettily furnished, light and airy with en suite bathrooms. The menu is surprisingly extensive, very reasonably priced and changes daily. Excellent local produce is given added flavour by the chef's individuality and flair. The Wheatsheaf has 1 AA Rosette. Winner of The Macallan Taste of Scotland Hotel of the Year Award 1997.

Open all year except last week Oct + 1 to 14 Jan
Closed Mon
🏠 Rooms: 6 en suite
🛏 B&B £32–£52
SP Special rates available
✗ Lunch except Mon ££
✗ Dinner except Mon £££
Ⓥ Vegetarians welcome
🕴 Children welcome
♿ Facilities for disabled visitors
🚭 No smoking in restaurant

Warm king scallop and crispy leek salad on a lemon butter sauce. Local roe deer loin with poached pear and spiced red cabbage in a sloe gin sauce. Iced praline soufflé with a warm butterscotch sauce.

STB ★★★★ Restaurant with Rooms
💳 Credit cards: Mastercard/Eurocard, Visa, Switch
🕴 Proprietors: Alan & Julie Reid

GLENMORANGIE HOUSE AT CADBOLL
Fearn, by Tain, Ross-shire IV20 1XP
Tel: 01862 871 671 Fax: 01862 871 625
E-mail: relax@glenmorangieplc.co.uk
Web: www.glenmorangie

33 miles north of Inverness on A9. Turn right at roundabout signposted B9175 Nigg. Drive 2 miles to left turn signposted Balintore and Hilton. 5 miles through village of Hilton to the end of lane.

Country house with exquisite cuisine, offering comfort of the highest standard.

• Restored 17th century house.
• Scottish cuisine.
• "A unique dining experience - excellent food in understated luxury."

This really is the ultimate in hospitality. Glenmorangie House is truly a welcoming home located in a breathtakingly beautiful part of Scotland. The house is run by Hugh Boyd who will organise anything for his guests. The house itself has been decorated in Highland style offering comfort, modern amenities (no televisions) and warmth. Menus are presented in a classical style with modern influences, using only excellent locally-sourced produce.

Open all year
🏠 Rooms: 9 en suite
🛏 DB&B £90–£160   B&B £70–£140
SP Special rates available
✗ Non residents – by appointment only
✗ Food available all day – by appointment only ££££
✗ Lunch – by appointment only ££
✗ Dinner- by appointment only ££££
Ⓥ Vegetarians welcome
🕴 Children welcome
🚭 No smoking in dining room

Mille feuille of Cadboll salmon and Moray lobster with a warm pine nut salad. Roast loin of Ross-shire lamb wrapped in leek and puff pastry with rosemary-glazed potatoes. Crabbies green ginger wine and white chocolate cheesecake with fresh strawberry coulis.

STB ★★★★★ Hotel
💳 Credit cards: Mastercard, Visa, Switch
🕴 Manager: Hugh Boyd

MANSFIELD HOUSE HOTEL
Scotsburn Road, Tain
Ross-shire IV19 1PR
Tel: 01862 892052 Fax: 01862 892260
E-mail: mansfield@cali.co.uk
Web: www.mansfield-house.co.uk

Approaching Tain from south, ignore first entrance
and continue north on A9 to second turning,
signposted to police station and Royal Academy.

A family-run luxury country house hotel.

* 19th century baronial house.
* Good Scottish cooking.
* "An international standard with a Scottish
  theme."

Visitors to the Royal Burgh of Tain, chartered in
1066, are able to enjoy many architectural features
of interest. Mansfield House was built in 19th
century baronial-style by Donald Fowler, the
former Provost of Tain between 1898 and 1912. The
house has been lovingly maintained and offers
every comfort for travellers. The kitchen prides itself
in preparing well-chosen Scottish produce for a
selection of familiar and popular dishes. There is a
friendly and relaxed atmosphere and the Lauritsen
family, highly skilled and experienced, are excellent
hosts – assisted by their two golden retrievers!
Investor in People Award. *See advert page 261.*

Open all year
🏠 Rooms: 18 en suite
🍴 B&B £50–£65
SP Special rates available
✗ Food available all day £-£££
✗ Lunch £
✗ Dinner £-£££
Ⅴ Vegetarians welcome
☩ Children welcome
♿ Facilities for disabled visitors
✘ No smoking in restaurants
🐄 Member of the Scotch Beef Club

**Tempura of squid with seared West Highland
scallops. Fillet of Highland venison with wild
mushroom risotto. Selection of Scottish soft and
hard cheeses.**

STB ★★★★ Hotel
Green Tourism ⟮ꝑꝑꝑ⟯ GOLD Award
💳 Credit cards: Mastercard/Eurocard, American
Express, Visa, Switch
🅺 Proprietors: Norman, Norma & David Lauritsen

MORANGIE HOUSE HOTEL
Morangie Road, Tain
Ross-shire IV19 1PY
Tel: 01862 892281 Fax: 01862 892872

Just off the A9 Inverness-Wick road on northern
outskirts of Tain.

Fine old Victorian mansion.

* Victorian mansion with tastefully extended and
  pleasing conservatory dining area.
* Traditional Highland fayre.
* "Popular traditional hotel offering a wide choice
  of good food."

This fine Victorian mansion is steeped in history and
has been tastefully renovated and extended by the
Wynne family. It offers an ideal base for golfing,
fishing and touring the Highlands. The Wynne family
have put a lot of effort into making this hotel what it
is today. In their dining room they serve good local
dishes using some of the freshest ingredients from
the Dornoch Firth, opposite the hotel. They offer bar,
table d'hôte and à la carte menus. Investor in
People Award.

Open all year
🏠 Rooms: 26 en suite
🍴 DB&B £55–£80   B&B £40–£60
SP Special rates available
✗ Food available all day £
✗ Lunch £
✗ Dinner ££
Ⅴ Vegetarians welcome
☩ Children welcome
♿ Facilities for disabled visitors
✘ No smoking in dining room

**Moules marinière using fresh mussels from the
Dornoch Firth. Pan-fried saddle of venison on a bed
of vegetable ribbons and served on a pool of apple
and cider jus. Home-made date sponge topped with
a sweet, enriched butterscotch sauce.**

STB ★★★★ Hotel
💳 Credit cards: Mastercard/Eurocard, American
Express, Visa, Diners Club, Switch
🅺 Proprietor: John Wynne

LOCH MAREE HOTEL
Talladale, by Achnasheen
Wester Ross IV22 2HL
Tel: 01445 760288
Fax: 01445 760241
E-mail: lochmaree@easynet

Midway between Kinlochewe (10 miles) and
Gairloch (10 miles) on the A832.

Traditional Victorian fishing lodge.

* Highland fishing lodge.
* Quality traditional Scottish.
* "Land your own catch for supper, in a beautiful setting."

Barbara and Matthew Wylie have come into this Highland hotel as managers. They are very keen and their enthusiasm is infectious as the staff are charming and attentive. The hotel is being returned to its former glory as a delightful retreat. Matthew oversees the cooking with a small team and sets very high standards. The menu is carefully balanced offering a selection of quality dishes which reflect the produce available. Loch Maree is an excellent base from which to explore the many local sights whilst enjoying the comforts of a bygone era.

Open all year except Christmas Day
🏨 Rooms: 20 en suite
🛏 DB&B £42.50–£70 B&B £30–£50
SP Special rates available
✗ Food available all day £££
✗ Dinner £££
Ⓥ Vegetarians welcome
🧍 Children welcome
♿ Facilities for disabled visitors
🚭 No smoking in dining room

Fresh Gairloch Bay scallops pan-fried with garlic and parsley. Seared loin of local venison with a rich red wine jus. Loch Maree summer pudding.

STB ★★ Hotel
💳 Credit cards: Mastercard/Eurocard, Visa, Switch, Delta
👤 General Manager: Matthew Wylie

THE OLD MILL HIGHLAND LODGE
Talladale
Loch Maree
Ross-shire
IV22 2HL
Tel: 01445 760271

On A832 at Talladale – 10 miles north of Kinlochewe and 10 miles south of Gairloch.

Converted old mill, now a Highland lodge.

* Attractive converted mill.
* Skilled home cooking.
* "Soufflés are a speciality at the Mill and the kitchen is the hub of the household here."

The Old Mill Highland Lodge is set in a delightful, peaceful haven overlooked by the impressive grandeur of the Mountain Slioch and surrounded by two acres of landscaped garden through which meanders a Highland stream and where glorious flowers, trees and shrubs abound. This is a charming and elegantly furnished house where Joanna and Chris Powell look after their guests with genuine warmth and charm. Chris is an enthusiastic cook and produces imaginative and colourful dishes utilising much locally-sourced Highland produce, while Joanna uses her experience in the wine trade to complement the mouthwatering dishes with just the right wine. No TV or radio disturbs the tranquillity here where you can be at one with nature – and watch with delight the pinemarten, known affectionately as *Major*, who visits the kitchen sill each evening to eat bread and jam!

Open all year except 15 Oct to 15 Dec
🏨 Rooms: 6, 5 en suite
🛏 DB&B £45–£65
SP Special rates available
✗ Residents only
🍷 Restricted hotel licence
✗ Dinner £££
Ⓥ Vegetarians welcome – by prior arrangement
🚭 No smoking throughout

Shitake mushrooms with goats cheese, hazelnuts and salad leaves. Fillet of Highland lamb wrapped in spinach and Parma ham with potato and herb layers. Dark chocolate soufflé with a raspberry coulis.

STB ★★★★ Hotel
💳 No credit cards
👤 Partners: Chris & Joanna Powell

THE COLUMBA HOTEL
East Pier Road, Tarbert
Argyll PA29 6UF
Tel/Fax: 01880 820808
E-mail: columbahotel@fsbdial.co.uk
Web: www.kintyre-scotland.org.uk

On East Pier Road, ½ mile to the left around the harbour. Hotel on roadside.

A well-appointed family-run hotel close to harbour at Tarbert.

- A Victorian waterfront hotel refurbished by the present owners as a comfortable and pleasant establishment.
- Scottish modern cooking.
- "A small, friendly hotel with very good food and wonderful views."

This delightful family-run hotel overlooks Loch Fyne at the entrance to Tarbert Harbour. It has been a labour of love to Gina and Bob Chicken, who have worked hard at sympathetically refurbishing this Victorian hotel and continue to do so. The decor is in keeping with the building; there is a cosy bar with an open fire, which is popular for its wholesomely different bar food (and its 30 malt whiskies). The restaurant has been elegantly restored; it offers a relaxed atmosphere and a menu which makes imaginative use of the excellent local produce. The seafood on the menu is of exceptional quality and well-cooked in an unpretentious manner. Game is from Inveraray Castle. Extremely good value for money eating experience. Walkers and cyclists welcome. *See advert page 26.*

Open all year except 25 + 26 Dec
- 🏠 Rooms: 10 en suite
- 🛏 DB&B £39.95–£57 B&B £33.95–£42
- SP Special rates available
- ✕ Lunch £
- ✕ Dinner ££
- Ⅴ Vegetarians welcome
- ⚱ Children welcome
- ✄ No smoking in restaurant

Warm salad of Tarbert smoked salmon with an Arran wholegrain mustard cream dressing. Roast rack of West Highland lamb with rosemary and bramble sauce and honey roast vegetables. Butterscotch meringue pie.

STB ★★★ Hotel
Green Tourism 🖉 **BRONZE** Award
- 🖭 Credit cards: Mastercard/Eurocard, Visa
- 🋐 Partners: Bob & Gina Chicken

STONEFIELD CASTLE HOTEL
Tarbert, Loch Fyne
Argyll PA29 6YJ
Tel: 01880 820836 Fax: 01880 820929

3 miles north of Tarbert on A83 to Lochgilphead.

Baronial Victorian mansion with famous gardens.

- A grand country house redolent of the past.
- Modern/traditional Scottish cooking.
- "Well-worth a visit to let the good food and marvellous scenery replenish the soul."

Stonefield Castle is set in 60 acres of woodland gardens which contain some of the finest Himalayan rhododendrons and other exotic shrubs and is therefore a joy for the garden lover. The castle dates back to 1837 and is a fine example of the Baronial style retaining many original furnishings and features. In addition to this the castle's location on Loch Fyne affords splendid views. The cooking here offers good local produce - seafood is caught locally – presented in a traditional style with modern influences and is served by well-trained and friendly staff. *See advert page 263.*

Open all year
- 🏠 Rooms: 33 (32 en suite, 1 with private facilities)
- 🛏 DB&B £65–£85
- SP Special rates available
- ✕ Lunch £
- ✕ Dinner £££
- Ⅴ Vegetarians welcome
- ⚐ Facilities for disabled visitors
- ✄ No smoking in restaurant

Islay king scallops with smoked bacon and garlic and chive butter. Fillet of Buccleuch beef with Dunsyre rarebit and port jus. Warm Drambuie and raspberry soufflé.

STB ★★★★ Hotel
- 🖭 Credit cards: Mastercard/Eurocard, American Express, Visa, Diners Club, Switch, Delta
- 🋐 General Manager: Peter Llewellyn

VICTORIA HOTEL
Barmore Road, Tarbert
Argyll PA29 6TW
Tel: 01880 820 236 Fax: 01880 820 638
E-mail: aliatvic@aol.com

First hotel as you enter the village (on A83 from
Lochgilphead) on your right-hand side.

Seaside hotel on the harbour at Tarbert.

- Distinctive hotel with enviable position.
- Modern Scottish cooking.
- "Enjoy local seafood and tasty wholesome fayre
  in this stylish location where every table has a
  view of the harbour."

The Victoria Hotel has been under the same
ownership and chef for the last nine years and has
built an enviable reputation for informal bar meals.
The conservatory offers a more formal dining
experience and its perfect location affords diners
an excellent view of the activities on the harbour
and distant hills. Menus are interesting and offer
locally-sourced produce described and presented
with skill and flair, with the eating experience
matching the description on the menus.

- Open all year except Christmas Day
- ⚓ Rooms: 5 en suite
- 🛏 DB&B £46–£48 B&B £26–£28
- SP Special rates available
- ✗ Lunch £
- ✗ Dinner ££
- Ⓥ Vegetarians welcome
- ⚘ Children welcome
- ♿ Facilities for disabled visitors
- ✄ No smoking in restaurant

**Loch Fyne queenies baked with a lemon and dill
pesto. Roasted Isle of Jura monkfish on a smoked
bacon and pea purée, accompanied with a lime
hollandaise. Colonsay honey and walnut tart with
a Drambuie Mascarpone.**

STB ★★★ Inn
- 💳 Credit cards: Mastercard/Eurocard, Visa,
  Switch, Delta
- 𝕂 Manager: Alistair Wilkie

TAYVALLICH INN
Tayvallich
Argyll PA31 8PL
Tel: 01546 870282
Fax: 01546 870333
E-mail: tayvallich.inn@virgin.net

2 hours from Glasgow via A82 to Tarbert. Then take
A83 to Lochgilphead. Follow signs to Oban then
take B841 at Carinbaan. After 4 miles take B8052 to
Tayvallich, 6 miles on single-track road.

**An informal bistro-style restaurant in Tayvallich
village now under new ownership.**

- Both a popular local hostelry and a destination
  for the discerning.
- Good Scottish cooking with some innovation.
- "Delicious seafood is a speciality in this popular
  restaurant with magnificent location."

Now under the new and very enthusiastic
ownership of Andrew, Jilly and Alyson Wilson, the
Tayvallich Inn continues to be a perennial favourite
place for visitors. It is beautifully situated with a
spectacular outlook onto Tayvallich Bay and offers
a very hospitable welcome to all visitors. The inn
prides itself on the use of fresh local produce, well-
presented and offering good value for money. The
decor is rustic with a nautical theme reflecting the
many yachtsmen who frequent this area. The new
owners are keen to preserve the inn's previous
reputation for good food and have made their own
mark on menus with some new ideas.

- Open all year except Christmas Day + New
  Year's Day
- ✗ Lunch except Mon Nov to Feb ££
- ✗ Dinner except Sun-Thu Nov to Mar ££
- ✗ Bar suppers except Mon Nov to Mar
- Ⓥ Vegetarians welcome
- ⚘ Children welcome
- ♿ Access only for disabled visitors

**Sound of Jura whole jumbo prawn salad with lime
mayonnaise. Grilled scallops with sweet chilli
sauce and crème fraîche. Chocolate bread and
butter pudding with cream.**

- 💳 Credit cards: Mastercard/Eurocard, Visa,
  Switch, Delta, JCB
- 𝕂 Proprietors: Andrew, Jilly and Alyson Wilson

TRIGONY HOUSE HOTEL
by Thornhill
Dumfries DG3 5EZ
Tel: 01848 331211 Fax: 01848 331303

Situated off A76, 13 miles north of Dumfries. 1 mile south of Thornhill on the Dumfries-Ayr trunk road.

An Edwardian country house standing in its own gardens.

- An attractive converted shooting lodge standing in its own gardens.
- Simple, elegant Scottish cooking.
- " A popular local haunt for meals and relaxation."

Trigony is a small country house hotel built of pink sandstone, standing amidst its own four acres of mature trees and lawns. It was once the home of the oldest woman in Scotland (Miss Frances Shakerley, who lived to be 107) and became a hotel 20 years ago. Its owners, Robin and Thelma Pollock, take justifiable pride in their hotel and provide homely comfort and good food made from local produce. Public and private rooms are bright and airy, prettily decorated and with charming views over the surrounding country. *See advert page 265.*

Open all year
🏠 Rooms : 8 en suite
🛏 DB&B £52.50–£62.50   B&B £35–£45
SP Special rates available
✗ Lunch £
✗ Dinner ££
Ⓥ Vegetarians welcome
🕏 Children over 8 years welcome
🚭 No smoking in dining room

Sauté of mushrooms, Dunsyre blue cheese, garlic and cream served in a vol-au-vent. Fillet of salmon poached in white wine and served with a lime and ginger sauce. Passion fruit parfait set on a fruit coulis.

STB ★★★★ Hotel
💳 Credit cards: Mastercard/Eurocard, Visa
🛡 Proprietors: Robin & Thelma Pollock

FORSS COUNTRY HOUSE HOTEL
by Thurso
Caithness
KW14 7XY
Tel: 01847 861201/202
Fax: 01847 861301

4 miles from Thurso heading west on A836. Secluded setting at Bridge of Forss.

Country house hotel set in 20 acres of woodland.

- Country house hotel.
- Traditional Scottish cooking.
- "A truly delightful country house where if an understated 'salmon' appears on the menu you can be assured that it is wild salmon from the River Forss, caught by the proprietor."

Forss Country House Hotel has been run by the MacGregor family for the past few years. Jamie MacGregor is 'mein host' looking after guests from arrival and even playing the bagpipes on special occasions for them. Catriona McLean does most of the cooking under the watchful eye of Jackie MacGregor. Best use of local produce is made in particular, locally-caught fish brought to the kitchen by Jamie. This is a place from which to enjoy the splendour of the Highlands.

Open 5 Jan to 23 Dec
🏠 Rooms: 10 en suite
🛏 DB&B £66–£75   B&B £45–£54.50
SP Special rates available
✗ Food available all day ££
✗ Lunch – residents only £-££
✗ Dinner ££
Ⓥ Vegetarians welcome
🕏 Children welcome
♿ Facilities for disabled visitors
🚭 No smoking in dining room

Local seafood wrapped in a pancake and served wtih Gruyere cheese topping. Stuffed breast of pheasant on a bed of haggis, served with a game sauce. Fluffy chocolate and Glayva mousse with freshly baked shortbread fingers.

STB ★★★★ Hotel
💳 Credit cards: Mastercard/Eurocard, American Express, Visa
🛡 Proprietors: Jamie & Jackie MacGregor

ROYAL HOTEL
Shore Road, Tighnabruaich
Argyll PA21 2BE
Tel: 01700 811 239 Fax: 01700 811 300
E-mail: royalhotel@btinternet.com
Web: www.royalhotel.org.uk

Overlooking the Kyles of Bute at the end of the A8003 in Tighnabruaich.

Comfortable hotel standing on the waters edge.

- White traditional hotel.
- Best modern Scottish.
- "The neat traditional facade belies the stylishly refurbished interior where local produce is served to perfection."

The Royal is a traditional stone-built hotel of considerable size owned by Roger and Bea McKie. Inside, the clever designer's eye of Bea is at work and has transformed the hotel into a haven of modern comfort. There is a stylish modern restaurant which overlooks the Kyles and island of Bute, and an informal friendly bar-brasserie where the local game and seafood is served straight from the fishermen's nets. Food at the Royal is very popular and, as it is often full, it is advised to arrive early for the brasserie and booking is essential for the restaurant. Investor in People Award.

Open all year
🏨 Rooms: 11 en suite
🛏 DB&B £50–£65   B&B £30–£47
SP Special rates available
✘ Food available all day ££
✘ Lunch £
✘ Dinner ££-£££
Ⓥ Vegetarians welcome
🕯 Children welcome
🚭 Smoking permitted in some areas of dining room

Carpaccio of venison with rocket leaves and shavings of Pecorino. Fillet of Black Faced lamb with Loch Striven mussels and a shellfish reduction. Chocolate mille feuille with almond thins and praline custard.

STB ★★★★ Hotel
💳 Credit cards: Mastercard/Eurocard, Visa, Switch, Delta
👤 Owners: Roger & Bea McKie

BORGIE LODGE HOTEL
Skerray, Tongue, Sutherland KW14 7TH
Tel/Fax: 01641 521 332
E-mail: jacqui@borgie.demon.co.uk
Web: www.s-h-systems.co.uk/hotels/borgie.htm

Take A836 for 7 miles from Tongue, turn left at the Torrisdale Road. Borgie Lodge is ½ mile along on the right.

A traditional hunting and fishing lodge in pleasant gardens on Scotland's northern seaboard.

- Spacious country house hotel.
- Modern Scottish cooking.
- "Jacqui MacGregor's first-class cooking proves without a doubt that it is possible to find top quality produce even in the most remote of Scottish locations – no shortcuts here!"

Quiet and secluded, Borgie Lodge is the home of Peter and Jacqui MacGregor. This hunting and fishing lodge has been tastefully upgraded to provide comfortable accommodation while keeping its traditional Highland image by way of Clan Sutherland tartan carpets, sporting prints and crackling log fires. A self-taught cook, Jacqui makes excellent use of the Caithness beef and lamb available to her, and the daily changing choice dinner menu will often feature the salmon and brown trout caught by the guests! Should you decide to contribute to the dinner menu, Borgie Lodge has salmon fishing rights on the Rivers Borgie and Halladale and boats for wild brown trout on the hotel's 20 hill lochs! Shooting and stalking on the 12,600 acre Tongue Estate. Peter can supply all the necessary ghillies, equipment and tuition. *See advert page 24.*

Open all year except 24 Dec to 3 Jan
🏨 Rooms: 7, 6 en suite
🛏 DB&B £62.50–£72.50   B&B £40–£50
✘ Lunch £
✘ Dinner £££
Ⓥ Vegetarians welcome
🕯 Children welcome
🚭 No smoking in dining room + bedrooms

Open ravioli of pigeon breast with red wine, lentils and smoked bacon. Lemon sole with pesto, sauce vierge and crispy courgette. Baked egg custard tart with nutmeg ice cream and blackberry sauce.

STB ★★★★ Hotel
💳 Credit cards: Mastercard/Eurocard, Visa
👤 Proprietors: Peter & Jacqui MacGregor

LOCH TORRIDON COUNTRY HOUSE HOTEL
Torridon, by Achnasheen
Wester Ross IV22 2EY
Tel: 01445 791242 Fax: 01445 791296
E-mail: enquiries@lochtorridonhotel.com
Web: www.lochtorridonhotel.com

Turn off the A832 at Kinlochewe and take the A896 to Torridon – do not turn off to Torridon village but carry on. Hotel 1 mile on right-hand side.

Luxury hotel with magnificent setting.

- Victorian shooting lodge.
- Fine Scottish cooking.
- "A luxurious Highland retreat with the added warmth of caring family ownership."

The Loch Torridon Country House Hotel offers a true Highland welcome. The building is a luxurious Victorian shooting lodge surrounded by outstanding scenery. It is set on the shore of Loch Torridon in 58 acres of parkland, with resident Highland cattle. The hotel has been lovingly restored to its Victorian splendour, with ornate ceilings, wood panelling and open log fires. The kitchen garden grows many herbs and vegetables which are used in the excellent daily changing menu. Investor in People Award. Loch Torridon Hotel has 2 AA Rosettes. *See advert page 259.*

Open all year
⊞ Rooms: 20 en suite
⨝ DB&B £75–£145 B&B £55–£125
SP Special rates available
✗ Food available all day ££
✗ Lunch ££
✗ Dinner ££££
Ⓥ Vegetarians welcome
⚊ Children welcome
⚹ Facilities for disabled visitors
⚸ No smoking in dining room

A roulade of home-smoked salmon and Torridon crab with crusted avocado. Bisque of Loch Torridon prawn. Pan-fried medallions of monkfish with roasted scallops and a salmon tartare. Lemon parfait wrapped in a tuile with a home-grown berry compote.

STB ★★★★ Hotel
Green Tourism 〔ₚₚ〕 SILVER Award
⊞ Credit cards: Mastercard/Eurocard, American Express, Visa, Diners Club, Switch
ⓧ Proprietors: David & Geraldine Gregory

CELLARS RESTAURANT AND COCKTAIL BAR
147 Templehill, Troon
Ayrshire KA10 6BQ
Tel: 01292 317448 Fax: 01292 318508
E-mail: anchor1812@aol.com

On arriving in Troon follow directions to Troon harbour which will lead you to Templehill. The Cellars is located half a kilometre along on the left-hand side.

Created out of the cellars of an old coaching inn.

- C. 1812 coaching inn with a 1930s Art Deco theme throughout.
- Modern Scottish cooking.
- "A vibrant, contemporary restaurant with a fine Scottish menu."

Cellars is steeped in local history of the 19th century where it was once the home of a local fisherman and his family of seven, offering the services of a coaching inn. Today it still features the original flooring and stone walls. Candles burn in profusion creating a highly charged and romantic atmosphere. From the restaurant you enter into the elegant scene of a 1930s style cocktail bar, similar to those on an ocean-going liner. Here the furnishings are of a high quality and have been used to good effect. Dishes are created from locally-sourced seafoods and the best of Scottish beef, fruits and vegetables. International touches are created by Robbie O'Keefe. An extensive cheeseboard is available.

Open all year
Closed Tue
✗ Lunch except Tue £-££
✗ Dinner except Tue ££
Ⓥ Vegetarians welcome
⚊ Children welcome
⚹ Facilities for disabled visitors
⚸ No smoking in restaurant
Smoking permitted in cocktail bar

King scallops with toasted brioche and a lobster dressing. Loin of Perthshire venison carpaccio, balsamic roast tomato and mixed berry salad. Chocolate tart, compote of raspberries, clotted cream.

⊞ Credit cards: Mastercard/Eurocard, American Express, Visa, Switch
ⓧ Proprietors: Malcolm & Karen Ronney

PIERSLAND HOUSE HOTEL
15 Craigend Road, Troon
Ayrshire KA10 6HD
Tel: 01292 314747 Fax: 01292 315613

South corner of Troon, opposite Royal Troon
Golf Club.

A fine country house hotel in the town of Troon.

- A beautifully restored Tudor style mansion in the heart of Ayrshire golfing country.
- International cuisine.
- "A well-presented and popular hotel in the heart of golf country."

Piersland was built for Sir Alexander Walker, grandson of the Johnnie Walker who founded the whisky firm of the same name. Tudor outside, and very impressive, the house has some fine Jacobean-style features. It stands in beautifully landscaped grounds that include an oriental garden. The hotel has 13 cottage suites for guests wanting that little bit extra. All have their own lounge and twin-bedroom and are fully equipped. Piersland has an informal dining area which overlooks the magnificent gardens. The recently refurbished upmarket Brasserie restaurant has 2 AA Rosettes.

Open all year
🏨 Rooms: 28 en suite
🛏 DB&B £75–£90   B&B £55–£70
SP Special rates available
✕ Lunch ££
✕ Dinner £££
Ⓥ Vegetarians welcome
🕏 Children welcome
♿ Facilities for disabled visitors

Tower of king scallops, black pudding and potato rösti with piquant pimento sauce. Roast loin of venison with thyme-flavoured scone, creamed lentils, celeriac traced with port jus. Warm orange sponge pudding served with Dundee marmalade ice cream.

STB ★★★★ Hotel
💳 Credit cards: Mastercard/Eurocard, American Express, Visa, Diners Club, Switch
Ⓜ General Manager: Karel Kuhler

MALIN COURT HOTEL
Turnberry
Ayrshire KA26 9PB
Tel: 01655 331457 Fax: 01655 331072
E-mail: info@malincourt.co.uk
Web: www.malincourt.co.uk

On A719 Ayr-Girvan, south of Maidens.

A modern country hotel with spectacular views.

- Popular, purpose-built country hotel.
- Modern Scottish cooking.
- "An expertly-run hotel offering very good customer care and delightful Scottish cuisine."

Malin Court is a very attractive, low-level , modern country hotel with superb views overlooking the Ayrshire coast. The hotel is very professionally-run and each member of staff takes an obvious pride in their work. The atmosphere is friendly and relaxed yet the hotel has very high standards and achieves much success. Chef Andrea Beach is a highly committed and competent young woman, who with her team has earned the hotel a second AA Rosette. Menus are imaginative and complemented by a short, well-priced wine list. The pleasure of dining is enhanced by spectacular sunset views of Arran. The hotel is ideal for a wide range of occasions. *See advert page 260.*

Open all year
🏨 Rooms: 18 en suite
🛏 DB&B £65–£95   B&B £52–£82
SP Special rates available
✕ Food available all day ££
✕ Lunch ££
✕ Dinner £££
Ⓥ Vegetarians welcome
🕏 Children welcome
♿ Facilities for disabled visitors
🐂 Member of the Scotch Beef Club

Timbale of pheasant topped with straw potatoes and whisky marmalade. Marinated lamb cutlets on a pineapple cous cous laced with chilli oil. Lavender cream with poached strawberries and a saffron tuille.

STB ★★★★ Hotel
Green Tourism 🌿🌿 SILVER Award
💳 Credit cards: Mastercard/Eurocard, American Express, Visa, Diners Club, Switch, Delta
Ⓜ General Manager: W R Kerr

TURNBERRY HOTEL

Turnberry, Ayrshire KA26 9LT
Tel: 01655 331000 Fax: 01655 331706
Web: www.turnberry.co.uk

A77 – 17 miles south of Ayr. 2 miles after
Kirkoswald.

One of Scotland's most exclusive hotels.

- Resort hotel of international standing.
- Grand hotel cooking; also spa and
  grill-room styles.
- "A grand Scottish golfing hotel offering world-
  class standards in all areas."

Turnberry was purpose-built as a golfing resort
hotel at the turn-of-the-century, and retains many
opulent Edwardian features. Service is gracious and
supremely professional, yet friendly. The hotel's
main restaurant offers the best classical cooking
using fresh, local ingredients. Chef Stewart
Cameron who is a member of the Academie
Culinaire de France was awarded The Macallan
Personality of the Year 1996. During the week lunch
is served in the Terrace Brasserie where a blissful
menu for the health-conscious is presented. The
Turnberry Clubhouse serves roasts, grills, fries and
sandwiches. Turnberry has 2 AA Rosettes.
Shortlisted and Commended for The Macallan Taste
of Scotland Awards 1999.

Open all year
🏨 Rooms: 132 en suite
🛏 DB&B £150–£217.50 B&B £100–£167.50
🆂🅿 Special rates available
✖ Food available all day ££
✖ Lunch £££
✖ Dinner ££££
Ⓥ Vegetarians welcome
🧍 Children welcome
♿ Facilities for disabled visitors
🐂 Member of the Scotch Beef Club

Marinaded Scottish salmon with orange, rosemary,
herbed mousse and caviar oil. Noisettes of
Highland venison with juniper celeriac purée,
bitter chocolate port pan juices and cranberry
syrup. White chocolate and Glayva délice
flavoured with raspberry compote and pistachio.

STB ★★★★★ International Resort Hotel
💳 Credit cards: Mastercard/Eurocard, American
   Express, Visa, Diners Club, Switch
👤 Director and General Manager: Kenneth Millar

FIFE ARMS HOTEL

The Square, Turriff
Aberdeenshire AB53 7AE
Tel: 01888 563124
Fax: 01888 563798

Situated in Turriff town square on A947. 10 miles
from Banff, 17 miles from Oldmeldrum.

**A pleasant and relaxing restaurant with rooms
offering traditional and modern dishes.**

- Old market square building.
- Freshly cooked local produce.
- "I was looked after as a friend."

There is a tradition of a hostelry on this site since
the early 1900s. Situated at the top of the square the
Fife Arms with its Poachers Restaurant offers a
cosy and informal venue for travellers and locals
alike. The restaurant menu is written on a
blackboard and changes daily according to
availability of local produce, particularly the
seafood which comes from Macduff. The lounge bar
is a relaxing place with oak beams, stained glass
windows, an open fire, and friendly service.

Open all year
🏨 Rooms: 9 en suite
✖ Lunch from £
✖ Dinner from £-££
Ⓥ Vegetarians welcome
🧍 Children welcome
🚭 No smoking in restaurant

Deep-fried langoustine tails in tempura-style
batter, with tartar sauce. Sauteed medallions of
venison in brandy and raspberry sauce with fresh
seasonal vegetables. Home-made sticky toffee
pudding with ice cream and cream.

💳 Credit cards: Mastercard/Eurocard, Visa,
   Switch, Delta
👤 Manager: Sandra Corless

THE CLIFTON COFFEE HOUSE
Tyndrum
Central Scotland FK20 8RY
Tel: 01838 400271 Fax: 01838 400330
E-mail: clifton@tyndrum12.freeserve.co.uk

On A85 to Oban and Fort William. 5 miles north of Crianlarich.

Excellent self-service restaurant.

- Craft and souvenir shopping eaterie.
- Home cooking.
- "Hearty portions of real home-made Scottish fayre served in a warm and friendly family-run restaurant."

What began as a simple self-service restaurant has become a tourist attraction in its own right. The shopping complex which has grown up around it sells books, crafts, woollens, gifts and food, but the restaurant is still the focal point. The owners constantly review their standards. Service is friendly and reliable, and good home baking and cooking along with a wide variety of traditional Scottish meals and snacks on offer. The tasteful decor along with the pleasing ambience and excellent facilities make this a well-kept and inviting establishment. 'Real' Highland hospitality and warmth are offered here. Very popular with visitors to Glencoe. In the year 2000 the owners celebrate their 35th anniversary in the business!

Open 8 Feb to 4 Jan except Christmas Day, Boxing Day + New Year's Day
✘ Food available 8.30 am – 5 pm £
✘ Lunch £
Ⓥ Vegetarians welcome
🕏 Children welcome
♿ Facilities for disabled visitors
✄ No smoking area in restaurant

Curried apple and parsnip soup. Venison casserole. Vegetarian selection. Home-baking: bread and butter pudding, shortbread and carrot cake.

▣ Credit cards: Mastercard/Eurocard, American Express, Visa, Diners Club, Switch, Delta
🅗 Partners: DD, LV & IL Wilkie/L P Gosden/ F D Robertson & E S Robertson

SCOTLAND'S LARDER
Upper Largo
Fife KY8 6EA
Tel: 01333 360 414 Fax: 01333 360 427
Web: www.scotlands-larder

Take East Neuk tourist route to Upper Largo, on A915. Scotland's Larder is at eastern edge of village.

Restaurant and coffee shop.

- Farm steading.
- Modern/traditional Scottish fayre.
- "Delightful Scottish food shop and restaurant."

Scotland's Larder is a unique centre providing a range of Scottish quality food, be it in the restaurant, the shop or weekly seasonal cookery demonstrations. Based in a 200 year old farm steading it has flagstone floors and an Aga in the corner. This rustic, charming restaurant offers a range of foods from morning coffee to meals served all day. Diners may choose from a set menu and 'specials board'. A set price dinner menu is offered on Friday and Saturday evenings. An interesting variety of Scottish produce is featured on the menu as well as local seasonal ingredients. With this combination, it allows the the natural flavours of the dishes to develop.

Open all year except 3 weeks from 5 Jan
✘ Food available all day £-££
✘ Lunch £-££
✘ Dinner ££
Ⓥ Vegetarians welcome
🕏 Children welcome
♿ Facilities for disabled visitors
✄ No smoking throughout

Cullen skink. Arisaig king scallops with leek and ginger. Macerated Freuchie strawberries with hazelnut parfait.

▣ Credit cards: Mastercard/Eurocard, Visa, Switch, Delta
🅗 Proprietor: Christopher Trotter
Manager: Anne Kinnes

THE 2001 TASTE OF SCOTLAND GUIDE

is scheduled to be published in October 2000.

To reserve a copy at a special post inclusive price, just complete the coupon below indicating your method of payment and send it to:

Taste of Scotland (Guide Sales)

33 Melville Street

Edinburgh EH3 7JF

Tel: 0131-220 1900. Fax: 0131-220 6102

You will be placed on the priority list to receive the Guide as soon as it is published.

For your convenience, we accept Mastercard, Visa and also cheques in £ sterling.

-- ✂

I wish to reserve _____ copy/copies of the Taste of Scotland 2000 Guide.

Name: _____

Address: _____

_____

_____

_____

Post Code: _____ Country: _____

Comments on meals in places listed in
The Taste of Scotland Guide are welcomed.
Send to Taste of Scotland, 33 Melville Street, Edinburgh EH3 7JF

Establishment visited _____

Date of visit _____Meal(s) taken _____

Comments_____

_____

_____

_____

_____

_____

_____

Name _____

Address_____

_____

_____

Comments on meals in places listed in
The Taste of Scotland Guide are welcomed.
Send to Taste of Scotland, 33 Melville Street, Edinburgh EH3 7JF

Establishment visited _____

Date of visit _____Meal(s) taken _____

Comments_____

_____

_____

_____

_____

_____

_____

Name _____

Address_____

_____

_____

THE MACALLAN TASTE OF SCOTLAND AWARDS 2000

Send to: Taste of Scotland, 33 Melville Street, Edinburgh EH3 7JF

I nominate_____ (Establishment)

for a Macallan Taste of Scotland Award.

Comments

_____

_____

_____

Name _____

Address _____

_____

_____

Date of visit _____

Meal (if appropriate) _____

Closing date for entries: 30 June 2000

--✂

THE MACALLAN TASTE OF SCOTLAND AWARDS 2000

Send to: Taste of Scotland, 33 Melville Street, Edinburgh EH3 7JF

I nominate_____ (Establishment)

for a Macallan Taste of Scotland Award.

Comments

_____

_____

_____

Name _____

Address _____

_____

_____

Date of visit _____

Meal (if appropriate) _____

Closing date for entries: 30 June 2000

FRIENDS OF TASTE OF SCOTLAND

We are presently developing a programme for 'Friends of Taste of Scotland',
details of which will be sent to all readers of the Guide who have purchased a
copy within the last two years from Taste of Scotland Scheme direct.
If you would like to be sure to receive information on
'Friends of Taste of Scotland', which will include details of special
offers and promotions at Taste of Scotland member establishments,
please complete the form below and we will send these to you in due course.
Thank you for your interest.

Name _____

Address _____

_____

_____

Post Code: _____ Country: _____

Tel No: _____ Fax No: _____

E-mail: _____

✂ --

FRIENDS OF TASTE OF SCOTLAND

We are presently developing a programme for 'Friends of Taste of Scotland',
details of which will be sent to all readers of the Guide who have purchased a
copy within the last two years from Taste of Scotland Scheme direct.
If you would like to be sure to receive information on
'Friends of Taste of Scotland', which will include details of special
offers and promotions at Taste of Scotland member establishments,
please complete the form below and we will send these to you in due course.
Thank you for your interest.

Name _____

Address _____

_____

_____

Post Code: _____ Country: _____

Tel No: _____ Fax No: _____

E-mail: _____

Reputation for Excellence

As with all other products which have earned a reputation for excellence it takes time, skill and dedication to produce Specially Selected Scotch Beef and Lamb.

Taste of Scotland members have a commitment to quality, reflected in their presentation of Scotland's own natural foodstuffs. Two of those, Specially Selected Scotch Beef and Lamb, are the end-products of a chain of traceability which reaches out from Scottish farmers to the finest tables in the land.

Specially Selected Scotch Beef and Lamb are available from accredited stockists around Britain so if you would like to learn more about the traditional production standards, now coupled to the pioneering assurance schemes of Scotland's farmers, hauliers, auctioneers and meat plants, and have details of your local retail stockists, then please contact

Scotch Quality Beef and Lamb Association,
Rural Centre – West Mains,
Newbridge, Midlothian EH28 8NX.
Tel: 0131 472 4040; Fax: 0131 472 4038

SCOTCH LAMB – NATURALLY ONE OF THE TRADITIONAL TASTES OF SCOTLAND...

The glories of Scotland's natural larder are acclaimed by chefs and diners alike. Our country generously yields an abundance of excellence – game from both land and air; fish from sea, rivers and lochs; fruits and berries; the barley for our national drink; and our Scotch beef and Scotch lamb.

The Taste of Scotland Scheme is itself an on-going celebration of Scotland's cornucopia. Scotch Lamb is, arguably, the traditional taste of Scotland and, like other cuisines our traditional dishes reflect the needs of an often harsh rural past, and the constraints of one-pot cooking. Food was the fuel for heavy labour, ingredients were solely those available in season.

Today's Scotch lamb is the end-product of those same husbandry skills which were notable even in the Middle Ages, now coupled with the high standards of quality assurance provided by a modern Scottish meat industry. But, though tradition still rightly influences many a Bill of Fare, today's tastes, appetites, chefs' skills, and culinary expectations are firmly of the 20th century.

It was this which seven years ago prompted the Scotch Quality Beef and Lamb Association – an organisation whose strong links with the Taste of Scotland Scheme date back to the early days of both bodies – to offer sponsorship of an annual chefs' competition for Scotch lamb. One objective of the competition was to develop a canon of contemporary recipes for this versatile meat.

For many of the world's top chefs Scotland is an instinctive choice when sourcing beef or lamb – they know that the traditional stock rearing skills are linked to high standards of quality assurance. For all chefs working in Taste of Scotland restaurants, large or small, the Scotch Lamb Challenge offers an opportunity to further demonstrate their skills and creativity. Many of the dishes developed for the competition have become regular features on members' menus.

The competition grows in importance ... 1999 saw 12 finalists – from an initial field of over 80 chefs – competing for the honour of winning The Taste of Scotland Scotch Lamb Challenge 1999 trophies and titles.

CHALLENGE 1999

Winning smiles (left to right): Amanda Clarke, Garry Watson and John Ross, Chairman of SQBLA.

Garry's winning lamb dish.

WINNER CATEGORY 1
Richard Hall, Ballathie House Hotel, nr Perth
Category 1 Runners-Up: Scott Dougall, Balbirnie House Hotel, Glenrothes;
Rob Watkinson, The Stagger Inn, Inverarnan
Category 1 Finalists: Andrew Hill, Victoria Hotel, Tarbert; Mark Petrie, Chapelbank House
Hotel, Forfar; Dale Smyth, The Rock Restaurant, Edinburgh.

WINNER CATEGORY 2
and Overall Winner of The 1999 Taste of Scotland Scotch Lamb Challenge
Garry Watson, Gordon's Restaurant, Inverkeilor
Category 2 Runners-Up: Andrew Hamer, The Gleneagles Hotel, Auchterarder;
Andrew May, Uplawmoor Hotel, Glasgow (Outskirts)
Category 2 Finalists: David Haetzman, blue bar cafe, Edinburgh; Scott Kirkham, Howies
Restaurant, Edinburgh; Ronny McDonald, Dalmunzie House Hotel, Blairgowrie.

Canon of Blackfaced Lamb with Slow Braised Shank, Minted Pea Mousse and White Bean Mash, Soubise and Rosemary Jus

Garry Watson, Sous Chef
Winner Category 2 and Overall Winner –
Scotch Lamb Challenge Competition 1999
Gordon's Restaurant, Inverkeilor

Ingredients

Canon of Lamb
1 best end of Blackfaced lamb
100g fresh brioche crumbs
75g fresh mint
75g flat leaf parsley
2 teaspoons Arran mustard
2 teaspoons black onion seeds

White Bean Mash
400g broad beans
400g haricot beans
1 Litre lamb stock
1 teaspoon garlic paste
50g butter
150ml cream
1 fresh bouquet garni

Potato Anna
450g potatoes – turned and sliced on a mandolin
2 tablespoons vegetable oil
mill salt and pepper

Shank of Lamb
4 Blackfaced lamb shanks
1 Litre light lamb stock
1 teaspoon tomato purée
50ml red wine
25ml port
4 sprigs thyme
1 bay leaf
4 sprigs rosemary

Soubise Sauce
1 large onion – finely diced
30g butter
pinch of caster sugar
150ml double cream
150ml light lamb stock
4 tablespoons white wine
1 clove garlic – crushed

Minted Pea Mousse
1Kg frozen peas
50g mint
2 tablespoons double cream
1 small baked potato
20g butter

Red Wine and Rosemary Jus
125ml red wine
1 Litre lamb stock
125g shallots
25g butter
4 sprigs fresh rosemary
seasoning

Method

■ Canon of lamb: remove canon from best end. Season with salt & pepper then coat in the Arran mustard. Blitz brioche crumbs & herbs in robot coupe, remove crumbs onto tray & add black onion seeds. Coat canon in the crust mixture. Seal in a hot pan on both sides then place in oven GM9/240°C/ 475°F for 6 mins (3 mins on both sides). Remove & allow to rest for 10 mins in a warm place. Cut diagonally into four pieces ready to serve.

■ Shank of lamb: braise the lamb shanks in the light lamb stock with tomato purée, rosemary, red wine, port, thyme & bay leaf until tender & sticky.

■ Minted pea mousse: blanch the peas then blitz with the remaining ingredients until thick & bright green. Pass through a mouli then quenelle to shape ready for service.

■ White bean mash: cook the beans with the rest of the ingredients, except cream until soft and thick (when cooking keep topping up with stock until they are cooked out). Pass the thick mash through a mouli or metal sieve & add cream (the mixture should be thick & white). Again, as the minted pea mousse, quenelle ready for service.

■ Soubise sauce: sweat the onion & garlic & add white wine, then reduce. Add remaining ingredients & cook until the onion is soft. Blitz and strain.

■ Red wine & rosemary jus: reduce the red wine & shallots & season. Add lamb stock and simmer with rosemary for 10 mins before straining and whisking in butter.

■ Potato Anna: heat oil in a 6 inch Pomme Anna mould on stove until very hot. Pack in the sliced potatoes (seasoning lightly between each layer). Bake in a hot oven at GM7/220°C/425°F for 20 mins, then turn out onto a tray & cut into four portions.

■ For the assembly of the dish, place the shank & canon off-centre on the plate. Quenelle on the white bean mash & minted pea mousse. Finish with soubise sauce to the left & rosemary jus to the right of the plate. Garnish with rosemary sprig & some sautéd wild mushrooms. *Serves 4*

Shank of Baby Scotch Lamb, Red Onion Daube, Kidney and Arran Mustard Sausage accompanied by Carrot and Parsnip Mash, Boulangère Potato, Sauteed Broad Beans and Madeira Glacé

Richard Hall, Sous Chef
Winner Category 1 – Scotch Lamb Challenge Competition 1999
Ballathie House Hotel, Perth

Ingredients

Lamb		Mirepoix	Vegetables and Potatoes
4 shanks of baby lamb	1 bunch rosemary	2 shallots	2 carrots
(cut 10cm below	1 bunch parsley – chopped	1 carrot – chopped	1 large parsnip
the 2nd knuckle)	2 shallots – finely chopped	2 sticks celery	400g peeled potatoes
2 lambs' kidneys	2 egg yolks	1 bunch thyme – chopped	100ml reduced brown
4 small red onions	10g dried cèpes (powdered)	2 cloves garlic	lamb stock
2 slices of streaky bacon	25ml olive oil		150g broad beans
1 sheet of crépinette	25g butter		salt, pepper and nutmeg
1 tblsp Arran mustard	salt and pepper		1 onion – finely sliced
1 glass red wine	2 bay leaves		
1 glass Madeira	1 Ltr brown lamb stock		

Method

■ Lamb shanks: cut a ring around the bone 3-4cm from the knuckle & trim the bone. Saw off the knuckle, cut through the knee joint & set aside the shanks. Remove the bone from the remaining meat. From two pieces trim all the fat, sinew & mince finely. From the other two pieces remove any excess fat & sinew & dice into half cm pieces.

■ Season the lamb shanks. Heat a spoonful of olive oil in a deep roasting tin. Seal the lamb & remove. Add the mirepoix & sauté until golden. Add the rosemary, bay leaf, red wine, Madeira and ¼ litre of lamb stock. Bring to the boil & add the lamb shanks & braise in a medium oven for 1½ hours, basting occasionally with the stock.

■ To make the daube, chop the bacon & sauté with the diced lamb & half the shallots until browned. Season with salt & pepper & cepe powder.

■ Add remaining wine & stock (reserving a teaspoon of stock for the potatoes) & simmer for 1½ hours. Peel the red onions, cut off the top & save. Leave the two outside layers of onion & remove the inner layers. Fill the onion with the stew mixture & put the onion lids back in place in an earthenware dish with any remaining stock.Put the lid on & cook in a medium oven for 35-45 mins.

■ Kidney & Arran mustard sausage: chop the kidneys into half cm cubes & quickly sauté with the remaining shallot & cool down. Mix the lamb mince, chopped parsley, Arran mustard, egg yolk & season. Cut the crépinette into four & pipe the mix on, 1cm thick &

6cm long. Wrap the crépinette round each sausage & trim any excess. Gently seal in butter & add to the lamb shanks & braise for 30 mins.

■ Carrot & parsnip mash: boil the carrots (peeled & chopped) in salted water until soft. Drain, purée & season. Return to the stove & dry excess juice. Repeat with the parsnip also adding the nutmeg. Place the purées into separate piping bags then place both in one piping bag with a 1cm plain nozzle & keep warm.

■ Boulangère potato: cut the potatoes into 5cm cylinders & slice finely. Line four 5cm ramekins with buttered greaseproof paper. Sauté the sliced onion until soft. In the ramekins alternately layer with potato & onion with a teaspoon of stock & season with salt & pepper on each layer until full. Cover with buttered greaseproof paper & cook in a moderately hot oven for 40 mins. Keep warm.

■ Broad beans: blanch the beans for 2 minutes in boiling water, refresh & set aside.

■ To assemble: remove the shanks, sausages & onions from the cooking liquors. Combine the liquors, pass through muslin & reduce to a sauce consistency, skimming off any fat. With a knob of butter sauté the broad beans. On four warm plates turn out the Boulangère potatoes, pipe the purée next to the potato in a semi-circle. Lay the shank & onion in between the potato and purée. Place the sausage on top of the potato. Scatter the beans at the bottom of each plate & pour some of the sauce over the lamb shanks & around the plate. Serve. *Serves 4*

BAKED COD WITH A PESTO CRUST, TOMATO AND BACON CONCASSÉ

Andy Cumming, Executive Head Chef
City Merchant, Glasgow

INGREDIENTS

4 x 175g thick cod fillets
100g fresh basil
50g grated parmesan cheese
olive oil
40g pine nuts
1 clove garlic, peeled
8 plum tomatoes, concassé (peeled, seeded & diced)
6 rashers smoked Ayrshire bacon (thick cut)
500g Ayrshire potatoes

TO GARNISH
coriander oil
fresh coriander

METHOD

■ Remove any fine bones from the cod steaks.
■ To prepare the pesto: using a food blender, place basil, garlic, pine nuts & parmesan into bowl. Blend at high speed, slowly adding olive oil until mixture becomes a firm paste.
■ Cut potatoes into barrel shapes & roast in olive oil.
■ Place cod fillets onto baking tray & spread pesto crust over. Bake in the oven GM8/230°C/450°F for 12 mins.
■ Cut bacon into ½ cm pieces & sauté. Add tomato concassé.
■ Set on heated plate with cod & garnish with potatoes, coriander oil & fresh coriander.
Serves 4

Pan Seared Hand Dived Scallops

Jennifer M Craig, Proprietor
Udny Arms Hotel, Newburgh, Aberdeen

Ingredients

2 large shallots
30ml white wine
120ml white wine vinegar
120ml fish stock
180ml double cream
1 small bunch snipped chives
125g unsalted butter
salt & freshly ground pepper
2 tblsps olive oil
20 medium scallops, fully trimmed & cleaned
250g spinach, lightly blanched & well drained, pinch nutmeg

Method

■ To make the sauce, sweat the shallots in 30g butter until soft. Add white wine & white wine vinegar & reduce by ⅔. Add fish stock & reduce by ⅔. Add double cream & bring to the boil, reduce to thicken. Remove from the heat & add chives & remaining butter. Stir & season.

■ For the scallops – in a heavy pan, heat olive oil & sear seasoned scallops. After 30 seconds turn scallops.

■ For the spinach – heat the last of the butter in a small pan & add spinach. Season with salt, pepper & nutmeg. Sauté until hot.

■ To serve – place the spinach on the plates & dress scallops on top. Gently reheat the butter sauce (but do not boil). Drizzle around the scallops. Garnish with chives. *Serves 4*

Photo: John Paul Photography

WARM SALAD OF SEARED SCALLOPS AND ROAST BREAST OF MALLARD WITH HEATHER HONEY AND GRAINY MUSTARD DRESSING

Shirley Spear, Chef
Three Chimneys Restaurant, Isle of Skye

INGREDIENTS

1 tblsp sliced toasted hazelnuts
12 good sized scallops, preferably with roe on
4 mallard duck breasts, skin on
olive oil
unsalted butter
selection of mixed salad leaves & baby vegetables (eg. asparagus tips,mange tout)
salt & black pepper

DRESSING

1 tblsp orange juice & rind of half an orange, finely grated
1 tblsp sherry vinegar
2 tsps grainy Dijon mustard
2 tsps heather honey
salt & black pepper
250ml good quality hazelnut oil

METHOD

For dressing

■ Mix all ingredients (except oil) together. Pour in oil slowly, whisking together as you go. Keep refrigerated until ready to use.

To assemble dish

■ Heat olive oil & butter in a heavy-based frying pan until very hot. Seal seasoned duck breasts on both sides & place on top shelf of hot over GM7/220°C/425°F & roast for approx. 5 mins.

■ Place salad leaves & summer vegetables in centre of individual serving dishes. Sprinkle with some dressing.

■ Sear scallops in very hot olive oil for a few seconds on each side. Remove from pan & place on top of salad leaves.

■ Remove duck breasts from oven & slice each one into 5 thin slices. Arrange around scallops.

■ Sprinkle with toasted hazelnuts & pour warmed dressing over completed dish.

■ Serve immediately with home-baked bread. *Serves 4*

BLACK PUDDING AND CLAPSHOT CAKE
WITH ARRAN MUSTARD SAUCE

Rob Watkinson, Head Chef
The Stagger Inn, Inverarnan

INGREDIENTS

2 half inch slices of black pudding per person
50ml double cream
1 tblsp Arran mustard
75g clapshot (equal amounts potato & turnip mashed)
seasoning
1 tsp chopped parsley

METHOD

■ Warm cream & mustard together. Reduce until required consistency.
■ Grill black pudding for 30 seconds each side.
■ Re-heat clapshot.
■ Place 1 slice of black pudding in centre of plate. Cover with scone cutter & fill with clapshot.
■ Remove cutter & place on other slice of black pudding. Mask with mustard sauce & garnish with parsley & serve. *Serves 4*

ROAST SALAD OF VENISON WITH SPICED RED CABBAGE AND PORT AND JUNIPER SAUCE

Neil Mellis, Head Chef
Kilcamb Lodge Hotel, Strontian

INGREDIENTS

1 saddle venison – 675g
rock salt & freshly ground
pepper
2 tblsps hazelnut oil
rowan & apple jelly to serve

Spiced Red Cabbage

200g red cabbage, finely
shredded
100g Granny Smith apples,
peeled,
cored & sliced
50g onions, finely chopped
pinch of each:powdered
nutmeg, allspice, cinnamon,
thyme & caraway seeds
½ tblsp wine vinegar
25g butter
freshly ground black pepper
1 clove garlic
juice & finely grated rind of
2 oranges
75ml red wine
½ tsp of brown sugar

Port and Juniper Sauce

150ml red wine
2 shallots, finely chopped
1 stick celery, finely chopped
20 juniper berries
150ml ruby port
1 carrot, finely chopped
1 clove garlic, finely chopped
450ml game stock

METHOD

■ Trim off all visible fat & sinew from venison, brush with hazelnut oil. Season & rest for 6 hours in refrigerator.

■ Toss cabbage in melted butter, evenly coating leaves. Layer 1cm into the base of the casserole dish. Sprinkle on some apples & onions, black pepper & a little orange rind. Repeat layering until all ingredients are used.

■ Liquidise together garlic, spices, wine & wine vinegar with the orange juice & sugar. Pour over the top of the dish. Bring to the boil on top of the stove, then bake in a preheated oven at GM5/190°C/375°F/ for 20 mins.

■ For the sauce, sauté the shallots, garlic, celery, carrot & juniper berries until a rich caramel colour. Add red wine, reduce until base of pan is almost dry. Add port, reduce liquid by half, then add stock & reduce to thicken. Sieve through muslin & set aside.

■ Pan fry venison on high heat to seal juices – thirty seconds each side. Place on oiled baking tray & bake in a preheated oven at GM9/240°C/500°F for 4 mins. Rest for 10 mins.

■ To serve, place red cabbage in the centre. Slice venison & fan around cabbage. Pour sauce round edge of plate. Serve with rowan & apple jelly. *Serves 4*

See entry page 150

Dungallan House Hotel

GALLANACH ROAD, OBAN, PA34 4PD
TEL: 01631 563799 FAX: 01631 566711

AA ★★ ❀ STB★★★

George and Janice Stewart look forward to welcoming you to their lovely Victorian Villa set high above Oban. Only half a mile away from the town centre with all its facilities yet far enough to be at peace amidst 5 acres of steep craggy tree-lined cliffs and lawns

See entry page 193

Sláinte

Heather Ale Ltd
Craigmill, Strathaven, Lanarkshire, ML10 6PB
Tel: 01357 529 529 Fax: 01357 522 256
www.heatherale.co.uk email:fraoch@heatherale.co.uk

See entry page 160

HOTEL EILEAN IARMAIN
Isle Ornsay Hotel

The Gaelic Inn on the Sea

*The Taste of Skye
- mostly landed at our own wharf. Oysters and mussels, herrings and halibut. Relish our seafood and relax in a seaview room. Open all year. Centrally heated. Full menus and information available from:*

Morag MacDonald, Hotel Eilean Iarmain, Sleibhte, Isle of Skye, IV43 8QR.
Telephone: 01471 833332 Fax: 01471 833275

Houstoun House
HOTEL & COUNTRY CLUB
UPHALL • Nr EDINBURGH

AA ★★★★ ❀ ❀ STB ★★★★

At Houstoun House, a unique 16th century
quality Tower House, a traditional Scottish
welcome awaits you

• Award winning Chefs • Wood panelled
Dining rooms • Roaring log fire • 20 Acres of
Glorious Gardens • Outstanding new Pelican
Leisure Club opened December 1997 •
Peligrino's Italian Bistro for more informal
dining • 72 Luxurious Bedrooms • 6 Stunning
Banqueting and Conference Suites

We look forward to welcoming you soon

**Uphall, West Lothian, Nr Edinburgh, EH52 6JS
Tel 01506 853831 Fax 01506 854220**

MACDONALD
hotels

enjoy the difference

See entry page 99

See entry page 182

Inver Lodge Hotel

**Lochinver, Sutherland, IV27 4LU.
Tel (01571) 844496 Fax (01571) 844395**

The hotel commands panoramic views of Loch
Inver Bay with great peaks of Sutherland: Cansip
& Suliven in the background.

Inver Lodge offers high standards in service,
accommodation, and cuisine, making the most of
locally landed fish and crustacea, using the best
Aberdeen Angus beef, Highland lamb and local
venison.

Guests can enjoy salmon and trout fishing in the
most spectacular scenery. Prices on application.

Lochinver is an ideal base for touring the
Northern Highlands with easy day trips to
Inverewe Gardens, Smoo Caves and Dunrobin
Castle. Numerous famous golf courses are within
an easy 1½ hours drive.

Please contact Nicholas Gorton for a brochure.

Kinloch Lodge

Sleat, Isle of Skye IV43 8QY.
Tel 01471 833214 Fax 01471 833277
Website www.kinloch-lodge.co.uk
and www.claire-macdonald.com

Kinloch Lodge is the ancestral home of Lord Macdonald of Macdonald, who runs the 15-bedroom hotel with his wife, the world-renowned cook and writer, Claire Macdonald. Here, in view of Skye's spectacular Cuillin Hills, the Macdonalds dispense the warmest hospitality from their family home. The atmosphere is very relaxed, with comfortable rooms decorated in traditional country house style, log fires in winter and a five-course dinner menu that features the freshest of ingredients that are naturally in season.

See entry page 160

See entry page 195

★★★★ *Kirroughtree* HOUSE   🌸🌸🌸 3AA ROSETTES FOR FOOD

This beautiful mansion, dating back to 1719, is set in 8 acres of garden on the edge of the Galloway Forest. There are two attractive dining rooms, and the hotel is rightly proud of its 3 AA rosettes for food. Chef Ian Bennett who trained with the Roux Brothers oversees a daily changing menu of mouthwatering dishes using only the finest local produce. A large oak panelled lounge with open fire and individually styled bedrooms are all part of the charm of Kirroughtree House.

Kirroughtree House
Newton Stewart DG8 6AN
Tel 01671 402141 Fax 01671 402425
www.mcmillanhotels.com

See entry page 192

See entry page 232

LOCH MELFORT
HOTEL

The finest location on the West Coast for magnificent views down the Sound of Jura. Superb "Taste of Scotland" cuisine in our award-winning restaurant friendly and attentive service.

Visit **"The Skerry"**
our informal Café Bistro
open daily for snacks, cream teas,
lunches and suppers.

Spring and Autumn Breaks available.

 🌸🌸   *Good Hotel Guide César*
Award for Hospitality

Arduaine, by Oban, Argyll PA34 4XG
Tel 01852 200233 Fax 01852 200214
Email lmhotel@aol.com
www.loch-melfort.co.uk

SCOTLAND'S HOTELS OF DISTINCTION

Loch Torridon
Country House Hotel

Set at the foot of the most spectacular of the Scottish Mountains, on the shore of Loch Torridon in 58 acres of parkland with resident Highland Cattle. The hotel has carefully been restored to its Victorian splendour. Bedrooms feature magnificent en suite bathrooms and views of the ever changing Highland Scenery. Scottish dishes carefully prepared and served in the stylish dining room overlooking the loch and mountains.

Torridon, by Achnasheen, Wester Ross IV22 2EY
Tel +44(0) 1445 791242 Fax +44(0)1445 791296
Email enquiries@lochtorridonhotel.com
Website www.lochtorridonhotel.com

LOVAT ARMS HOTEL

BEAULY NR. INVERNESS IV4 7BS

TELEPHONE: (01463) 782313
FAX: (01463) 782862

Friendly family managed hotel offering great comfort and excellent value for money, with Aberdeen Angus Beef and North Country Cheviot lamb from our own farm. 10 minutes from Inverness, and central to the whole Highland area. Bar Lunches, High Teas, Bar Suppers and Lairds Table for Dinner.

See entry page 56

See entry page 196

MALIN COURT

Where to stay, where to eat

INVESTOR IN PEOPLE   Best Western   RAC ★★★

AA ★★★ ❀ ❀   STB ★★★★

Malin Court Hotel & Restuarant
Turnberry, Ayrshire, Scotland KA26 9PB
Tel 01655 331457 Fax 01655 331072
Email info@malincourt.co.uk
Internet www.malincourt.co.uk

See entry page 233

See entry page 128

THE MANOR HOUSE

AA ❀ ❀   STB ★★★★

ℐN AN ENVIABLE POSITION ON FORESHORE OF OBAN BAY – A FEW MINUTES WALK FROM TOWN CENTRE. HIGH QUALITY IN COMFORT OF ACCOMMODATION.

The Manor House, Gallanach Road, Oban.
Tel 01631 562087 Fax 01631 563053

Mansfield House Hotel

WEENSLAND ROAD, HAWICK.
Tel 01450-373988 Fax 01450-372007
email ian@mansfield-house.com

Standing in its own wooded grounds overlooking Hawick this charming Victorian House Hotel is now considered one of the best restaurants in the Scottish Borders.

The magnificent Dining Room which has been restored to its original glory makes dining out a real pleasure.

The menus which have a Scottish flavour feature the very best of local and Scottish produce and are complemented by an excellent wine list.

We are sure you will enjoy a memorable meal in the most memorable of surroundings.

MANSFIELD HOUSE HOTEL

At the Mansfield House Hotel we have all you need to help you enjoy your holiday ... good food, friendly service and a lovely atmosphere ... they're all to be found at the Mansfield. So whether you're touring or golfing, shooting or fishing, alone or with a small group, give us a call. We will tell you about our 18 rooms, several with jacuzzis, and about our special rates for weekends and week-long holidays. We can make your mouths water with the food in our restaurants and you can enjoy our more than 80 malt whiskies and our real ales. We will help book your tee-off times at Tain, Royal Dornoch and many other nearby courses and pass on discounts. We can suggest touring itineraries and we can arrange car hire. In short, we will do anything and everything to ensure that you enjoy your stay at the Mansfield House Hotel.

AA ❀ ❀   STB★★★★   **RAC**★★★

RAC Merit Awards
Restaurant, Hospitality & Comfort

Scotsburn Road, Tain, Ross-shire IV19 1PR
Tel. 01862-892052 Fax. 01862-892260
Email mansfield@cali.co.uk
Website www.mansfield-house.co.uk

See entry page 226

Monachyle Mhor

Small family run, 18th Century award winning hotel is set in its own 2000 acres.
All bedrooms en-suite with the most magnificent views overlooking Lochs Voil & Doine.
The hotel is delightfully furnished with family period furniture & country fabrics.
Robert & Jean Lewis and son, Tom – the chef invite you to dine in our restaurant with delicious dishes including game and fresh herbs from our own estate. The hotel is fully licensed & non-residents are most welcome to dine with us.

LUNCH 12PM UNTIL 2PM • DINNER 7PM UNTIL 8.45PM

Glasgow/Edinburgh 1 hour. Private fishing & stalking to guests
Featured in the Good Food Guide. Open all year.

STB★★★   **AA** ★★ ❀ ❀

Please write or telephone for bookings or further details.
Balquhidder, Lochearnhead, Perthshire FK19 8PQ
Tel 01877-384 622 • Fax 01877-384 305

See entry page 52

See entry page 35

*C*onservatory *R*estaurant

Specialising in
Fresh Lobster, Seafood, Aged Beef,
Steaks cut to order
and all local produce

The Marcliffe at Pitfodels

North Deeside Road, Pitfodels,
Aberdeen AB15 9YA
Tel: 01224 861000 Fax: 01224 868860
http://www.nettrak.co.uk/marcliffe/
E-mail: enquiries@marcliffe.com

THE
ᴛ**ARTAN**
COLLECTION

★★★★★
S.T.B.

NETHER UNDERWOOD

COUNTRY HOUSE
Luxury Dinner, Bed and Breakfast

"There is no compromise at
Nether Underwood, only the guests' total
comfort and personal pampering will do"

"Felicity Thomson is a talented cook"

STB★★★

Nether Underwood, By Symington,
Kilmarnock KA1 5NG.
Tel 01563 830 666 Fax 01563 830 777

See entry page 65

Fall in love with our food, seriously Scottish, supremely good.

Pool House Hotel

STB★★★★ Johansens Ashley Courtenay

By Inverewe Garden, Poolewe,
Wester Ross, IV22 2LD.
Tel 01445 781272 Fax 01445 781403
www.inverewe.co.uk

See entry page 213

See entry page 161

THE ROMAN CAMP HOTEL
CALLANDER FK17 8BG
TEL 01877-330003 FAX 01877-331533

Nestling in the heart of the beautiful Trossachs, the
Roman Camp Hotel offers a magical mixture of
gracious living and historic atmosphere.

Surrounded by 20 acres of superb gardens on the
banks of the River Teith, the hotel's picturesque
interior reflects the original charm of this 17th
century building.

All bedrooms have private bathrooms, and
facilities which make for a welcoming,
comfortable stay. Guests can enjoy peace and
tranquillity in a truly unique style.

Fresh produce and fine wines will tempt the most
discerning diner and friendly personal service
creates an atmosphere of leisured living.

The Roman Camp invites you to relax and
enjoy the warmest of welcomes and the greatest
of pleasure.

For brochure, tariff and reservations write,
telephone or fax.

THE ROSEDALE HOTEL

The Rosedale Hotel is ideally situated on the
harbour front at Portree and affords
magnificent views across the Bay towards the
Isle of Raasay. The hotel is a family run hotel
where an old fashioned Scottish welcome
awaits you.

23 en suite rooms • award winning restaurant
using only fresh and locally produced
ingredients • comfortable guest lounge •
lounge bar • coffee bar / wine bar

THE ROSEDALE HOTEL
Baurmont Street, Portree, Isle of Skye
Tel: 01478 613131 Fax: 01478 612531

THE ROXBURGHE

HOTEL AND GOLF COURSE · KELSO · SCOTTISH BORDERS

*Lazy days with only yourself to please –
sporty days with experts only too happy to pass on
their skills – wining and dining days with chefs
and cellars to tantalise the palate –
sleepy days with roaring log fires and
cosy quiet corners.*

*The Roxburghe Hotel and Golf Course
offers luxurious Country House Hotel
accommodation, a 72 par championship
Golf Course, clay pigeon shooting, riding,
fishing, tennis, falconry and the Elixir
Health and Beauty Clinic.*

01573 450 331

Please quote TOS1 when calling.

See entry page 166

See entry page 162

COUNTRY HOUSE
HOTEL

The Sandford Hotel, one of the Kingdom of Fife's most picturesque, listed, country house hotels, is renowned for its fine Scottish and European cuisine and comfortable accommodation.

Seasonal dishes in particular, served in the oak beamed restaurant, are the hallmark of the Sandford. An extensive wine list has been carefully chosen in order to complement the variety of dishes on the extensive table d'hôte menu.

The Sandford is located near to both St Andrews and Dundee, and provides an ideal venue for those touring, fishing, golfing or shooting in this region of Scotland.

*Bar Lunch 12.00 to 2.30 pm
Bar Supper and Dinner 6.00 to
9.30 pm. Open January to
December (inclusive).*

 AA ★★★ ❀

**The Sandford Country House Hotel
Newton Hill, Wormit, nr Dundee, Fife DD6 8RG
Tel 01382-541802 • Fax 01382-542136
Email sandford.hotel@btinternet.com
Website www.sandfordhotelfife.com**

See entry page 218

See entry page 228

SKEABOST HOUSE HOTEL *on Skye is a luxurious establishment rich with contrasts. Set amidst beautifully landscaped gardens it overlooks Loch Snizort and is a picture of tranquillity. Dating back to 1870 the Scots pine panelling is a feature. There has been constant upgrading since the McNab/Stuart family bought the hotel in 1969 and additions have included the very popular conservatory which blends in with the building.*

SKEABOST HOUSE HOTEL

**Skeabost Bridge, Isle of Skye,
Inverness-shire IV51 9NP
Tel: 01470 532202 Fax 01470 532454**

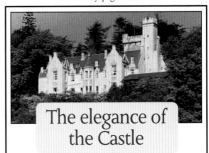

The elegance of the Castle

Breathtaking natural beauty surrounds the baronial elegance of the Castle.

Add spectacular views over the Loch, the tranquillity of the garden grounds, fine food and wines and you have all that is best in Scottish hospitality.

A regal experience
that won't cost a King's ransom

Scottish Tourist Board★★★★ AA & RAC★★★
Taste of Scotland Awarded

Stonefield Castle
——————HOTEL——————

Tarbert, Loch Fyne, Argyll.
Tel: 01880 820 836 Fax: 01880 820 929

263

TAYCHREGGAN

With a cobbled courtyard as its centrepiece, this 350 year old drovers Inn offers the best in fresh local produce beautifully presented and professionally served. Situated on the shores of Loch Awe, its unique location and ambience combines to make a perfect venue for any special occasion

Lunch and dinner served daily – Open all year
AWARD WINNING CUISINE AND
FINE WINE LIST

For reservations please call:

**Taychreggan, Kilrenan, Taynuilt,
Argyll PA35 1HQ. Tel 01866 833 211/366**

STB★★★★ RAC★★★   AA ❀ ❀

INVESTOR IN PEOPLE   PRODUCT OF *Scotland*

See entry page 168

THAINSTONE
HOUSE HOTEL

Thainstone Estate Inverurie Aberdeenshire AB51 5NT
Tel: 01467 621643 Fax: 01467 625084

On A96 north of Aberdeen (8 miles from airport)

A country house hotel and country club near Aberdeen. Two Red Rosettes and an award winning restaurant.

**CONVERTED COUNTRY MANSION
COUNTRY HOUSE COOKING
"THAINSTONE RANKS AMONG THE BEST
COUNTRY HOUSE HOTELS IN SCOTLAND"**

This charming house has been modernised to become a comfortable hotel and country club. Behind its imposing facade the house has been radically altered to create a luxurious modern hotel and leisure centre. The Head Chef, Martin Ward, offers both à la carte and table d'hôte menus in Simpson's Restaurant. There is an ambitious and bold feeling about many of the dishes; the presentation is influenced by nouvelle cuisine, but portion sizes and the quality of the raw materials are influenced only by the rich farming country within which Thainstone stands. You can also eat in Cammie's Bar, where the food and the atmosphere is more informal.

See entry page 137

The GLENLIVET®

DISCOVER THE DISTILLERY

Visit **The Glenlivet Distillery** and go on a fascinating journey to the source of one of the greatest names in Scotch whisky. At this special place experience the essence of The Glenlivet, explore the distillery's turbulent history, delve into the mysteries of distilling, and of course, sample the golden magic that is *The Glenlivet – the very spirit of Scotland.*

OPENING TIMES
Mid-March to end of October, Monday to Saturday 10am to 4pm Sunday 12.30pm to 4pm July & August open until 6pm daily.

ADMISSION
Adults £2.50 (includes £2 voucher) Under 18s admitted free.
For safety reasons, children under the age of 8 are not admitted to production areas.

The Glenlivet Distillery, Ballindalloch, Banffshire AB37 9DB. Tel/fax 01542 783220

INDEX

New Member for 2000**

A

36: Edinburgh — 83
Acarsaid Hotel: Pitlochry — 207
Aithernie Restaurant At Old Manor Hotel,
   Lundin Links: St Andrews (Outskirts) — 217
Albannach, The: Lochinver — 181
Allan Cottage Guest House, Tarbert: Isle of Harris — 143
Allt-Chaorain House, Inverherive: Crianlarich — 70
Allt-nan-Ros Hotel: Onich, by Fort William — 199
Almara: Isles of Shetland ** — 154
Altamount House Hotel: Blairgowrie — 59
An Crann, Banavie: Fort William — 107
Anchorage Hotel & Restaurant, The: Dunoon — 82
Apple Lodge, Lochranza: Isle of Arran — 138
Ardanaiseig Hotel: Kilchrenan — 167
Ardconnel House: Grantown-on-Spey — 124
Ardfenaig House, by Bunessan: Isle of Mull — 147
Ardlarig, The: Grantown-on-Spey — 125
Ardoe House Hotel: Aberdeen — 33
Ards House, Connel: by Oban — 193
Ardsheal House: Kentallen — 167
Ardvourlie Castle: Isle of Harris — 143
Argentine House Hotel, Whiting Bay: Isle of Arran — 138
Assapol House Hotel, Bunessan: Isle of Mull — 148
Atholl Hotel, The: Aberdeen — 33
Atholl House Hotel & Chimes Restaurant,
   Dunvegan: Isle of Skye — 156
Atrium: Edinburgh — 84
Auchen Castle Hotel: Beattock — 55
Auchendean Lodge Hotel: Dulnain Bridge — 78
Auchrannie Country House Hotel,
   Brodick: Isle of Arran — 139
Auchterarder House: Auchterarder — 43
Auld Alliance Restaurant: Kirkcudbright — 174

B

Babbity Bowster: Glasgow — 110
Balbirnie House Hotel, Markinch Village:
   by Glenrothes — 123
Balcary Bay Hotel: Auchencairn — 43
Balgonie Country House Hotel: Ballater, Royal Deeside — 48
Ballathie House Hotel, Kinclaven: nr Perth — 204
Balmoral Hotel, The: Edinburgh — 84
Banff Springs Hotel: Banff — 54
Bank Restaurant, The: Crieff — 71
Beardmore Hotel, Clydebank: Glasgow (Outskirts) — 119
Beaumont Lodge Guest House: Anstruther — 41
Birchwood: Gairloch — 109
Birkwood Lodge: Aboyne — 38
Bistro at Fern Grove: Kilmun by Dunoon — 169
blue bar cafe: Edinburgh — 85
Boath House: Nairn ** — 187
Borgie Lodge Hotel, Skerray: Tongue — 231
Bosville Hotel, Portree: Isle of Skye — 157
Bouquet Garni Restaurant: Elie ** — 101
Bouzy Rouge: Airdrie — 40
Bouzy Rouge: Edinburgh ** — 85
Bouzy Rouge: Glasgow — 111
Bowfield Hotel & Country Club: Howwood — 130

Braidwoods: Dalry — 74
Brasserie, The: Glasgow — 111
Brasserie At The Hydro, Crieff Hydro Hotel: Crieff ** — 71
Bridge of Orchy Hotel: Bridge of Orchy ** — 62
Brodick Castle Restaurant (NTS), Brodick:
   Isle of Arran — 139
Budda: Glasgow ** — 112
Bunchrew House Hotel: Inverness ** — 132
Bunrannoch House: Kinloch Rannoch — 171
Burrastow House: Isles of Shetland ** — 155
Burts Hotel: Melrose — 185
Busta House Hotel, Brae: Isles of Shetland — 155
Butterchurn, The: Kelty by Dunfermline — 166
Buttery, The: Glasgow — 112

C

Cabin Restaurant, The: Glasgow — 113
Cafe 1: Inverness — 133
Cafe Hub: Edinburgh ** — 86
Caledonian Hotel: Edinburgh — 86
Calgary Farmhouse Hotel, Calgary: Isle of Mull — 148
Cameron House Hotel and Country Estate:
   Loch Lomond — 179
Cargills Restaurant & Bistro: Blairgowrie — 60
Carlin Maggie's: Kinross ** — 172
Carradale Hotel: Carradale — 67
Cawdor Tavern, Cawdor: Nairn — 188
Cellars Restaurant & Cocktail Bar: Troon ** — 232
Channel Restaurant: North Queensferry ** — 192
Channings Brasserie: Edinburgh — 87
Chapelbank House Hotel & Restaurant: Forfar — 105
Chatters Restaurant: Dunoon — 82
Chirnside Hall Country House Hotel: Chirnside — 68
City Merchant: Glasgow — 113
Cleaton House Hotel, Westray: Isles of Orkney — 152
Clifton Coffee House, The: Tyndrum — 235
Clint Lodge: St Boswells — 218
Coach House Coffee Shop, Luss: Loch Lomond ** — 180
Coach House Restaurant, The, Glenfintaig:
   by Spean Bridge — 219
Cobbles Inn Restaurant: Kelso ** — 164
Collearn House Hotel: Auchterarder — 44
Columba Hotel, The: Tarbert, Argyll — 228
Conchra House, nr Dornie: Kyle of Lochalsh — 176
Cook's Room, The, Giffnock: Glasgow (Outskirts) — 119
Corriegour Lodge Hotel, Loch Lochy:
   by Spean Bridge — 220
Corrour House Hotel, Inverdruie: by Aviemore — 45
Corsemalzie House Hotel, Port William:
   Newton Stewart — 191
Cosses Country House: Ballantrae — 48
Coul House Hotel, Contin: by Strathpeffer — 223
Courtyard Restaurants On The Lane: Aberdeen — 34
Craigadam: Castle Douglas — 68
Craigard House Hotel: Boat of Garten ** — 61
Craigellachie Hotel: Craigellachie — 70
Craigendarroch Hotel & Country Club:
   Ballater, Royal Deeside — 49
Craiglynn Hotel: Aberdeen — 34

Crannog Seafood Restaurant: Fort William 107
Creagan House Restaurant with Accommodation:
  Strathyre 223
Creebridge House Hotel: Newton Stewart 191
Creel Restaurant & Rooms,
  St Margaret's Hope: Isles of Orkney 153
Creelers Seafood Restaurant, Brodick: Isle of Arran 140
Crinan Hotel: Crinan 72
Cringletie House Hotel: Peebles 203
Croft Kitchen, The, Port Charlotte: Isle of Islay 145
Cromlix House, Kinbuck: By Dunblane ** 79
Cross, The: Kingussie 170
Crowne Plaza: Edinburgh 87
Cuilcheanna House: Onich, by Fort William 199
Cuillin Hills Hotel, Portree, Isle of Skye ** 157
Culdearn House Hotel: Grantown-on-Spey 125
Culloden House Hotel: Inverness 133
Culloden Moor Visitor Centre Restaurant,
  (NTS): Inverness 134

D

Dalhousie Castle, Bonnyrigg: Edinburgh (Outskirts) 99
Dalmunzie House Hotel: Glenshee 124
Dalrachney Lodge Hotel: Carrbridge 67
Darroch Learg Hotel: Ballater, Royal Deeside 49
Davaar House Hotel and Restaurant: Dunfermline 80
Daviot Mains Farm: Daviot nr Inverness 75
Deeside Hotel: Ballater, Royal Deeside 50
Dormy Clubhouse, The (The Gleneagles Hotel):
  Auchterarder 44
Doune: Knoydart ** 176
Druimard Country House, Dervaig: Isle of Mull 149
Druimnacroish Hotel, Dervaig: Isle of Mull ** 149
Drum and Monkey, The: Glasgow 114
Dryburgh Abbey Hotel: Melrose 185
Dryfesdale Hotel: Lockerbie ** 182
Dubh Prais Restaurant: Edinburgh 88
Duck's at Le Marché Noir: Edinburgh 88
Duisdale Country House Hotel, Sleat: Isle of Skye 158
Dunain Park Hotel: Inverness 134
Dungallan House Hotel: Oban 193
Dunlaverock Country House: Coldingham Bay 69
Dunnikier House Hotel: Kirkcaldy 173
Dunorin House Hotel, Dunvegan: Isle of Skye 158

E

East Haugh Country House Hotel & Restaurant:
  Pitlochry 207
East Lochhead, Lochwinnoch: Glasgow (Outskirts) 120
Ednam House Hotel: Kelso 165
Eisenhower Apartment, The, Culzean Castle (NTS),
  Maybole: Ayr 46
Enmore Hotel: Dunoon 82
Exceed: Perth 204

F

Falls of Shin Visitor Centre: Invershin ** 137
Farleyer House Hotel: Aberfeldy 37
Farriers Country Hotel: Alva ** 40
Feorag House, Glenborrodale: Ardnamurchan 42
Fernhill Hotel: Portpatrick ** 213
Fife Arms Hotel: Turriff 234
Fifty Five BC, Bearsden: Glasgow (Outskirts) 120
Fins Seafood Restaurant: Fairlie 102

Fish Market, The: Mallaig ** 184
Flodigarry Country House Hotel & The Water Horse
  Restaurant, Staffin: Isle of Skye 159
Forss Country House Hotel: by Thurso 230
Four Seasons Bistro & Bar, Inchree:
  Onich, by Fort William 200
Fouters Bistro Restaurant: Ayr 47
Foveran Hotel & Restaurant, Kirkwall:
  Isles of Orkney ** 153

G

Garvock House Hotel: Dunfermline ** 80
Gathering, The: Kilmarnock 169
Gathering Restaurant and O'Donnell's
  Irish Bar, The: Oban 194
Glasgow Hilton International (Camerons Restaurant):
  Glasgow 114
Glasgow Moat House: Glasgow 115
Gleddoch House Hotel & Country Estate, Langbank:
  Glasgow (Outskirts) 121
Glen Cloy Farm Guest House, Brodick: Isle of Arran 140
Glen Loy Lodge Hotel, Glen Loy: Banavie ** 52
Glen Lui Hotel: Ballater, Royal Deeside 50
Glendruidh House Hotel: Inverness 135
Glenisla Hotel, The: Alyth ** 175
Glenmachrie, Port Ellen: Isle of Islay 145
Glenmorangie House at Cadboll: Fearn, by Tain 225
Glenturret Distillery: Crieff 72
Glenview Inn & Restaurant, The, Staffin: Isle of Skye 159
Golf View Hotel & Leisure Club, The: Nairn 188
Gordon's Restaurant: Inverkeilor 132
Grain Store Restaurant: Edinburgh 89
Granary, The: Comrie 69
Grange Hotel, The: Edinburgh 89
Grange Inn, The: St Andrews 214
Grange Manor, The, Grangemouth: Falkirk 103
Grape Vine Restaurant, The: Bothwell ** 62
Green Inn Restaurant With Rooms, The:
  Ballater, Royal Deeside 51
Green Park Hotel, The: Pitlochry 208
Greywalls: Gullane 127
Grouse & Claret Restaurant, The: Kinross 173
Guinach House: Aberfeldy 38

H

Haldanes Restaurant: Edinburgh 90
Handa, (Ceos) Lochs: Isle of Lewis 146
Harold's Restaurant, Lochranza: Isle of Arran 141
Hartree Country House Hotel: Biggar 56
Haven Hotel, The: Plockton 212
Heathbank – The Victorian House: Boat of Garten 61
Henderson's Salad Table: Edinburgh 90
Highland Cottage, Tobermory: Isle of Mull ** 150
Hoebridge Inn Restaurant: Melrose 186
Holly Tree Hotel, Seafood & Game Restaurant, The,
  Kentallen: nr Glencoe 122
Hotel Eilean Iarmain, Sleat: Isle of Skye 116
House of Bruar Ltd, The: by Blair Atholl 58
Houstoun House Hotel, Uphall:
  Edinburgh (Outskirts) 99
Howgate Restaurant: Howgate ** 129
Howies Stockbridge: Edinburgh ** 91
Howies Restaurant (Dalry Road): Edinburgh 91
Huntingtower Hotel: Perth 205

I

Igg's Restaurant: Edinburgh 92
Inchyra Grange Hotel, Polmont: Falkirk 103
Inn at Lathones, The, Lathones, by Largoward:
 St Andrews (Outskirts) 217
"Inn Town" at the Merchants House: St Andrews ** 215
Inver Lodge Hotel: Lochinver 182
Isle of Eriska, Ledaig: by Oban 194

J

Jackson's Restaurant: Edinburgh 92
Jedforest Hotel: Camptown ** 66
Johnstounburn House Hotel, Humbie:
 Edinburgh (Outskirts) 100

K

Keavil House Hotel, Crossford: nr Dunfermline 81
Keepers Restaurant: Edinburgh 93
Kilcamb Lodge Hotel: Strontian 224
Kilfinan Hotel: Kilfinan 168
Killiechronan House, Killiechronan: Isle of Mull 150
Killiecrankie Hotel, The: by Pitlochry 208
Kilmeny Country Guest House, Ballygrant:
 Isle of Islay 146
Kilmichael Country House Hotel, by Brodick:
 Isle of Arran 141
Kind Kyttock's Kitchen: Falkland 104
Kinkell House, Easter Kinkell: Dingwall 75
Kinloch House Hotel: by Blairgowrie 60
Kinloch Lodge, Sleat: Isle of Skye 160
Kirkton House, Cardross: Helensburgh 128
Kirroughtree House: Newton Stewart 192
Knipoch Hotel: Knipoch ** 195
Knockendarroch House Hotel: Pitlochry 209
Knockinaam Lodge: Portpatrick 214
Knockomie Hotel: Forres 106

L

La Bonne Auberge (Holiday Inn): Glasgow 115
Ladyburn: by Maybole 184
Lairhillock Inn & Restaurant, Netherley: Aberdeen 35
Lang Bar & Restaurant, The, Perth Theatre: Perth 205
Langass Lodge, Locheport: Isle of North Uist ** 152
Le Café Saint–Honoré: Edinburgh 93
Leachin House, Tarbert: Isle of Harris 144
Letham Grange Resort Mansion House Hotel,
 Colliston: Carnoustie 66
Let's Eat: Perth 206
Let's Eat Again: Perth ** 206
Little Lodge: Gairloch 109
Livingston's Restaurant: Linlithgow 179
Loch Fyne Oyster Bar: Cairndow 65
Loch Maree Hotel: Talladale 227
Loch Melfort Hotel and Restaurant,
 Arduaine: by Oban 195
Loch Torridon Hotel: Torridon 232
Lochnagar, The: Bridge of Weir 63
Lochside Lodge & Roundhouse Restaurant,
 Bridgend of Lintrathen: by Kirriemuir 175
Lodge at Carfraemill, The: Lauder ** 178
Lodge on Loch Lomond Hotel & Restaurant,
 The: Loch Lomond 180
Lodge On The Loch Hotel, The: Onich,
 by Fort William 200

Loft Restaurant, The: Blair Atholl 59
Lovat Arms Hotel: Beauly 56
Low Kirkbride Farmhouse, Auldgirth: Dumfries 79
Lux: Glasgow ** 116
Lynwilg House: Aviemore 45

M

Mackeanston House: Doune 77
Maitlandfield House Hotel: Haddington 127
Makerston House: Paisley 202
Malin Court Hotel: Turnberry 233
Mallin House Hotel: Dornoch 76
Malt Barn Inn, Newton of Falkland: Falkland ** 105
Manor House, The: Oban 196
Mansefield House Hotel: Elgin 101
Mansfield House Hotel: Hawick 128
Mansfield House Hotel: Tain 226
March House, Feshiebridge: Kincraig 170
Marcliffe at Pitfodels, The: Aberdeen 35
Marine Hotel: Mallaig 183
Marque, The: Edinburgh ** 94
Martins Restaurant: Edinburgh 94
Meldrum House: Oldmeldrum 198
Milton Restaurant, The, Crathes: Banchory 53
Minmore House: Glenlivet 123
Monachyle Mhor: Balquhidder 52
Montgreenan Mansion House Hotel: Irvine ** 137
Monty's Bistro, Lerwick: Isles of Shetland 156
Moorings Hotel, The, Banavie: Fort William ** 108
Morangie House Hotel: Tain 226
Muckrach Lodge Hotel & Restaurant,
 Dulnain Bridge: Grantown-on-Spey 126
Myrtle Bank Hotel: Gairloch 110

N

Nairns: Glasgow 116
Navidale House Hotel: Helmsdale 129
Nether Underwood, near Symington: Ayr 47
New Farm Bed & Breakfast Restaurant,
 Mount Stuart: Isle of Bute 142
New Lanark Mill Hotel: New Lanark ** 190
Newton Hotel, The: Nairn 189
No 4 Cameron Square: Fort William ** 108
No Sixteen: Glasgow ** 117
Norton House Hotel, Ingliston: Edinburgh (Outskirts) 100
Norwood Hall Hotel: Aberdeen 36

O

Obinan Croft: Opinan 201
Old Armoury, The: Pitlochry ** 209
Old Bridge Inn, The: Aviemore 46
Old Byre Heritage Centre, The, Dervaig: Isle of Mull 151
Old Course Hotel Golf Resort & Spa, The: St Andrews 215
Old Library Lodge & Restaurant, The: Arisaig 42
Old Manse of Marnoch, The: by Huntly 130
Old Mill Highland Lodge, The: Talladale 227
Old Monastery Restaurant, The: Buckie ** 64
Old Pines Restaurant with Rooms: Spean Bridge 220
Old Priory & Coach House, The: Kelso 165
Old Schoolhouse Restaurant, The: Erbusaig,
 by Kyle of Lochalsh 102
Old Smiddy Guest House, The: Laide 178
Old Station Restaurant: Spean Bridge 221
Old West Manse, The: Banchory ** 53

Olivia's Restaurant: Stirling 221
Onich Hotel: Onich, by Fort William ** 201
Open Arms Hotel, The: Dirleton 76
Orasay Inn, Lochcarnan: Isle of South Uist 163
Ord House Hotel: Muir of Ord by Inverness 187
Osprey Hotel, The: Kingussie 171
Ostlers Close Restaurant: Cupar 73
'Oven Bistro, The', At Drumnacree House: Alyth ** 41

P

Park Guest House & Restaurant, The,
    Stornoway: Isle of Lewis 147
Peat Inn, The: Peat Inn 202
Peebles Hotel Hydro: Peebles 203
Pend, The: Dunkeld ** 81
Perthshire Visitor Centre: Bankfoot 55
Piersland House Hotel: Troon 233
Pines, The: Grantown-on-Spey 126
Pitlochry Festival Theatre Restaurant: Pitlochry 210
Pittodrie House Hotel, Chapel of Garioch: by Inverurie 136
Plockton Hotel, The: Plockton ** 212
Pool House Hotel: Poolewe ** 213
Poplars, The: Pitlochry ** 210
Portnacraig Inn and Restaurant: Pitlochry 211
Potting Shed Restaurant At The Bruntsfield Hotel,
    The: Edinburgh 95
Prince's House, The: Glenfinnan 122
Puppet Theatre, The: Glasgow 117

Q

Quenelles Restaurant: Falkirk ** 104

R

Ramnee Hotel: Forres 106
Ravenswood Hotel: Ballater, Royal Deeside 51
Reform Restaurant, The: Edinburgh ** 95
Restaurant At The Bonham: Edinburgh 96
Riverhouse Restaurant, The: Inverness 135
Rock, The: Edinburgh 96
Rockvilla Hotel & Restaurant: Lochcarron 181
Roman Camp Hotel: Callander 65
Rosebank House: Strathyre ** 224
Rosedale Hotel, Portree: Isle of Skye ** 161
Roskhill House, by Dunvegan: Isle of Skye 161
Roxburghe Hotel and Golf Course, The, Heiton: Kelso 166
Royal Golf Hotel, The: Dornoch 77
Royal Hotel: Tighnabruaich 231
Royal Marine Hotel: Brora 63
Rufflets Country House & Garden Restaurant:
    St Andrews 216

S

St Andrews Links Clubhouse: St Andrews ** 216
Sandford Country House Hotel, Wormit:
    St Andrews (Outskirts) 218
Saplinbrae House Hotel: Old Deer 198
Scarista House, Scarista: Isle of Harris 144
Scholars Restaurant At Stirling Highland Hotel: Stirling 222
Scoretulloch House Hotel: Darvel 74
Scotland's Larder: Upper Largo, nr St Andrews** 235
Seafield Hotel, The: Cullen 73
Seafood Restaurant, The: Kyle of Lochalsh 177
Seafood Restaurant, The: St Monans 219

Seagreen Restaurant & Bookshop: Kyle of Lochalsh 177
Selkirk Arms Hotel, The: Kirkcudbright 174
Sheraton Grand Hotel: Edinburgh 97
Shieldhill, Quothquan: Biggar ** 57
Simply Scottish: Jedburgh 164
Simpsons Hotel Bar/Brasserie: Aberdeen 36
Skeabost House Hotel, Skeabost: Isle of Skye 162
Skiary, Loch Hourn: Kinlochourn 172
Skirling House, Skirling: Biggar 57
Somerton House Hotel: Lockerbie 183
South Kingennie House, Kellas: by Broughty Ferry 64
Stac Polly: Edinburgh 97
Stagger Inn, The: Inverarnan 131
Stepping Stone Restaurant, Balivanich: Isle of Benbecula 142
Stonefield Castle Hotel: Tarbert, Argyll 228
Stravaigin: Glasgow 118
Summer Isles Hotel: Achiltibuie 39
Sunny Brae Hotel: Nairn ** 189

T

Talisker House, Talisker: Isle of Skye 162
Taste of Speyside, A: Dufftown 78
Taychreggan Hotel: Kilchrenan 168
Tayvallich Inn: Tayvallich ** 229
Thainstone House Hotel & Country Club: Inverurie 136
Three Chimneys Restaurant And The House Over-By,
    Glendale: Isle of Skye 163
Toftcombs Country House Hotel and Restaurant:
    Biggar ** 58
Topps, The, Denny: Stirling (Outskirts) 222
Tor-Na-Coille Hotel: Banchory 54
Tower Restaurant: Edinburgh ** 98
Traquair Arms Hotel: Innerleithen 131
Trigony House Hotel: by Thornhill, Dumfries 230
Turnberry Hotel: Turnberry 234

U

Ubiquitous Chip: Glasgow 118
Udny Arms Hotel: Newburgh 190
Uplawmoor Hotel, Uplawmoor: Glasgow (Outskirts) 121

V

Victoria Hotel: Tarbert, Argyll 229
Victoria Restaurant, The: Aberdeen ** 37

W

Waterfront Restaurant, The: Oban ** 196
Well View Hotel: Moffat 186
Western Isles Hotel, The, Tobermory: Isle of Mull 151
Westlands of Pitlochry: Pitlochry 211
Wheatsheaf Hotel, The: Swinton 225
White Cottage Restaurant, The: Aboyne 39
Willowburn Hotel, Clachan-Seil: by Oban 197
Witchery by the Castle, The: Edinburgh 98
Woodwick House, Evie: Isles of Orkney 154

Y

Yacht Corryvreckan, Kilmore: nr Oban 197

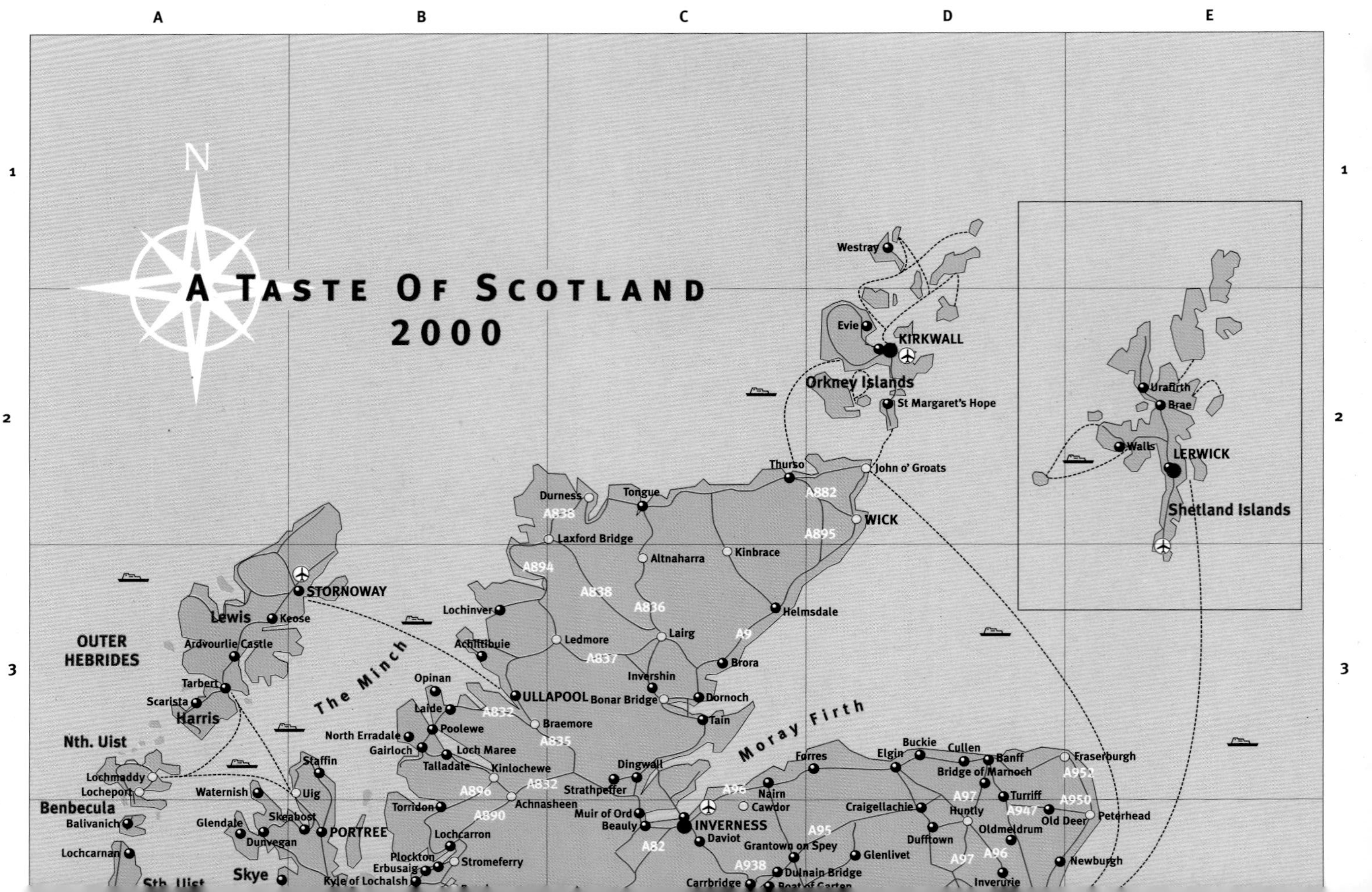
A TASTE OF SCOTLAND
2000
A
B
C
D
E
1
2
3
N
OUTER HEBRIDES
Lewis
STORNOWAY
Keose
Ardvourlie Castle
Tarbert
Scarista
Harris
Nth. Uist
Lochmaddy
Locheport
Benbecula
Balivanich
Lochcarnan
Waternish
Uig
Staffin
Glendale
Dunvegan
Skeabost
PORTREE
Skye
Kyle of Lochalsh
Erbusaig
Plockton
Stromeferry
Lochcarron
Torridon
The Minch
Opinan
Laide
North Erradale
Poolewe
Gairloch
Loch Maree
Talladale
Kinlochewe
Achnasheen
A896
A890
A832
A835
Lochinver
Achiltibuie
ULLAPOOL
Braemore
Ledmore
A837
A894
A838
Durness
Laxford Bridge
Tongue
Altnaharra
A836
Lairg
Invershin
Bonar Bridge
Dornoch
Tain
Brora
A9
Helmsdale
Kinbrace
Thurso
A882
A895
WICK
John o' Groats
Westray
Evie
KIRKWALL
Orkney Islands
St Margaret's Hope
Urafirth
Brae
Walls
LERWICK
Shetland Islands
Moray Firth
Dingwall
Strathpeffer
Muir of Ord
Beauly
INVERNESS
A82
Daviot
A96
Nairn
Cawdor
Forres
A95
Grantown on Spey
A938
Dulnain Bridge
Carrbridge
Glenlivet
Elgin
Buckie
Cullen
Banff
Bridge of Marnoch
Craigellachie
Huntly
A97
Dufftown
Turriff
A947
Oldmeldrum
A96
Inverurie
Fraserburgh
A952
A950
Old Deer
Peterhead
Newburgh

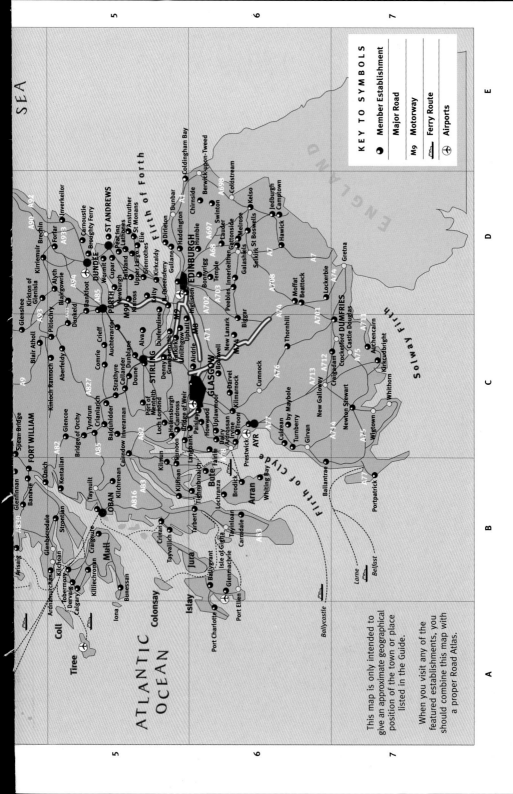

ATLANTIC OCEAN

SEA

ENGLAND

Firth of Forth

Firth of Clyde

Solway Firth

KEY TO SYMBOLS

● Member Establishment

— Major Road

M9 Motorway

⚓ Ferry Route

✈ Airports

This map is only intended to give an approximate geographical position of the town or place listed in the Guide.

When you visit any of the featured establishments, you should combine this map with a proper Road Atlas.

NOTES